KU-180-200

Programs, machines, and computation

Programs, machines, and computation:

An introduction to the theory of computing

Keith Clark

Queen Mary College, University of London

Don Cowell

Thames Polytechnic, London

London · New York · St Louis · San Francisco · Auckland · Düsseldorf · Johannesburg · Kuala Lumpur · Mexico · Montreal · New Delhi · Panama · Paris · São Paulo · Singapore · Sydney · Tokyo · Toronto

Published by
McGRAW-HILL Book Company (UK) Limited
MAIDENHEAD · BERKSHIRE · ENGLAND

07 084067 9

Library of Congress Cataloging in Publication Data

Clark, Keith L
Programs, machines, and computation.
Includes bibliographical references and index.
1. Machine theory. 2. Formal languages.
I. Cowell, Don, joint author. II. Title.
QA267.C54 001.6'4'01 76-2665

ISBN 0-07-084067-9

54321 WmC & S 79876
Printed in Great Britain

To my mother, for so much help and encouragement.

Keith

Contents

Preface

The purpose of this book is to introduce students of Computer Science or Mathematics to the idea of abstract models of computers and formal proofs using these models. It differs from most other books on the subject in using a single framework within which particular machines are defined. (See the notes at the end of chapter 1.) This is used consistently throughout the book and makes possible a systematic approach to machine-equivalence proofs, as well as a novel treatment of some of the results relating to formal languages and machines. Because programs have a central role in the theory, program manipulation becomes an important proof technique. This renders the abstract theory much more accessible to students whose strength is in programming rather than in mathematics.

Chapter summaries The first chapter tries to motivate the theoretical framework adopted and introduces the Floyd method for proving the correctness of programs.

The second chapter defines the 'big' machines, i.e., those machines that are limiting models of digital computers. It concentrates on register machines and the Turing machine. The concept of machine equivalence is defined and the various machines are proved equivalent. The chapter ends with a brief discussion of Church's thesis.

Chapter 3 examines special forms of program for register machines, namely *while* programs and the more restricted *count* programs. While structure is established as a normal form for register programs. By devising methods for 'reading-off' the functions computed by a while program from its sub-program structure we arrive at an alternative characterization of the register-computable functions. We are able to define these as a class of functions closed under various forms of function definition. Finally these functions are identified with the partial recursive functions, and those computed by count programs are identified with the primitive recursive functions.

Chapter 4 makes substantial use of Church's thesis to establish the standard negative results concerning algorithmically unsolvable problems. The technique of problem reduction is used to show that the unsolvability of many problems is implied by the unsolvability of the halting problem for the Turing machine.

Chapter 5 introduces the idea of a machine with input and output streams computing partial functions from the set of input strings to the set of output strings. The domains and ranges of these functions become the acceptable and generable languages of the machine. This chapter contains material not normally covered in books on formal languages and machines. One result in particular, the essence of which is that finite increases in memory capacity bring no increase in computing power, enables us to give simple 'program-orientated' proofs of many of the theorems relating languages with machines.

In chapter 6 transition graphs are introduced as a normal form for programs for the automaton, a machine which has an input and an output stream but no internal memory. Standard results relating transition graphs with regular languages are given. Finally the solvability of the equivalence problem for transition graphs is used to establish the solvability of the equivalence problem for function-predicate program schemas.

The last chapter introduces the Chomsky hierarchy of generative grammars as devices for specifying languages. The languages generated by different types of grammar are identified with the generable languages of the Turing machine (type 0), the pushdown store machine (type 2) and the automaton (type 3). Derivation trees are used to prove several results concerning the type 2 or context-free languages.

Audience This book has grown out of an introductory course in the Theory of Computing given to second-year students at Queen Mary College, London University. The principal source of inspiration for the course was a paper by Scott[3] suggesting a new framework for the study of abstract machines. (This paper pre-dates Scott's fixed-point semantics. Ours is still very much a computational approach and we have made no use of the concepts of the fixed-point theory.) Much of the novelty of our approach stems from Scott's paper.

We have found the material quite accessible to students with a rudimentary background in mathematics. It assumes some facility in mathematical thinking of the level usually achieved after one or two first-year courses in Algebra or Analysis. Otherwise the few mathematical concepts that are used are explained in the text.

The first four chapters comprise an introduction to the theory of computability. The last three chapters, which together with chapter 1 form a relatively self-contained unit, are an introduction to the theory of formal languages and machines. The topics covered do not correspond exactly with any of the suggested courses of the Association for Computing Machinery Curriculum 68[1]. However, the book does cover nearly all the topics of a new intermediate level course proposed by Fischer[2] in a suggested revision of the Curriculum 68 proposals for courses in computing theory. This is course I-X, 'Introduction to Computability Theory and Formal Languages'.

Notes to the reader Many of the exercises given in the text play an essential role in the development of the theory. Whenever these might present difficulties detailed hints are given which amount to 'thumb-nail sketch' proofs. The more difficult exercises are starred.

Occasionally part or all of a section is starred. This material either contains developments of the theory aside from the main stream of the book, or might prove to be more demanding at first reading.

Acknowledgements We should like to thank Peter Landin, who first suggested that we give an introductory course based on the Scott paper[3], and Eric Wagner, whose careful reading and constructive comments were much appreciated. We should also like to thank our students, who had to suffer earlier versions of the book as lecture notes, and Ruth for doing so much of the typing. Last, but certainly not least, we must thank Krysia and Pauline. They were very patient!

References

1. *Curriculum 68,* Comm. ACM **11**, 3, 151–197 (March 1968)
2. Fischer, P. C., 'Theory of computing in computer science education', *Proc. AFIPS Spring Joint Comp. Conf.*, 857–864 (1972)
3. Scott, D., 'Some definitional suggestions for automata theory', *J. Comp. Sys. Sci.*, **1**, 187–212 (1967)

List of symbols used and first occurrence in text

1 A formal model of computation

1.1 Formalizing the idea of a programmable computer

This book is about abstract machines, computing devices that are specified on paper and not necessarily realized as some mechanical or electronic device. Yet they hopefully relate to real machines either as blueprints for how the latter ought to perform or as generalizations of how they might conceivably perform. So we start by trying to extract the essential properties of a programmable computer to use as the framework for the presentation of the abstract machines.

Memory sets Let us start by considering a very simple computer. Imagine that we have a pocket calculator with two memory locations each capable of recording any non-negative integer less than 2^{24}. Suppose also that the calculator can be programmed; that it can process and transform information recorded in its two memory locations under the control of a program. For the time being we shall not concern ourselves with the details of how the program is presented to the calculator but it might be as a sequence of instructions punched on a paper tape. The important thing to realize is that no matter what we use this calculator for, the data and each of its subsequent transformations must be capable of being recorded as an ordered pair of non-negative integers:

$$\langle m, n \rangle$$

stored in the calculator's first and second memory locations. The two integer-valued memory locations comprise the *information environment* of the calculator and the set of all ordered pairs of non-negative integers less than 2^{24}:

$$M = \{\langle m, n \rangle \mid 0 \leqslant m, n < 2^{24}\}$$

provides us with an abstract specification of this information environment. It indicates the *structure*–two locations with integer values–as well as the *capacity*– the range of values that can be stored. We call it the *memory set* of the machine.

We reap an immediate bonus by specifying the information environment as a set of mathematical constructs such as ordered pairs of numbers. It clearly divorces the information-recording requirement from its realization by a physical machine. Indeed any actual computer whose range of memory configurations can be put into 1-1 correspondence with the elements of the memory set of an abstract machine, and whose manipulations of the recorded information also correspond to those of the abstract machine, is a physical realization of that abstract machine. For example it is immaterial whether or not the memory set M defines the information environment of a binary or decimal machine. The contents of each location may actually be recorded as a sequence of 24 binary digits or as a sequence of 8 decimal digits. All that matters is that each location just records non-negative numbers less than 16 777 216, which is 2^{24}.

Potentially infinite memory Our strategy, then, is to use sets of mathematical constructs to define the information environment of an abstract machine. In general we shall use non-negative integers or strings of binary digits as these most obviously relate to the representation of information. Strings of binary digits (bit strings) are prime candidates, since we know that the information processed by actual digital computers is ultimately represented in this form. Non-negative integers are a convenient alternative, especially where the operations of the machine are best defined arithmetically.

The elements of the memory sets will therefore fairly obviously relate to the memory configurations of actual digital devices. However, we shall stretch the bounds of possibility in just one respect. We shall define abstract machines with memories of *unbounded capacity*.

For example the set of all ordered pairs of non-negative integers:

$$M' = \{\langle m, n\rangle \mid m, n \geqslant 0\}$$

will be used as the memory set of an abstract machine defined later in the chapter. Since there is no upper bound on the size of the numbers to be stored, the memory capacity of the machine must be able to increase without bound as and when required. Thus a physical realization of the machine presupposes that we can add on extra bits, or splice on extra lengths of magnetic tape, each time the existing memory capacity is about to be exhausted (i.e., to avoid overflow). In this respect it is an idealized machine, a machine with a *potentially infinite memory*. We use such abstract machines in order to investigate the limiting capabilities of instruction-obeying machines.

Machine operations and tests A computer not only records information but also manipulates it under the control of a program. We therefore endow our machines with a repertoire of *operations* and *tests*.

Let us consider again the two-location pocket calculator. Let us assume that it has a division operation, that it can divide the number held in the first location by that held in the second location with the result stored in the first location. Although only the value stored in the first location is changed we can treat the division as a machine operation applied to the total information environment of the calculator. In the formal model this becomes a function over the memory set of the machine which maps the memory element $\langle m, n\rangle$ into the memory element $\langle m \div n, n\rangle$. We indicate this mapping by the notation

$$\langle m, n\rangle \mapsto \langle m \div n, n\rangle.$$

Actually this specification of the division operation is not complete. We have not indicated what the result is when n, the content of the second location, is zero. Usually an attempt to divide by zero on a pocket calculator produces an error condition, that is an undefined result. It is appropriate therefore to specify the division operation by a function with *undefined* results. The idea of such functions, called *partial functions*, may be new to the reader, so we shall define them formally.

1.1.1 DEFINITIONS

A *partial function*, $f\colon A \to B$, from *source* set A to *target* set B is a set of ordered pairs $\langle a, b\rangle$ with $a \in A$ and $b \in B$ such that no two pairs have the same first member. If $\langle a, b\rangle \in f$ then we write $f(a) = b$. If $a \in A$ but there is no $b \in B$ such that $\langle a, b\rangle \in f$ then $f(a)$ is undefined and we shall denote this condition by writing $f(a) = \Omega$.

Ω is a special symbol which we reserve just for this purpose. We can think of it as denoting some special *undefined* object, or alternatively we can treat the equation $f(a) = \Omega$ as mere shorthand for '$f(a)$ is not defined'. We shall also write $f(a) \neq \Omega$ to mean that $f(a)$ has a defined value in the target set B.

When f and g are two partial functions the composition $f \circ g$ is defined only when the target set of g is the source set of f. It is then the set of all ordered pairs $\langle a, f(g(a))\rangle$ for which $g(a) \neq \Omega$ and $f(g(a)) \neq \Omega$. This accords with the convention that

$$f(\Omega) = \Omega$$

is true for every partial function f. Clearly composition is associative.

The *domain* of a partial function is the subset

$$\{a \mid a \in A \text{ and } f(a) \neq \Omega\}$$

of the source set for which the function is defined. The *range* of a partial function is the subset

$$\{b \mid b \in B \text{ and for some } a \in A,\ f(a) = b\}$$

of the target set which comprises all the defined values.

When the domain of a function is empty we say that it is *totally undefined*; when it is non-empty we say that the function is *partially defined*; when it is the entire source set we say that the function is *total.*

$f: A \to B$ is 1-1 if for each $b \in B$ there is at most one $a \in A$ such that $f(a) = b$. The *inverse* $f^{-1} : B \to A$ of a 1-1 function is the set of ordered pairs $\{\langle b, a\rangle \mid f(a) = b\}$. Thus $f^{-1} \circ f$ is a partial identity function on A with domain the domain of f, and $f \circ f^{-1}$ is a partial indentity function on B with domain the range of f.

A function $g : A \to B$ is an *extension* of a function $f : A \to B$ if the domain of f is a subset of the domain of g, and, for all a in the domain of f, $g(a) = f(a)$. ∎

We can now define the division operation of the pocket calculator as a partial function with source and target set the memory set of the machine. That is as the partial function *over* the memory set M:

$$\langle m, n\rangle \mapsto \begin{cases} \langle m \div n, n\rangle & \text{if } n \neq 0 \\ \Omega & \text{if } n = 0, \end{cases}$$

where $m \div n$ is the whole number of times that n divides m. Every operation of the pocket calculator would be defined by some partial function over M.

There is clearly no loss of generality if we assume that the application of a test never changes the state of the information environment of the machine. We can assume that a test just determines whether or not a certain condition prevails in the current state of the environment. So as the target set for test functions we take the pair of truth values {true, false} with the true or false value indicating the result of the test whenever this is defined. We call such functions *partial predicates* over the memory set of the machine.

As an example, a test on the pocket calculator for whether the contents of the first location exactly divide the contents of the second location is specified by the partial predicate:

$$\langle m, n \rangle \mapsto \begin{cases} \text{true} & \text{if } m \text{ exactly divides } n \\ \text{false} & \text{if } m \text{ does not divide } n \\ \Omega & \text{if } m = 0. \end{cases}$$

Computable functions By a *computable* function we mean a function that can be algorithmically specified; a function for which each defined value $f(a)$ can be determined, given a, by following a 'precisely specified set of instructions in a mindless and mechanical way'. As an example, the division operation of the pocket calculator can be algorithmically specified by precisely formulating the pencil-and-paper algorithm for the division of one decimal notation integer by another.

Part of the purpose of this book is to present a more precise and mathematical formulation of the concept of a computable function. We return to this topic at the end of chapter 2. For the time being we shall use the idea of a pencil-and-paper computation as a working criterion. Thus we shall consider that a function $f: A \to B$ is computable if and only if a pencil-and-paper algorithm can be specified which, when applied to a symbolic representation of domain element a, will eventually terminate and produce a symbolic representation of $f(a)$. There is no assumed restriction on the amount of paper or time that may be required. Given enough patience and space we can 'hand compute' any defined value of the function. If the same algorithm is applied to an element of the source set outside the domain then it must either not terminate, or terminate producing a result which does not represent an element of the target set B.

In this book we shall concern ourselves almost exclusively with computable functions. In fact this is the main reason for introducing the concept of a partial function. Whenever an algorithm is such that its computation does not always terminate, then the algorithm defines a *computable partial function.*

1.2 Programs defined

Essentially we take programs to be flowcharts. We expect that the reader is familiar with flowcharts but Fig. 1.1 is an example. The F_0, F_1, F_2 are operation names and the P_0 a test name.

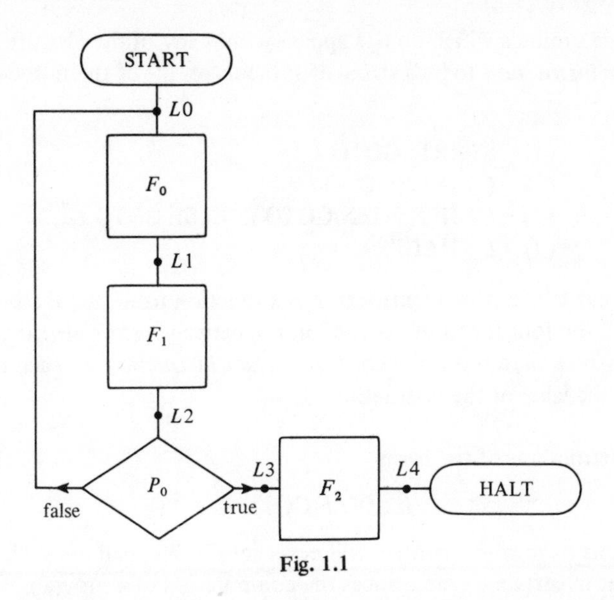

Fig. 1.1

We could attempt to give a definition of flowcharts as geometrical objects but it is easier to extract the essential structure by inserting labels between the boxes and representing them as sets of labelled instructions. In fact some labels have already been inserted in Fig. 1.1 and using these we can give a corresponding set of instructions:

START : GOTO $L0$;
$L0$: DO F_0 GOTO $L1$;
$L1$: DO F_1 GOTO $L2$;
$L2$: IF P_0 THEN GOTO $L3$ ELSE GOTO $L0$;
$L3$: DO F_2 GOTO $L4$;
$L4$: HALT;

We can define the allowed form of such sets of instructions much more easily.

First of all, instructions are made up from some basic symbols with the aid of identifiers chosen from certain sets: $\mathscr{L}$ (the labels), $\mathscr{F}$ (the function or operation names), and $\mathscr{P}$ (the predicate or test names). In practice it does not really matter whether these sets of identifiers are disjoint because the context in the instruction determines the use. However, it is convenient for the purpose of our subsequent more formal definition of a machine to require that the sets of function names and the sets of predicate names are disjoint. This can be simply guaranteed by insisting that all and only predicate names end with a '?' We shall adopt this convention. Otherwise think of an identifier as being any name made up from the symbols and characters used in this book, but with the following exceptions. We shall consider that

START GOTO DO IF THEN ELSE HALT ; :

are each single symbols which do not appear within any of the identifiers. Then we can define an *instruction* to be a string of symbols of one of the following four forms:

(1) START: GOTO L;
(2) L : DO F GOTO L';
(3) L : IF P THEN GOTO L' ELSE GOTO L'';
(4) L : HALT;

where L, L', and L'' are label identifiers, F is a function name and P a predicate name. We call the four forms of instruction respectively a *start instruction*, an *operation instruction*, a *test instruction* and a *halt instruction*. In each case we refer to L as the label of the instruction.

Ω-*loops* Instructions of the form

L : DO F GOTO L;

are instructions from which control will never return. We shall use such instructions to ensure that in certain circumstances the computation of a program never terminates. In the flowchart of the program we shall indicate the use of an instruction of this form, called an *Ω-loop*, by a circled Ω.

1.2.1 DEFINITION

A *program schema* is a finite set π of instructions that contains exactly one start instruction and for each label occurring anywhere in any instruction in π exactly one instruction beginning with that label. ∎

1.2.2 EXERCISE

The definition of a program schema has been kept as simple as possible subject to the requirement that it captures the essential properties of a flowchart. However, it does allow some silly, but harmless, program forms. For example:

START : GOTO $L0$;
$L0$: DO F_0 GOTO $L2$;
$L1$: DO F_1 GOTO $L2$;
$L2$: HALT;

is a legal program schema but it corresponds to a flowchart with an inaccessible box. Give an alternative definition which ensures that each instruction is accessible from the start. ∎

We have called the lists of instructions program *schemas* to emphasize that they are mere strings of symbols. They only become programs in the normal sense when the function and predicate names are given an interpretation as certain operations and tests of an abstract machine. Since the same function name may 'mean' a different operation on a different machine the same program schema can become several different programs. However, we shall allow ourselves the licence of referring to program schemas as programs.

Finally we shall in practice exhibit programs as flowcharts as these are easier to assimilate. However, the rewriting and manipulation of programs that we shall sometimes specify, and all the definitions which refer to them, should be understood relative to the above definition of a program schema as a finite set of strings.

1.3 Machines defined

We have suggested that a machine can be thought of as something that gives an interpretation to a program schema by assigning the functions and predicates that comprise its operation and test repertoire as the meanings of the various function and predicate names that appear in the schema. However, this suggests that we treat the machine itself as a function, a function from the set of all function and predicate names to the operation and test repertoire of the machine.

1.3.1 DEFINITION

A *machine* is a function $\mathbf{M}$ defined on the set $\mathscr{F} \cup \mathscr{P}$ of all function and predicate names for which there exists a set M, called the *memory set* of the machine, such that:

(1) $\mathbf{M}_F$ is a partial function over M for each $F \in \mathscr{F}$

(2) $\mathbf{M}_P$ is a partial predicate over M for each $P \in \mathscr{P}$. ∎

We have used the subscript notation $\mathbf{M}_F$ instead of the more usual $\mathbf{M}(F)$ since it enables us to avoid expressions such as $\mathbf{M}(F)(m)$. Instead we write $\mathbf{M}_F(m)$ to indicate the value of the function assigned by $\mathbf{M}$ to F for argument m.

We understand that implicit in the above definition is the requirement that each function $\mathbf{M}_F$ and each predicate $\mathbf{M}_P$ is computable, and that given any name we can *effectively find* the function or predicate that is the assigned interpretation of that name. (In other words a machine is a computable function from strings to computable functions.) This does not preclude the possibility that quite elaborate processing (or parsing) of the name may be required before the assigned operation or test can be found.

In practice we shall define particular abstract machines by tables which assign the operations and tests of the machine to names with suitable mnemonic content. Since we shall nearly always have fewer operations and tests than there are function and predicate names, we shall simply assign the totally undefined function over M as the value of every spare function and predicate name. This is of course just a tidying up device, but it means that we can talk about the machine interpretation for every function and predicate name that can appear in a program schema. It also corresponds to the reasonably intuitive notion that an 'illegal' operation or test name appearing in a program to be 'run' on a particular machine should always produce an undefined result. Looking up a name in the table obviously constitutes an effective method for finding the interpretation of the name as supplied by the machine.

1.3.2 DEFINITION

An **M**-*program*, or a *program for* **M**, is a program in which no instruction, except perhaps Ω-loops, makes use of an operation or test name that is interpreted as the totally undefined function by **M**. ∎

We shall think of the partially defined functions and predicates as comprising the operation and test repertoire of the machine. So a program *for* the machine is one which uses only the operations and tests of the machine.

1.4 Computation defined

Given a program π and a machine **M** we need to define what it means to follow the flow of the program on the machine.

1.4.1 DEFINITION

A *completed computation* by a program π on a machine **M** is a finite sequence

$$L_0, m_0, L_1, m_1, \ldots, L_n, m_n$$

of alternating labels of π and elements of M, where L_0 is the label contained in the start instruction of π, the label L_n is contained in some halt instruction of π, and where for $i < n$ we either have an instruction of the form

$$L_i : \text{DO } F \text{ GOTO } L';$$

belonging to π, in which case $L_{i+1} = L'$ and $m_{i+1} = \mathbf{M}_F(m_i)$, or an instruction of the form

$$L_i : \text{IF } P \text{ THEN GOTO } L' \text{ ELSE GOTO } L'';$$

belonging to π, in which case $m_{i+1} = m_i$, and either $\mathbf{M}_P(m_i) = \text{true}$ and $L_{i+1} = L'$, or $\mathbf{M}_P(m_i) = \text{false}$ and $L_{i+1} = L''$. ∎

Given a value of m_0, the start instruction of π provides the label L_0, and the computation sequence is strictly determined. As we attempt to follow the program we may find that the developing sequence is *uncompletable* for one of the following reasons:

(1) A label of a halt instruction will never be reached, and the sequence is forced to go on forever;
(2) an instruction

$$L_i : \text{DO } F \text{ GOTO } L';$$

is reached where $\mathbf{M}_F(m_i) = \mathbf{\Omega}$; or
(3) an instruction

$$L_i : \text{IF } P \text{ THEN GOTO } L' \text{ ELSE GOTO } L'';$$

is reached where $\mathbf{M}_P(m_i) = \mathbf{\Omega}$.

The overall effect of a computation is to map some initial element m_0 into a final element m_n. As m_0 varies over the memory set of a machine the corresponding m_n will vary although its value will be sometimes undefined. This occurs whenever the computation sequence is uncompletable. So the program and machine implicitly determine a computable partial function comprising all the pairs $\langle m_0, m_n \rangle$ of memory elements that begin and end a completed computation.

1.4.2 DEFINITION

The (*partial*) *function* $\mathbf{M}_\pi$ *computed* by a program π on a machine **M** is that function over the memory set of the machine comprising all the ordered pairs $\langle m_0, m_n \rangle$ such that

$$L_0, m_0, L_1, m_1, \ldots, L_n, m_n$$

is a completed computation. ∎

Intuitive model of program machine interaction The reader will perhaps find it helpful to pin the above rather abstract definitions on a simple and intuitive model. However, he should remember that it is just a model and that the formal definitions are the authority on what constitutes a program, a machine and a computation.

The finite set of strings that make up a program can be written as one long string of symbols which can then be punched on a paper tape. The program tape can then be fed to a control mechanism which acts as an intermediary between the program and the machine. The main task of the control mechanism is to search up and down the program tape looking for the instruction which begins with a particular label. It can remember one label at a time, the label of the next instruction to be obeyed. When it has found the instruction it dispatches the function or predicate name contained in that instruction and waits for the machine to respond. Figure 1.2 illustrates the idea.

On receiving the name the machine processes it to find the corresponding operation or test which is then applied to the current state of the information environment of the machine. If it is an operation, and the application has a defined

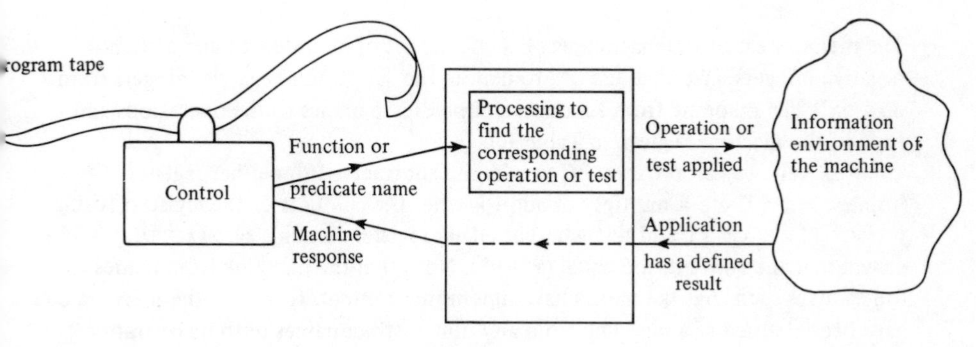

Fig. 1.2

result, this will generally transform the information environment to a new state. The machine then responds, say by returning the name of the operation, and waits for a new signal from the control. If a test is applied this will not change the state of the information environment. Again the machine will respond if the application has a defined result, this time returning the 'true' or 'false' result. No response is sent from the machine if either an operation or test has been applied with an undefined result.

When it receives a machine response the control finds and extracts the label of the next instruction to be obeyed from the current instruction (taking into account the 'true', 'false' result in the case of a test instruction) and the whole cycle repeats. The exceptional events are at the beginning, when the control scans the program tape looking for the start instruction, to get hold of the first label, and whenever the instruction to be obeyed next is a halt instruction; in which case it simply halts.

We expect in the normal course of events that a halt instruction is eventually reached. When this happens the information environment of the machine will have been transformed as a result of the application of the sequence of operations whose names have been dispatched from the control. This final state of the information environment is the result of the computation. The computation will fail to halt if an attempt is made to apply an operation or test with an undefined result for the state of the information environment to which it is applied, or because a halt instruction is never encountered. In either case the result of the computation is undefined.

The reader should note that we treat the program and the machine as quite separate entities. He is probably more familiar with the idea of the program being stored inside the machine and perhaps being modified by its own instructions. We shall keep the idea of a program and a machine quite separate. It enables us to establish properties of programs independently from properties of machines.

1.5 A simple machine

1.5.1 DEFINITION OF MACHINE **PC**

The memory set of the machine is $\mathcal{N} \times \mathcal{N}$, the set of all ordered pairs of non-negative integers. (We shall use $\mathcal{N}$ to denote the set of non-negative integers from now on.) The mapping from function and predicate names to the operations and tests of the machine is given in Table 1.1.

Intuitively we can program **PC** to add and subtract 1 from either register (using $x \leftarrow x + 1$, etc.), multiply or add together the contents of the registers (using $y \leftarrow x \times y, y \leftarrow x + y$), and test whether either register contains zero ($x = 0?, y = 0?$) or whether the contents are equal ($x = y?$). Note that the mapping from names to functions is such that the names have mnemonic content. However, the machine could have been defined as a mapping from any nine distinct names onto its operation and test repertoire.

Table 1.1

		Interpretation: result when applied to memory set element $\langle m, n\rangle$
Function names	$x \leftarrow x + 1$	$\langle m+1, n\rangle$
	$x \leftarrow x - 1$	$\begin{cases}\langle m-1, n\rangle & \text{if } m > 0\\ \langle 0, n\rangle & \text{if } m = 0\end{cases}$
	$y \leftarrow y + 1$	$\langle m, n+1\rangle$
	$y \leftarrow y - 1$	$\begin{cases}\langle m, n-1\rangle & \text{if } n > 0\\ \langle m, 0\rangle & \text{if } n = 0\end{cases}$
	$y \leftarrow x + y$	$\langle m, m+n\rangle$
	$y \leftarrow x \times y$	$\langle m, mn\rangle$
	All other function names	$\mathbf{\Omega}$
Predicate names	$x = 0?$	$\begin{cases}\text{true if } m = 0\\ \text{false if } m \neq 0\end{cases}$
	$y = 0?$	$\begin{cases}\text{true if } n \neq 0\\ \text{false if } n \neq 0\end{cases}$
	$x = y?$	$\begin{cases}\text{true if } m = n\\ \text{false if } m \neq n\end{cases}$
	All other predicate names	$\mathbf{\Omega}$

Consider the program Π given by the set of instructions:

START : GOTO $L0$;
$L0$: $y \leftarrow y + 1$ GOTO $L1$;
$L1$: IF $x = 0$? THEN GOTO $L4$ ELSE GOTO $L2$;
$L2$: DO $y \leftarrow x \times y$ GOTO $L3$;
$L3$: DO $x \leftarrow x - 1$ GOTO $L1$;
$L4$: HALT;

and the corresponding flowchart of Fig. 1.3

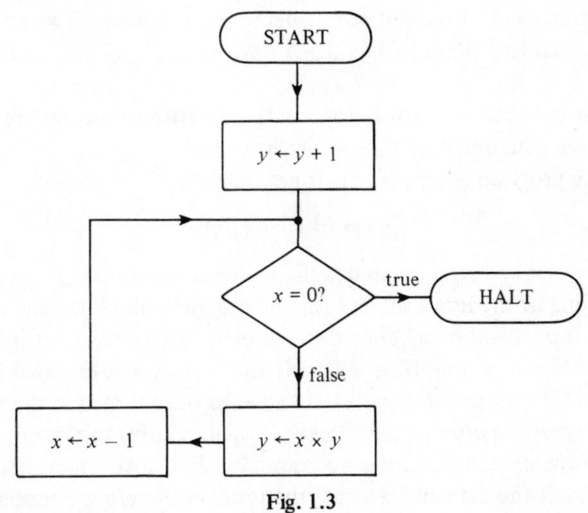

Fig. 1.3

We shall try to discover what function, $\mathbf{PC}_\Pi$, is computed by this program on the machine **PC**. First let us look at the computation sequence that is produced if the initial element of the memory set is the ordered pair $\langle 3, 0\rangle$. We leave it to the reader to check that we shall get the following completed computation;

$$\begin{array}{l}
L0, \langle 3,0\rangle, \\
L1, \langle 3,1\rangle, \text{(after } y \leftarrow y+1) \\
L2, \langle 3,1\rangle, \text{(test } x = 0\text{? is false)} \\
L3, \langle 3,3\rangle, \text{(after } y \leftarrow x \times y) \\
L1, \langle 2,3\rangle, \text{(after } x \leftarrow x-1) \\
L2, \langle 2,3\rangle, \text{(test } x = 0\text{? is false)} \\
L3, \langle 2,6\rangle, \text{(after } y \leftarrow x \times y) \\
L1, \langle 1,6\rangle, \text{(after } x \leftarrow x-1) \\
L2, \langle 1,6\rangle, \text{(test } x = 0\text{? is false)} \\
L3, \langle 1,6\rangle, \text{(after } y \leftarrow x \times y) \\
L1, \langle 0,6\rangle, \text{(after } x \leftarrow x-1) \\
L4, \langle 0, 6\rangle \text{ (test } x = 0\text{? is true)}
\end{array}$$

which maps $\langle 3,0\rangle$ into $\langle 0,6\rangle$. It is fairly easy to see that an initial element of the form $\langle k,0\rangle$ would be mapped into $\langle 0,k!\rangle$ and that the general element of the memory set $\langle m,n\rangle$ would be mapped into $\langle 0, (n+1)m!\rangle$. Thus we have

$$\mathbf{PC}_\Pi : \langle m,n\rangle \mapsto \langle 0, (n+1)m!\rangle$$

as the function computed by the program on the machine. Note that we have not proved that this is the case. We have just examined some sample data and generalized from the form of the computation that was produced. We shall return to the task of proving the correctness of the program in section 1.7.

Input encoding and output decoding functions Any program will now compute a partial function over the memory set of **PC**. However, unless we are specifically interested in computing a function over ordered pairs of integers we must specify how we are representing the actual data and how we are intending to read the result.

For example, suppose the above program Π was written to compute the factorial function. This is a function over the non-negative integers $\mathcal{N}$.

However, the program computes the function

$$\langle m,n\rangle \mapsto \langle 0,(n+1)m!\rangle$$

over the memory set and so it computes the factorial function only relative to a specified encoding of the input value, k, as the ordered pair $\langle k, 0\rangle$, and a decoding of the result as the second member of the ordered pair $\langle 0, k!\rangle$ which will then be the result of the computation. If for example the input k was encoded in the memory set of **PC** as the ordered pair $\langle 0, k\rangle$ and the output read as the second member of the resulting ordered pair $\langle 0, k+1\rangle$ then, relative to this encoding and decoding, the program computes the function: $k \rightarrow k+1$. An exact specification of how to represent the data and read off the result is therefore essential.

We can formalize this idea in the following way. We can specify an *input* set X and an *output* set Y which are understood to be the range of the data and the results respectively. Then given an *encoding* function

$$e : X \to M$$

and a *decoding* function

$$d : M \to Y$$

where M is the memory set of some machine, **M**, the composition

$$d \circ \mathbf{M}_\pi \circ e$$

for any program, π, will be a partial function from X to Y. We allow that e and d are themselves partial but computable functions.

We shall often refer to *standard* input and output sets and *standard* encoding and decoding functions associated with a given machine. For example, we shall say that $\mathcal{N}$ is the standard input/output set for **PC** and that the standard encoder is the function

$$\text{input} : k \to \langle k, 0 \rangle$$

and the standard decoder is the function

$$\text{output} : \langle j, k \rangle \to k$$

Then for every program π

$$\text{output} \circ \mathbf{PC}_\pi \circ \text{input}$$

is a function over $\mathcal{N}$. When π is the program of Fig. 1.3 output $\circ$ $\mathbf{PC}_\pi$ $\circ$ input is the factorial function.

The reader is perhaps thinking that this formal method of recording data and reading off the result, by once in and once out operations, is somewhat artificial; that in practical computing the data can arrive piecemeal and be read in as required during the computation. Likewise the output can be printed out piecemeal and need not be retained until the end of the computation. However, we were careful to describe the elements of the memory set as states of the information *environment* of a physical device precisely because we can define, and shall consider in chapter 5, machines where the appropriate physical interpretation incorporates input and output 'streams'. Then encoding the data is equivalent to the once only operation of recording the data as a string of characters on the input stream, decoding the result as the once only operation of reading off the results from the output stream. This is precisely what we must do when using an actual digital computer to process information; it computes a function from the input stream to the output stream which we then interpret as the processing of information relative to a particular representation of the information as the sequence of punched characters of the input stream, and the sequence of printed characters of the output stream.

1.5.2 EXERCISES

(1) A machine **SR4** can be intuitively described as follows. It has four registers, the x, y, z, w registers, each capable of holding any non-negative integer. For each register it has an operation to add or subtract one and a test for whether or not the register contents is positive. In each case the attempt to subtract 1 from 0 just leaves the zero value unchanged. The machine has no other operations and tests. Give a formal definition of **SR4**.

(2) Write a program $\Pi_{y \to w}$ such that

$$\mathbf{SR4}_{\Pi_{y\to w}} : \langle i, j, 0, 0 \rangle \mapsto \langle i, 0, 0, j \rangle.$$

(3) Write a program $\Pi_{y \leftarrow x+y}$ such that

$$\mathbf{SR4}_{\Pi_{y\leftarrow x+y}} : \langle i, j, 0, l \rangle \mapsto \langle i, i+j, 0, l \rangle.$$

(4) Write a program $\Pi_{y \leftarrow x \times y}$; making use of $\Pi_{y \to w}$ and $\Pi_{y \leftarrow x+y}$, such that

$$\mathbf{SR4}_{\Pi_{y\leftarrow x\times y}} : \langle i, j, 0, 0 \rangle \mapsto \langle i, ij, 0, 0 \rangle.$$

(5) Write a program $\Pi_{x=y}$ such that

$$\mathbf{SR4}_{\Pi_{x=y}} : \langle i, j, 0, 0 \rangle \mapsto \begin{cases} \langle i, j, 0, 0 \rangle & \text{if } i = j \\ \langle i, j, 1, 0 \rangle & \text{if } i \neq j. \end{cases}$$

Give an encoding function e from input set $\mathcal{N} \times \mathcal{N}$ to the memory set of **SR4**, and a decoding functional from the memory set to output set {true, false}, such that

$$d \circ \mathbf{SR4}_{\Pi_{x=y}} \circ e : \langle m, n \rangle \mapsto \begin{cases} \text{true} & \text{if } m = n \\ \text{false} & \text{if } m \neq n. \end{cases}$$

In each case give the program as a flowchart. In (4) make use of $\Pi_{y \to w}$ and $\Pi_{y \leftarrow x+y}$ by assuming that corresponding operations $y \to w$ and $y \leftarrow x + y$ are available. Function boxes that use these operations can always be replaced by the flowcharts of the programs that realize these operations to produce the actual program $\Pi_{y \leftarrow x \times y}$. ∎

1.6 Properties of programs

We can expect that there are many different ways of computing certain functions, and if two programs compute the same function over the memory set of a machine they are obviously equivalent in some sense.

1.6.1 DEFINITION

Two programs π and π' are **M**-*equivalent* if and only if

$$\mathbf{M}_\pi = \mathbf{M}_{\pi'}.$$

1.6.2 DEFINITION

Two programs are *equivalent* if and only if they are **M**-equivalent for every machine **M**. ▮

Definition 1.6.2 is possible because we have so defined machines that every program computes some partial function, even if it is totally undefined, over the memory set of every machine. **M**-equivalence obviously depends on the interpretation of the function and predicate names that appear in the two programs as supplied by the machine **M**. On the other hand equivalence is essentially a syntactic condition. Two equivalent programs will generally contain exactly the same function and predicate names and be structurally 'similar'. However, we can already prove some equivalence results.

1.6.3 THEOREM

(a) Every program is equivalent to one containing just one halt instruction.
(b) Every program is equivalent to one in which no test instruction leads directly into a test instruction involving the same predicate name.

Proof. (a) is fairly trivial. If a program contains no halt instruction we merely add one using a label that does not already appear in the program. If it has more than one we condense to one by making their halt labels identical.
(b) is rather more interesting. It is illustrated by Fig. 1.4.

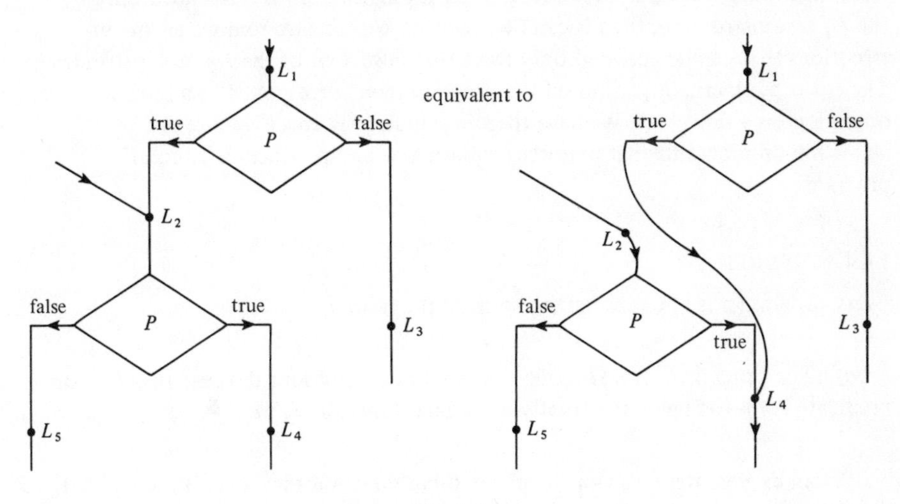

Fig. 1.4

The two test boxes of Fig. 1.4 will be represented in the program by the pair of instructions,

$$L_1 : \text{IF } P \text{ THEN GOTO } L_2 \text{ ELSE GOTO } L_3;$$
$$L_2 : \text{IF } P \text{ THEN GOTO } L_4 \text{ ELSE GOTO } L_5;$$

We must show that we can alter the first test instruction, replacing the label L_2 by the label L_4, and not change the function computed by the program on any machine. We do this by looking at differences in the computation sequences generated by the original program π and its updated version π' on any machine **M**.

Given some initial memory element m_0, the computation sequences of π and π' differ only if control passes through the L_1 instruction with the information environment of the machine in a state m with $\mathbf{M}_p(m)$ = true. In that case the computation sequence of π contains the subsequence

$$\ldots, L_1, m, L_2, m, L_4, m, \ldots,$$

where the computation sequence of π' contains the subsequence

$$\ldots, L_1, m, L_4, m, \ldots.$$

However, this difference between the computation sequences does not prevent either sequence from being completed when the other one is, nor change the final memory element of a completed computation. Hence π and π' compute the same function on every machine **M**. ∎

Note that the alteration of π did not include the removal of the L_2 instruction. Indeed if the label L_2 appears in some other instruction in the program this will result in an illegal program. However, if the L_2 instruction is referenced only by the L_1 test instruction, then it can be removed. We can also remove all the instructions that can be accessed only from the 'false' exit of the L_2 test instruction. The entire syntactic operation on the program then corresponds to a pruning operation on a flowchart. We have therefore indirectly specified a rewriting algorithm on programs that preserves equivalence and produces a 'simpler' program.

1.6.4 THEOREM

Every program π is **M**-equivalent to some **M**-program π'.

Proof. The program π' has Ω-loops where π has instructions that use function or predicate names assigned the totally undefined function by **M**. ∎

We can express the result of the above theorem in another way. It means that the set of functions

$$\{\mathbf{M}_\pi \mid \pi \text{ a program}\}$$

is identical to the set of functions

$$\{\mathbf{M}_{\pi'} \mid \pi' \text{ an } \mathbf{M}\text{-program}\}.$$

Both are the set of program-computable functions over the memory set of **M**.

1.6.5 EXERCISES

(1) Establish that the unfolding of loops preserves equivalence. Figure 1.5 illustrates the operation.

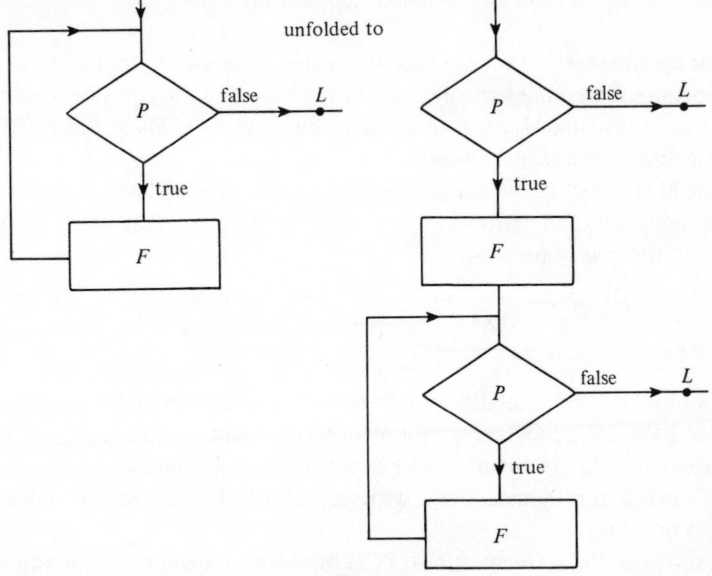

Fig. 1.5

(2) Establish that if two programs differ as illustrated in Fig. 1.6, then they are equivalent.

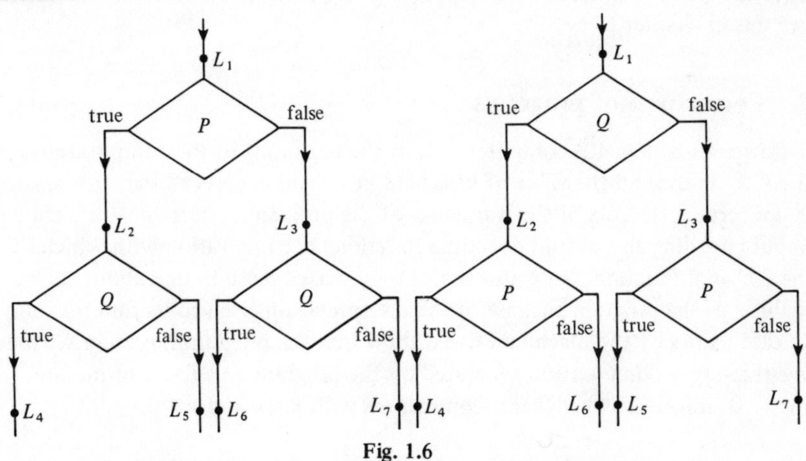

Fig. 1.6

1.6.6 DEFINITION

In a program π instruction I' is *accessible* from instruction I if there is a path in the flowchart of π from I to I'.

A *loop* in π is any set of instructions each of which is accessible from every other instruction in the set. ∎

1.6.7 EXERCISE

A loop has no exit points if there is no instruction outside the loop whose label occurs in an instruction in the loop. Show that every program can be pruned to an equivalent program whose only no-exit loops are Ω-loops. ∎

Testing for equivalence If we can specify an algorithm which, applied to any pair of programs, determines whether or not the programs are equivalent with respect to some machine **M**, then we say that the *problem of* **M***-equivalence of programs is (algorithmically) solvable.*

Suppose **M** is a machine which interprets every function and predicate name as the totally undefined function over its memory set. Any program which is not equivalent to the *empty* program,

which computes the total identity function, will compute the totally undefined function on **M**. Since a program is equivalent to the empty program only if its start instruction transfers directly to a halt we have an obvious syntactic check for **M**-equivalence of programs. Thus, with respect to this machine, equivalence of programs is solvable.

As we shall see, there are machines (**PC** is one) with respect to which equivalence of programs is not solvable; for these machines no program-equivalence testing algorithm exists. This will be one of the negative results of chapter 4. The problem of equivalence of programs (with respect to every machine) is solvable. We shall prove this in chapter 6.

1.7 Correctness of programs

The flowchart of Fig. 1.3 computes $k!$ if at the beginning of the computation $x = k$ and $y = 0$. At the end the value of $k!$ is held in y. You may recall that this assumption concerning the role of the 'variables' of the program corresponds to a choice of input encoding and output decoding functions in composition with which $\mathbf{PC}_\Pi$ is the factorial function. Note also that it only makes sense to talk about the 'variables' of the program because of the interpretation given to its function and predicate names by the machine **PC**. To show that the program is *correct* we must *prove* that every computation generated by the program on **PC** will terminate with $x = 0$ and $y = k!$ whenever it commences with $x = k$ and $y = 0$.

Associating assertions with points in the program The technique we employ involves proving that certain conditions on the information environment of the machine will hold each and every time the computation passes through a certain point in the program. In the case of the machine **PC** we can specify these conditions by referring to the values of the variables x and y (in other words the values held in the first and second memory locations), and we therefore attach assertions to

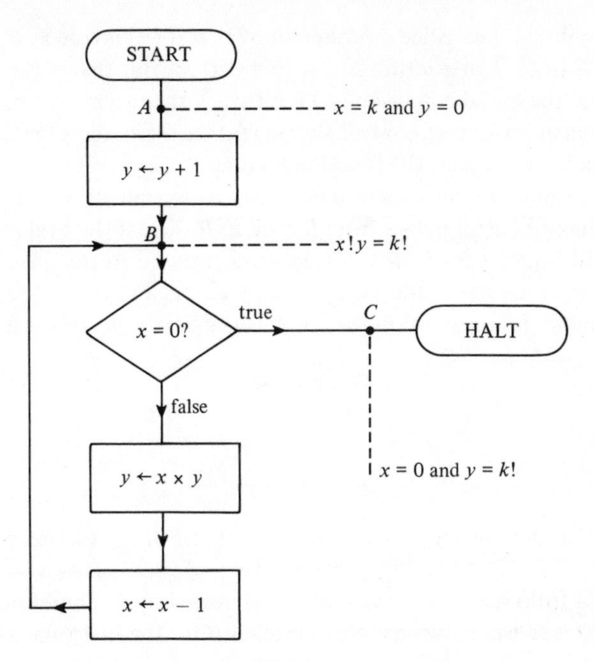

Fig. 1.7

various points in the program which refer to x and y. The flowchart of Fig. 1.3 has been reproduced in Fig. 1.7, and assertions have been attached to the three key points marked A, B and C.

A and C are the control points that begin and end any computation. We therefore associate with these points assertions

$$\text{(A)}\ x = k \text{ and } y = 0 \quad \text{and} \quad \text{(C)}\ x = 0 \text{ and } y = k!$$

that give the initial condition and the required final condition respectively. Point B is at the beginning of the only loop in the program and it will be traversed several times. We therefore associate with B an assertion

$$\text{(B)}\ x! \times y = k!$$

that specifies a relation between the values of the variables which will be satisfied each time control passes B.

By examination of the flowchart of Fig. 1.7 we can see that during any computation control moves from A to B; may traverse the loop several times from B back to B; then terminates at C. If on the assumption that assertion (B) is true at the beginning of one loop back to B we can show that it is true of the new values of the variables on return to B, then by induction, if once true of the values of the variables at B it is always true when control passes B. Next if we can show that if assertion (A) is true at A then assertion (B) is true the first time control reaches B, then we have established that (B) is always true when control passes B providing the initial condition is satisfied. We then show that if (B) is true at B, and control moves from B to C, then assertion (C) is true at C proving that if ever control reaches C, and the initial condition (A) is satisfied, then so is the final condition (C). It remains to prove that control always reaches C and the proof that the program computes the factorial function is complete.

The implications are fairly easy to establish. By examination of the flowchart we can see that if control moves from B back to B then at the beginning of the loop, since the 'false' exit of the test is taken, x must be greater than zero. At the end of the loop x has been reduced by 1 and y changed to the product of the old values of x and y. By assumption these old values satisfy the relation

$$x!\,y = k!;$$

but if $x > 0$, then

$$(x - 1)!(xy) = k!,$$

and so the relation is also satisfied by the new values of the variables on return to B.

On moving from A to B the value of y is increased by 1. Therefore if the initial condition (A) is satisfied, when control reaches B for the first time we shall have

$$x = k \quad \text{and} \quad y = 1,$$

and these values satisfy the relation (B).

Next if control passes from B to C, then $x = 0$. But at B the variables satisfy the relation

$$x!y = k!,$$

and since $x = 0$ we must have $y = k!$. This is exactly the final condition (C).

Finally, control always eventually reaches C, in fact after k iterations of the loop from B back to B, since each time round the loop the positive integer value of x is reduced by 1. Control leaves the loop when its value is reduced to zero.

We have spelled out every detail of the above proof as it is our first example of a correctness proof. In future we shall just attach the appropriate assertions to the flowchart program, and leave the reader to check that they establish the correctness of the program. For some further examples involving programs with variables, the reader may look ahead to the flowcharts of Fig. 2.5, Fig. 2.6 and Fig. 2.7 in the next chapter.

The general technique of a correctness proof A proof of program correctness is always relative to some machine interpretation of the operation and test names appearing in the program. We attach assertions to points on the flowchart of the program that refer to the memory states of this machine. They are such that each time control passes through an assertion point, the attached assertion is true of the memory state of the machine.

(1) First attach an assertion at the start of the program which characterizes the set of initial memory states for the computations of the program. Typically, this describes the memory state that encodes some arbitrary data item that is a parameter to the assertion.
(2) Next attach an assertion to each halt of the program. Each halt assertion should be such that, if it is true of the memory state when control reaches that halt, then the program is correct.
(3) Now attach as many assertions as you like to intermediary points in the flowchart. However:

(a) Make sure that each loop in the program includes at least one assertion,
(b) For every assertion-free control path that begins at an assertion A and ends at an assertion A', check that A implies A'. That is, assume that A is true of the memory state as control begins to move along the path from A to A'. By taking into account the sequence of operations that will be applied and the test exits that will be taken, prove that A' will be true of the memory state when control reaches the end of the path.

Note that because each loop contains at least one assertion point, there are only a finite number of path implications to validate. (We do not need to consider paths that involve an arbitrary number of loop traversals before they reach the next assertion.) Also note that when an assertion A is the only assertion that appears inside some loop then there is an assertion-free path that begins and ends at A. Checking this path implication means checking that A implies A after a traversal of the loop. Consequently such loop assertions are called *loop invariants.* Finally it may not be possible to attach assertions that make every path implication valid. Unless this is because the start or halt assertions need modifying, there is a 'bug' in the program. However, the failure to prove one of the path implications may enable you to identify the 'bug'.

Now consider some computation of the program. A truncated record of the computation is given by the sequence

$$A_1, A_2, \ldots, A_i, A_{i+1}, \ldots$$

of assertions passed during the computation. A_1 is the start assertion which we assume is true when the computation begins. In moving from A_i to A_{i+1}, the control must have followed an assertion-free path. Thus we know that if A_i is true when control reaches it, then A_{i+1} is true when control reaches it. By induction on i, it follows that every assertion reached during the computation is true of the memory state of the machine when control reaches it. Thus if control does reach a halt, the halt assertion is true providing the start assertion was true.

By attaching assertions we have established the *partial correctness* of the program. We have proved that whenever the computation of the program halts the result is as required. We now need to show that the computation does eventually halt. (If we intend the program to compute a partial function we must also check that the computation does not halt in those circumstances when the function value is to be undefined.)

(4) Check that the computation halts when it is supposed to halt. Do this by proving that control eventually leaves each loop in the program, and, if some non-total operations and tests are used, that they are defined whenever they are applied. Use the attached assertions to check that the computation does not stall at any of these operations and tests. To prove that control eventually leaves some loop in the program, try to prove that each traversal of the loop changes the memory state in such a way that the loop exit condition must hold after a finite number of loop traversals. (For example, show that the positive integer value of some function of the values of the variables that are changed is reduced each time round, and that control must leave the loop when its value is reduced to zero.)

1.7.1 EXERCISE

Prove the correctness of each of the programs of exercises 1.5.2. Note how easily you can prove the correctness of the program $\Pi_{y \leftarrow x \times y}$ once the correctness of $\Pi_{y \rightarrow w}$ and $\Pi_{y \leftarrow x+y}$ is established.

1.8 Notes and references

Our approach to the study of abstract computing devices follows the suggestions of Scott[9]. Indeed some of our definitions are taken verbatim from that paper. The more traditional approach does not so clearly separate the control and the memory components of a computation. Instead the next action of the machine is determined, not by a program, but by the current state of a control component of the memory which can take on a finite number of different states. Moreover the action is generally composite, involving a test, an operation and a change of state of the control component. The books of Minsky[8] and Hopcroft and Ullman[4] define machines in this way. The alternative that we have adopted, with the control component specified by a flowchart program, is used by Engeler[2] and Manna[7] although they also make use of the traditional definitions for certain machines. Kain[5] formally defines machines to have finite-state control but informally 'programs' them using flowcharts.

The technique for proving the partial correctness of programs is normally referred to as the Floyd *inductive-assertions method*[3]. Manna[7] has a whole chapter on program-verification techniques. He gives an excellent account of the Floyd method applied to programs that use one-dimensional arrays as well as integer-valued variables. We shall not need to prove the correctness of such complex programs. Manna also shows how, if the assertions are made in a formal logical language, the path implications that must be checked become theorems to be proved in that formal language. This fact has led to attempts to automate the check that assertions attached to a program satisfy the requirements of a correctness proof[6,10].

In connection with mechanical program verification, Cooper[1] has investigated transformations of flowchart programs that preserve equivalence. Independently he and Engeler proved a normal-form result for flowcharts. The normal form, and the proof that any flowchart program can be transformed into an equivalent program in that form, is clearly expounded in reference 2.

References

1. Cooper, D. C.,'Programs for mechanical program verification', *Machine Intelligence*, Vol. 6 (B. Meltzer and D. Michie, eds.), Edinburgh University Press (1971)
2. Engeler, E., *Introduction to the Theory of Computation*, Academic Press, London (1973)
3. Floyd, R. W., 'Assigning meanings to programs', *Mathematical Aspects of Computer Science* (J. T. Schwartz, ed.), *Proc. Symp. App. Math.,* **19**, 19–32, American Mathematical Society (1967)
4. Hopcroft, J. E., and J. D. Ullman, *Formal Languages and their relation to Automata*, Addison-Wesley, Reading, Mass. (1969)
5. Kain, R. Y., *Automata Theory, Machines and Languages*, McGraw-Hill, New York (1972)
6. King, N. J., 'A verifying compiler', *Debugging Techniques in Large Systems* (R. Rustin, ed.) pp. 17–40, Prentice-Hall, Englewood Cliffs, New Jersey (1971)
7. Manna, Z., *Mathematical Theory of Computation*, McGraw-Hill, New York (1974)
8. Minsky, M. L., *Computation: Finite and Infinite Machines*, Prentice-Hall, Englewood Cliffs, New Jersey (1967)
9. Scott, D., 'Some definitional suggestions for automata theory', *Journal of Computer and System Sciences*, **1**, 187–212 (1967)
10. Waldinger, R. J., and K. N. Levitt, 'Reasoning about programs', *Artificial Intelligence*, **5**, 235–316 (1974)

2 Limiting models of instruction obeying machines

In this chapter we shall define several abstract machines. One of these machines, **R**, is an idealization of a digital computer with a register memory. It calculates by manipulating the integer contents of a vector of memory locations using arithmetic operations and tests. In contrast, another machine, **TM**, calculates by shuffling to and fro along a paper tape, printing and erasing symbols. Despite their superficial differences each can be used to compute any function that can be computed on the other machine. They are *equivalent* machines.

2.1 Machine simulation and equivalence

Suppose **M** and **M**$'$ are two machines, π a program, and we want to compute the function $\mathbf{M}_\pi$ on **M**$'$. If **M** and **M**$'$ do not have identical memory sets, we shall have to make use of encoding and decoding functions, $g : M \to M'$ and $h : M' \to M$, and then find a program π' so that

$$\mathbf{M}_\pi = h \circ \mathbf{M}'_{\pi'} \circ g.$$

Ideally we want some algorithm which given π will 'compile' it into the corresponding program π'. We could then use **M**$'$ to compute any function we could compute on **M**. For suppose a function $f : X \to Y$ can be computed on **M** using some program π with $e : X \to M$ and $d : M \to Y$ as encoding and decoding functions. That is

$$f = d \circ \mathbf{M}_\pi \circ e.$$

If we plug π into the 'compilation' algorithm we shall produce a program π' such that

$$\mathbf{M}_\pi = h \circ \mathbf{M}'_{\pi'} \circ g.$$

Since function composition is associative, we have

$$f = (d \circ h) \circ \mathbf{M}'_{\pi'} \circ (g \circ e).$$

Thus f can be computed on **M**$'$ using π' with $d \circ h : X \to M'$ and $g \circ e : M' \to Y$ as the encoding and decoding functions.

2.1.1 DEFINITIONS

A machine **M**$'$ *simulates* a machine **M** if for some pair of encoding and decoding functions, $g : M \to M'$ and $h : M' \to M$ we can specify an algorithm which given any program π produces a program π' such that

$$\mathbf{M}_\pi = h \circ \mathbf{M}'_{\pi'} \circ g.$$

Machines $\mathbf{M}$ and $\mathbf{M}'$ are *equivalent* if each simulates the other. ∎

Note that the memory encoder g must be 1–1, that is it must uniquely encode the memory configurations of the simulated machine as memory configurations of the simulating machine. If it does not, there is no way of computing on $\mathbf{M}'$ the identity function over M, which is computed on $\mathbf{M}$ by the empty program

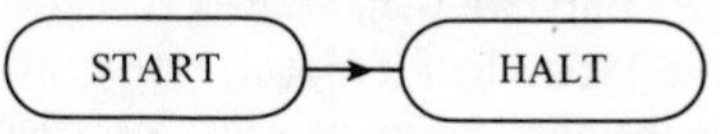

Usually h is the inverse g^{-1} or an extension of the inverse.

Clearly machine equivalence is reflexive and symmetric. It is transitive because simulation is transitive. Therefore it is an equivalence relation.

Stepwise simulation There is one general method for showing that a machine $\mathbf{M}'$ simulates a machine $\mathbf{M}$ that we shall find particularly useful. We show that each of the operations and tests of $\mathbf{M}$ can separately be 'simulated' by a computation on $\mathbf{M}'$. Then to compile a program π for $\mathbf{M}$ into the corresponding program π' for $\mathbf{M}'$ we simply replace each instruction of π by the program for $\mathbf{M}'$ that 'simulates' the operation or test of that instruction.

Suppose that we have some memory encoder $g : \mathbf{M} \to \mathbf{M}'$ enabling us to represent the memory configurations of $\mathbf{M}$ uniquely as memory configurations of $\mathbf{M}'$. The program π_F to simulate an operation $\mathbf{M}_F$ must be such that for all $m \in M$, $\mathbf{M}'_{\pi_F}(g(m)) = g(\mathbf{M}_F(m))$, as indicated in Fig. 2.1. Needless to say if the result of the application of $\mathbf{M}_F$ to memory configuration m is undefined, the result of the computation of $\mathbf{M}'_{\pi_F}(g(m))$ must likewise be undefined, that is, the computation of $\mathbf{M}'_{\pi_F}(g(m))$ should not be completed. More formally, π_F must satisfy

$$g \circ \mathbf{M}_F = \mathbf{M}'_{\pi_F} \circ g.$$

Remember that tests leave the memory configuration to which they are applied unchanged. Correspondingly the computation of a program to simulate a test should halt with the memory reset to its initial configuration. Moreover if the

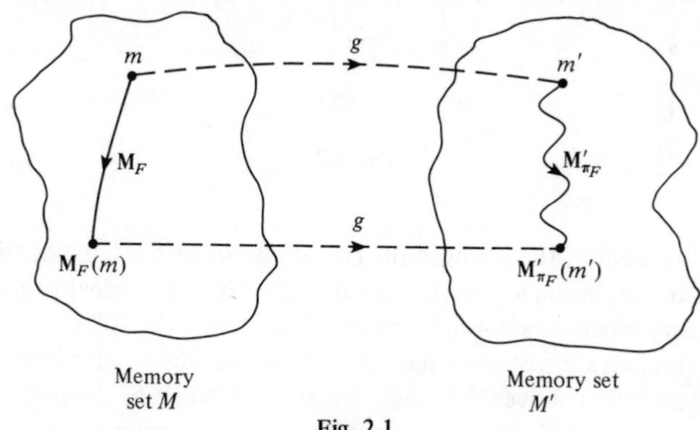

Fig. 2.1

result of the test was undefined then the result of the simulating computation should be undefined. In other words the program π_P to 'simulate' a test $\mathbf{M}_P$ must compute on $\mathbf{M}'$ a partial identity function such that for all $m \in M$ $\mathbf{M}'_{\pi_P}(g(m)) \neq \Omega$ iff $\mathbf{M}_P(m) \neq \Omega$. (Actually $\mathbf{M}'_{\pi_P}$ need only compute a partial identity function over the range of g. In the simulating computations $\mathbf{M}'_{\pi_P}$ is never applied to a memory configuration outside this range. Thus it does not matter what the result is for $m' \in M'$, where $m' \neq g(m)$ for some m.) Yet we must somehow indicate the result of the test when this is defined. We can do this by having two halt instructions in π_P, labelled TRUE and FALSE. We then arrange that the computation of $\mathbf{M}'_{\pi_P}(g(m))$ terminates at the TRUE half if $\mathbf{M}_P(m)$ = true, at the FALSE halt if $\mathbf{M}_P(m)$ = false. Now just as the application of a test $\mathbf{M}_P$ selects the appropriate exit of the test instruction, so the computation of test simulator $\mathbf{M}'_{\pi_P}$ selects the appropriate exit of the test program π_P.

Given for each function name F a program π_F, and for each predicate name P a program π_P, where the programs π_F and π_P satisfy the above conditions, we can transform a program π into the corresponding program π' as indicated in Fig. 2.2.

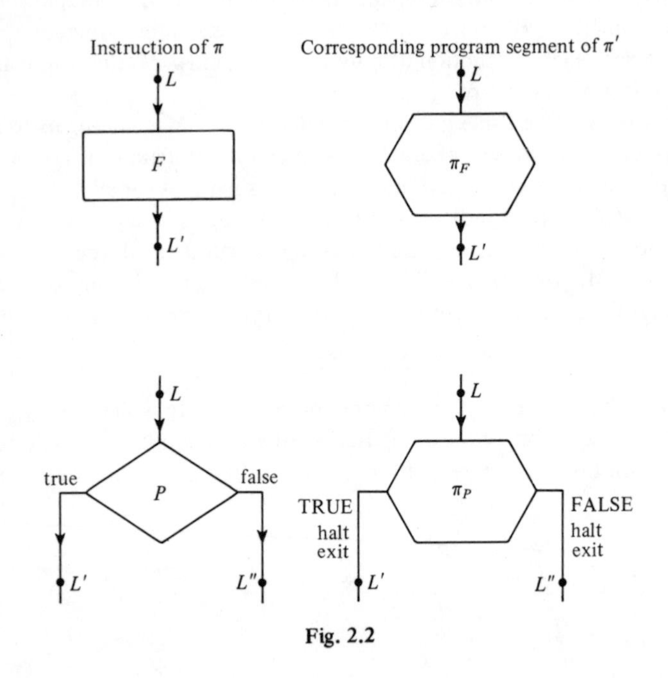

Fig. 2.2

Note that the label of the replaced instruction becomes the label of the first instruction of the replacing segment. Thus the labels of the original program π re-appear as entry labels of sub-programs of π'. Moreover, the sub-program with entry label L simulates the operation or test of the instruction of π labelled L in the manner specified above. Note also that the exit labels of the replaced instruction become the exit labels of the replacing sub-program.

By induction of the length of the computation sequence, it is easy to prove that if π generates on $\mathbf{M}$ a computation sequence (completed or otherwise) of the form

$$L_0, m_0, L_1, m_1, \ldots, L_{n-1}, m_{n-1}, L_n, m_n, \tag{1}$$

then π' generates on $\mathbf{M}'$ a computation sequence of the form

$$L_0, g(m_0), \ldots, L_1, g(m_1), \ldots, L_{n-1}, g(m_{n-1}), \ldots, L_n, g(m_n). \tag{2}$$

Moreover in (2), for $0 \leqslant i < n$, the memory configurations of the subsequence

$$L_i, g(m_i), \ldots, L_{i+1}, g(m_{i+1})$$

are those of the completed computation of the program π_F if in π L_i labels an operation instruction that uses F, and those of the completed computation of the program π_P if in π L_i labels a test that uses P.

Since computation sequence (2) is completed if computation sequence (1) is completed (L_n is a halt label terminating both computations), we have that whenever

$$\mathbf{M}_\pi (m_0) = m_n,$$

then

$$\mathbf{M}'_{\pi'} (g(m_0)) = g(m_n)$$

for all memory configurations m_0. This establishes that

$$g \circ \mathbf{M}_\pi = \mathbf{M}'_{\pi'} \circ g.$$

Rearranging the equation using the inverse g^{-1}, we get

$$\mathbf{M}_\pi = g^{-1} \circ \mathbf{M}'_\pi \circ g,$$

proving that $\mathbf{M}'$ simulates $\mathbf{M}$ using g and g^{-1} as memory encoding and decoding functions respectively.

2.1.2 DEFINITION

Machine $\mathbf{M}'$ *stepwise simulates* a machine $\mathbf{M}$ if for some 1-1 memory encoding function $g : M \rightarrow M'$ there is:

(a) for every function name F a program π_F such that

$$g \circ \mathbf{M}_F = \mathbf{M}'_{\pi_F} \circ g;$$

(b) for every predicate name P a program π_P, which has two halt instructions labelled TRUE and FALSE, such that for all $m \in M$,

$$\mathbf{M}'_{\pi_P}(g(m)) = \mathbf{\Omega} \quad \text{when } \mathbf{M}_P(m) = \mathbf{\Omega}$$

$$\mathbf{M}'_{\pi_P}(g(m)) = g(m) \quad \text{when } \mathbf{M}_P(m) \neq \mathbf{\Omega}$$

with the computation of $\mathbf{M}'_{\pi_P}(g(m))$ terminating at the TRUE halt if $\mathbf{M}_P(m)$ = true and at the FALSE halt if $\mathbf{M}_P(m)$ = false. ∎

2.1.3 EXAMPLE OF STEPWISE SIMULATION

If the reader has successfully attempted exercises 1.5.2 and 1.7.1 he has virtually proved that **SR4** stepwise simulates **PC**. As the memory encoding function we use

$$g : \langle m, n \rangle \mapsto \langle m, n, 0, 0 \rangle,$$

which transfers the contents of the x and y registers of **PC** to the x- and y-registers of **SR4**. In Fig. 2.3 we give the simulating programs Π_F and Π_P for each function name F and predicate name P.

$\Pi_{y \leftarrow x+y}$ is the program of exercise 1.5.2(3). Since this maps $\langle i, j, 0, l \rangle$ into $\langle i, i+j, 0, l \rangle$ it maps $\langle m, n, 0, 0 \rangle$ into $\langle m, m+n, 0, 0 \rangle$, exactly as required. $\Pi_{y \leftarrow x \times y}$ is the program of exercise 1.5.2(4) which likewise maps the images of the memory set elements of **PC** as required. As it stands $\Pi_{x=y}$ of exercise 1.5.2(5) does not quite simulate the test '$x = y$?'. It uses the contents of the z-register to indicate the result of the test and so is not an identity function over the memory set of **SR4**. We can either rewrite the program so as not to use z, or we can add extra instructions which branch to the appropriate halt instruction and reset z to zero as required. We chose the second alternative to produce the simulating program $\Pi_{x=y?}$. Finally note that when F or P is assigned the totally undefined function by **PC** the simulating program just comprises an Ω-loop. In future we shall take this substitution for granted, and just give the simulating programs for the operations and tests of the simulated machine.

2.1.4 EXERCISE *

Prove that **SR4** can be stepwise simulated on **PC**.
Hint: as memory encoding function, use

$$g : \langle i, j, k, l \rangle \mapsto \langle 2^i \times 3^j \times 5^k \times 7^l, 0 \rangle$$

This leaves the y-register of **PC** for use as working store for the simulating programs. In fact, none of these programs need to use $y \leftarrow x + y, y \leftarrow x \times y$ or $x = y?$, so that you will indirectly establish that **SR4** really needs only two registers. (Does this surprise you?) However, there is a consequence to note. Where **SR4** computes a function over the non-negative integers, using encoding and decoding functions

$$e : n \mapsto \langle n, 0, 0, 0 \rangle$$
$$d : \langle i, j, k, l \rangle \mapsto i,$$

with the data and result held in the first register, with the corresponding program for the two register version **SR2**, we must use

$$g \circ e : n \mapsto \langle 2^n, 0 \rangle$$

$$d \circ g^{-1} : \langle m, n \rangle \mapsto \begin{cases} i & \text{if } m = 2^i \times 3^j \times 5^k \times 7^l \text{ and } n = 0 \\ \Omega & \text{otherwise.} \end{cases}$$

So we have sneaked some computation into the new encoding and decoding functions. In order to have argument and result recorded directly as the contents

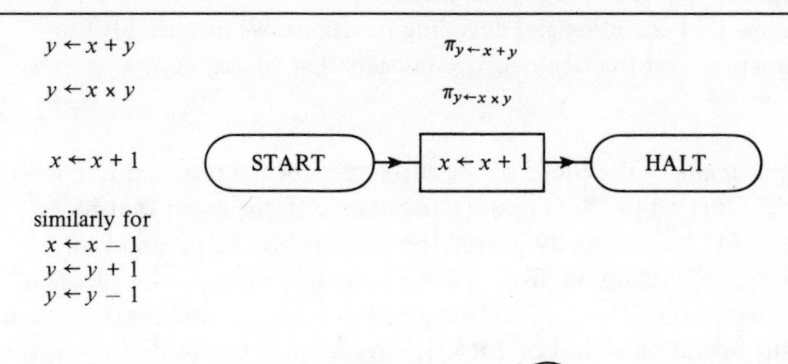

Every other function name

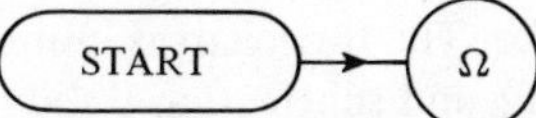

Predicate name

Simulating program

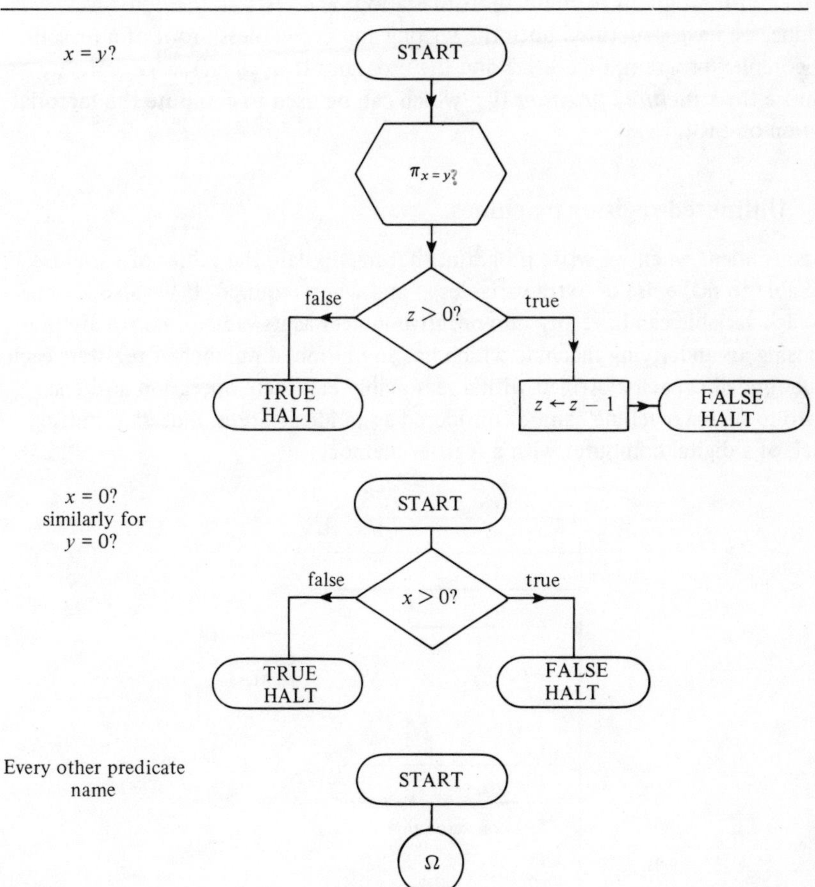

Fig. 2.3

of one of the registers we must use at least three registers (why?). However, by making use of these odd encoding and decoding functions, we can use **SR2** to compute any function over the non-negative integers that we can compute on **SR4.** ∎

Structured programming The proof of the correctness of the program to compute the factorial function on **PC** (Fig. 1.7), together with the proof that **SR4** stepwise simulates **PC**, has indirectly proved the correctness of a program to compute the factorial function on **SR4**. It is the program that is produced when we expand the flowchart of Fig. 1.7, replacing each box by the flowchart segment that simulates the operation or test on **SR4**. The reader may like to do the expansion to see what the program looks like. The flowchart is quite large and it naturally contains only operations of adding and subtracting 1 and tests for non-zero value. To attempt to write the program directly, and then to prove its correctness, will be no trivial matter. However, by writing a program for a more 'high-level' machine, together with programs to simulate its operations and tests on the 'low-level' machine, we have structured both the writing and correctness proof of a reasonably complex program. Figure 1.7 and the programs $\Pi_{y \leftarrow x \times y}$, $\Pi_{y \leftarrow x+y}$, $\Pi_{w \rightarrow y}$ comprise the *structured program* Π_{fac} which can be used to compute the factorial function on **SR4.**

2.2 Unlimited-register machines

It is convenient when we write programs that manipulate the values of variables to be able to make use of extra variables as and when required. If we also assume that each variable can have any non-negative integer as its value, then we are presupposing an underlying machine which has an unlimited number of registers each of unbounded capacity. Armed with a reasonably elaborate operation and test repertoire such a machine can be considered as an idealization, indeed a limiting model, of a digital computer with a register memory.

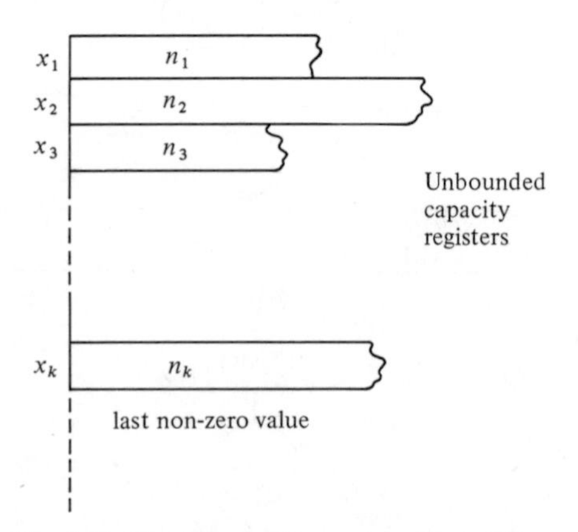

Fig. 2.4 The information environment of **R**

2.2.1 THE MACHINE R

The information environment of **R** is depicted in Fig. 2.4. The memory set of the machine is the set of all infinite sequences of non-negative integers

$$\{n_i\}_{i=1}^{\infty}$$

such that for some $k \geqslant 0, n_i = 0$ for all $i > k$. Thus only a finite initial segment of the register memory holds non-zero values and every state of the information environment could be recorded by a finite sequence.

The operations and tests of **R**, all totally defined, are listed below. Here i, j, k are positive integer subscripts and m is any non-negative integer.

operations

$x_i \leftarrow m$	constant m is assigned to x_i
$x_i \leftarrow x_j + m$	
$x_i \leftarrow x_j - m$	zero assigned to x_i if $m \geqslant$ value of x_j
$x_i \leftarrow x_j \times m$	
$x_i \leftarrow x_j \div m$	integer division with largest non-negative q such that $m \times q \leqslant$ value of x_j assigned to x_i; 0 assigned if $m = 0$
$x_i \leftarrow x_j$	
$x_i \leftarrow x_j + x_k$	
$x_i \leftarrow x_j - x_k$	0 assigned if value of $x_k \geqslant$ value of x_j
$x_i \leftarrow x_j \times x_k$	
$x_i \leftarrow x_j \div x_k$	integer division, again with 0 assigned if value of x_k is zero

tests

$x_i = m?$
$x_i > m?$
$x_i = x_j?$
$x_i > x_j?$

The functions and predicates over the memory set of **R** which define these operations and tests are trivially specified. For example,

$$\mathbf{R}_{x_3 \leftarrow 66} : \{n_i\}_{i=1}^{\infty} \mapsto \{n'_i\}_{i=1}^{\infty} \quad \text{where } n'_3 = 66 \text{ and for all } i \neq 3, n'_i = n_i$$

and

$$\mathbf{R}_{x_4 = x_7 ?} : \{n_i\}_{i=1}^{\infty} \mapsto \begin{cases} \text{true} & \text{if } n_4 = n_7 \\ \text{false} & \text{otherwise} \end{cases}$$

and in general

$$\mathbf{R}_{x_i \leftarrow x_j} : \{n_i\}_{i=1}^{\infty} \mapsto \{n'_i\}_{i=1}^{\infty} \quad \text{where } n'_i = n_j \text{ and for all } i \neq j, n'_i = n_i.$$

Input and output registers Suppose π is some program for **R**. We can implicitly define encoding and decoding functions such that $d \circ \mathbf{R}_\pi \circ e$ is a function from k-tuples to l-tuples by designating k registers $u_1, u_2, \ldots, u_k$ as *input registers* and l registers $w_1, w_2, \ldots, w_l$ as *output registers.* e is then the function that loads register u_i with the ith argument n_i, for $1 \leqslant i \leqslant k$, setting all other registers to zero. d is the function that extracts the jth result from register w_j for $1 \leqslant j \leqslant l$. Any registers used by π other than input or output registers we call *working registers.* Note that the encoding function initializes each non-input register with zero value.

2.2.2 AN EXAMPLE PROGRAM FOR R

Figures 2.5, 2.6 and 2.7 together comprise a structured program Π_{prime} which computes the nth prime number for argument n using x_1 as *input register*, x_2 as

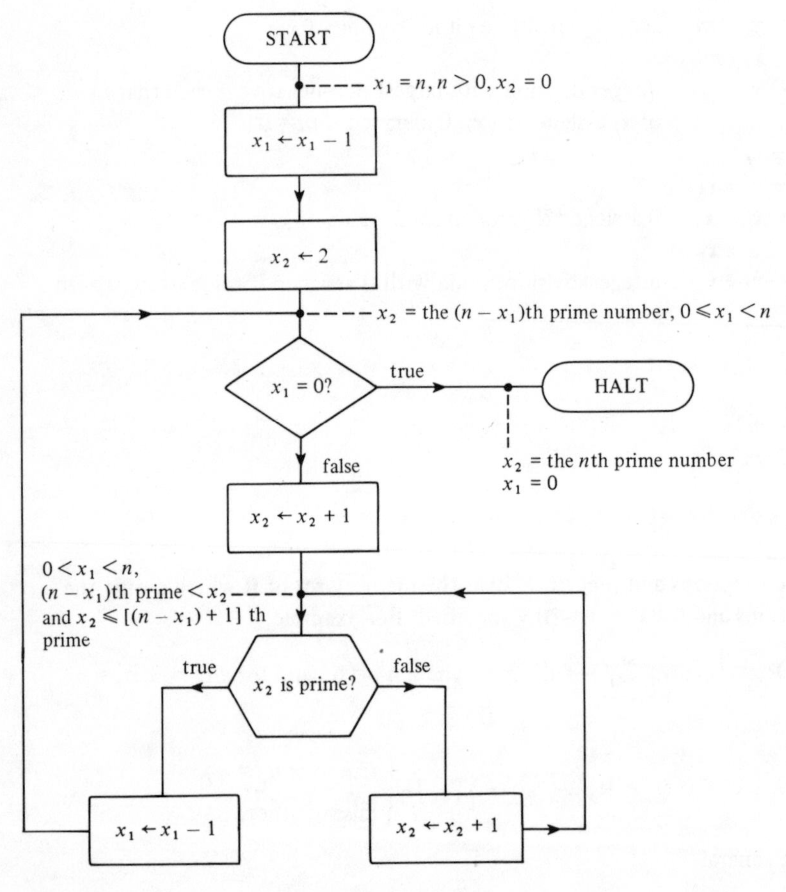

Fig. 2.5 Π_{prime}.

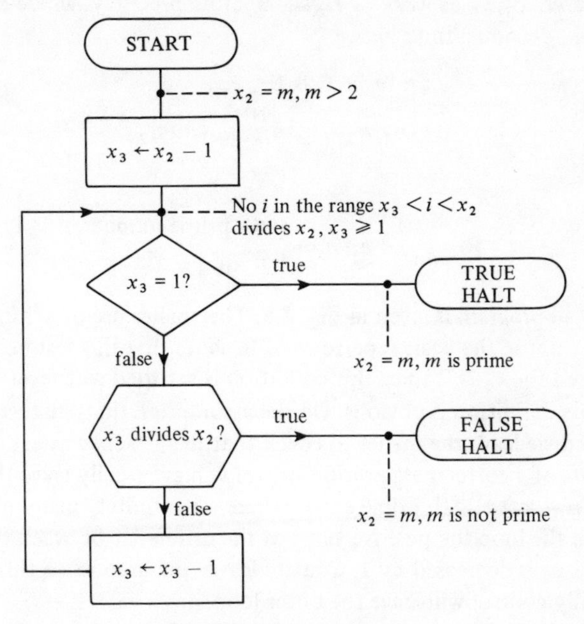

Fig. 2.6 Π_{x_2} **is prime?**

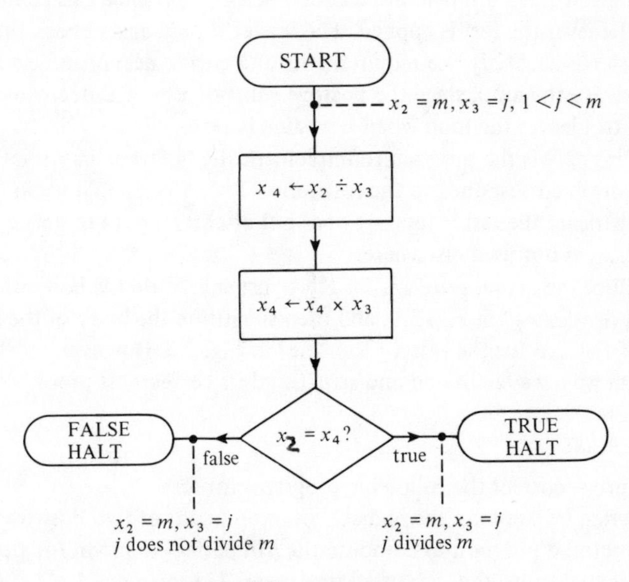

Fig. 2.7 Π_{x_3} **divides** x_2**?**

output register, x_3, x_4 as *working registers*. More precisely, where e and d are the encoding and decoding functions,

$$e : n \mapsto \{n, 0, 0, 0, \ldots\}$$

$$d : \{n_1, n_2, \ldots, n_i, \ldots\} \mapsto n_2$$

then

$$d \circ \mathbf{R}_{\Pi_{\text{prime}}} \circ e : n \mapsto \begin{cases} n\text{th prime number}, n \geqslant 1 \\ 2 \quad \text{if } n = 0 \end{cases}$$

The overall program is given in Fig. 2.5. This makes use of a 'high-level' test x_2 is prime? not in the basic repertoire of **R**. Note that this test need only be correctly defined for $x_2 > 2$ since this condition is satisfied whenever the test is applied. Otherwise its definition is obvious. On the assumption that the test is correctly implemented we leave the reader to check that the attached assertions satisfy the requirements of a correctness proof. Control will eventually leave the inner loop since the $[(n - x_1) + 1]$th prime exists (there are infinitely many primes) and each time around the loop the positive value of the difference between this next prime number and x_2 is decreased by 1. Control leaves the loop when this difference is zero. Trivially control will leave the outer loop.

Figure 2.6 is the program to implement the test x_2 is prime? Note that it does not alter its input register x_2 and that its working register x_3 is not used elsewhere. For our purpose this is equivalent to the requirement that it compute an identity function. The initial condition is $x_2 = m, m > 2$ since the prime test need only be defined for $x_2 > 2$ as noted above. This program makes use of an 'intermediary-level' test x_3 divides x_2? Like the 'high-level' test this need only return the correct result over a restricted domain, in fact for $1 < x_3 < x_2$, since this condition is satisfied whenever the test is applied. The reader should again check that the attached assertions satisfy the requirements of a correctness proof. Control must eventually leave the loop, since the positive value of $x_3 - 1$ is decreased each time round; control leaves the loop when the value is zero.

Finally Fig. 2.7 is the program to implement the 'intermediary-level' test. The initial condition corresponds to the restriction $1 < x_3 < x_2$ that we know is satisfied whenever the test is used. It does not alter its input registers x_2, x_3 and its working x_4 is not used elsewhere.

To produce the actual program for **R** we just substitute the body of Fig. 2.7 for the test x_3 divides x_2? in Fig. 2.6, and then substitute the body of the expanded program of Fig. 2.6 for the test x_2 is prime? in Fig. 2.5. However, by structuring the program we have facilitated and structured its correctness proof.

2.2.3 EXERCISE

Write and prove correct the following programs for **R**:

(1) A program to compute the highest common factor of two positive integers.

(2)* A structured program to compute the nth perfect number. i is a perfect number if it is equal to the sum of all its divisors j in the range $1 \leqslant j < i$. It is not expected that you will be able to prove that this program always terminates, for it is an open question whether or not there are an infinite number of perfect numbers. So the program will compute the function,

$$\text{perfect} : n \mapsto \begin{cases} n\text{th perfect number if there is one} \\ \Omega \text{ if there are less than } n \text{ perfect numbers.} \end{cases}$$

Register functions Suppose we designate the sequence $x_1, \ldots, x_k$ of the first k registers of **R** as input registers. Let f_i be the function from $\mathcal{N}^k$ to $\mathcal{N}$ computed by an **R**-program π using x_i, where $1 \leqslant i \leqslant k$, as the output register. We call the k functions $f_1, f_2, \ldots, f_k$ the *(k-adic) associated functions* of π.

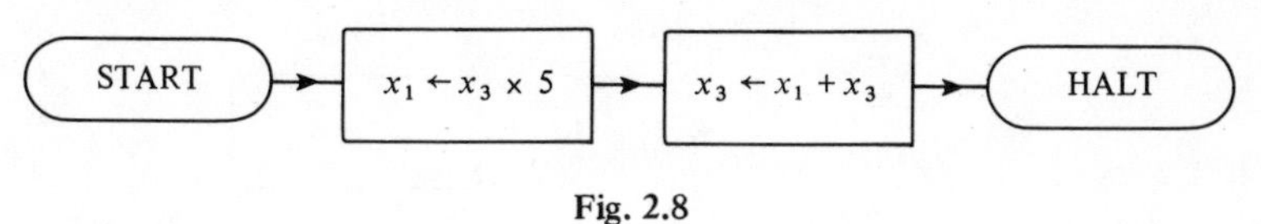

Fig. 2.8

As an example consider the program of Fig. 2.8. For any $k \geqslant 3$ its associated functions are

$$f_1: \langle x_1, x_2, \ldots, x_k \rangle \mapsto x_3 \times 5$$
$$f_2: \langle x_1, x_2, \ldots, x_k \rangle \mapsto x_2$$
$$f_3: \langle x_1, x_2, \ldots, x_k \rangle \mapsto x_3 \times 5 + x_3$$
$$f_4: \langle x_1, x_2, \ldots, x_k \rangle \mapsto x_4$$
$$\vdots$$
$$f_k: \langle x_1, x_2, \ldots, x_k \rangle \mapsto x_k,$$

and for $k = 2$ its two (dyadic) associated functions are

$$g_1: \langle x_1, x_2 \rangle \mapsto 0$$
$$g_2: \langle x_1, x_2 \rangle \mapsto x_2.$$

(g_1 returns a zero value of all arguments since x_3 is now a working register which is always initialized to zero.)

We shall be interested in the class of functions that are associated functions of programs for **R**.

2.2.4 DEFINITION

A *register program* is any program for **R**. A *k-adic register function* is any function which is a k-adic associated function of a register program. The class of all k-adic register functions, for all $k \geqslant 1$, is the class of *register functions.* ∎

We shall consider the register functions as *the* functions that are computable on **R**.

Using only a rudimentary operation and test repertoire We have already seen in the proof of the stepwise simulation of **PC** on **SR4** that at the expense of using some extra variables a program's use of addition and multiplication can be realized with a far more rudimentary repertoire. We shall see how much of the repertoire of **R** can be dispensed with in this way.

Let π be some register program. We give a method for rewriting π, making use of five extra registers y_1, y_2, y_3, y_4, y_5 not already used by π, to produce a program π' in which the only operations are of the form $x_i \leftarrow x_i + 1, x_i \leftarrow x_i - 1$, and the only tests are of the form $x_i > 0$? Moreover the new program computes the same function over the set of registers used by π.

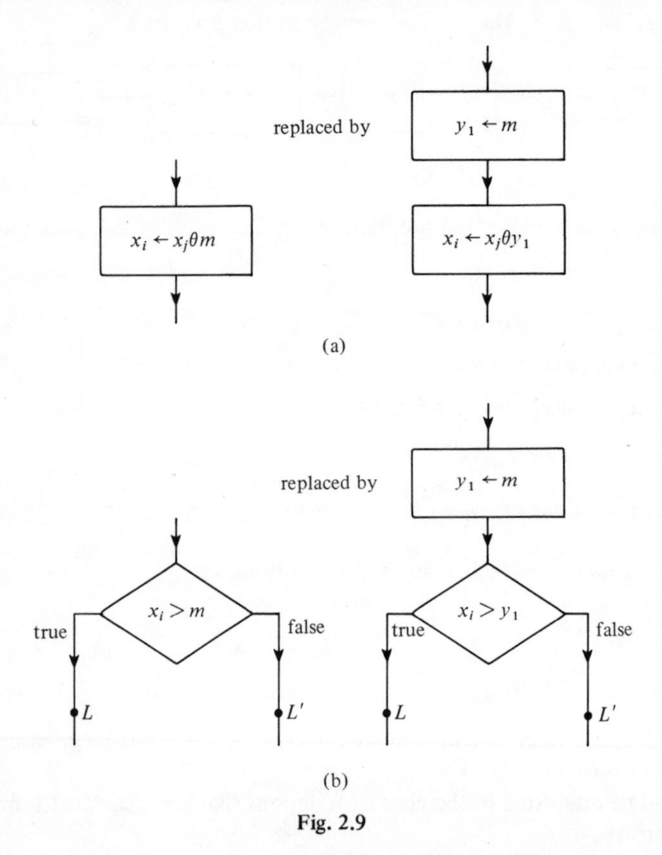

Fig. 2.9

The first step is to get rid of the inequality tests $x_i > m?$, $m \neq 0$, and the operations $x_i \leftarrow x_j \theta m$, $\theta = +, -, \times, \div$, which are not of the form $x_i \leftarrow x_i + 1$ or $x_i \leftarrow x_i - 1$. We simply make substitutions in the program as indicated in Fig. 2.9 using the first extra register y_1.

The next step is to jettison operations of the form $x_i \leftarrow x_j \times x_k$ and $x_i \leftarrow x_j \div x_k$. The appropriate substitutions are given in Fig. 2.10. Note that the substitutions do not re-introduce any operation or test already removed. This is of course essential. These substitutions make use of y_2.

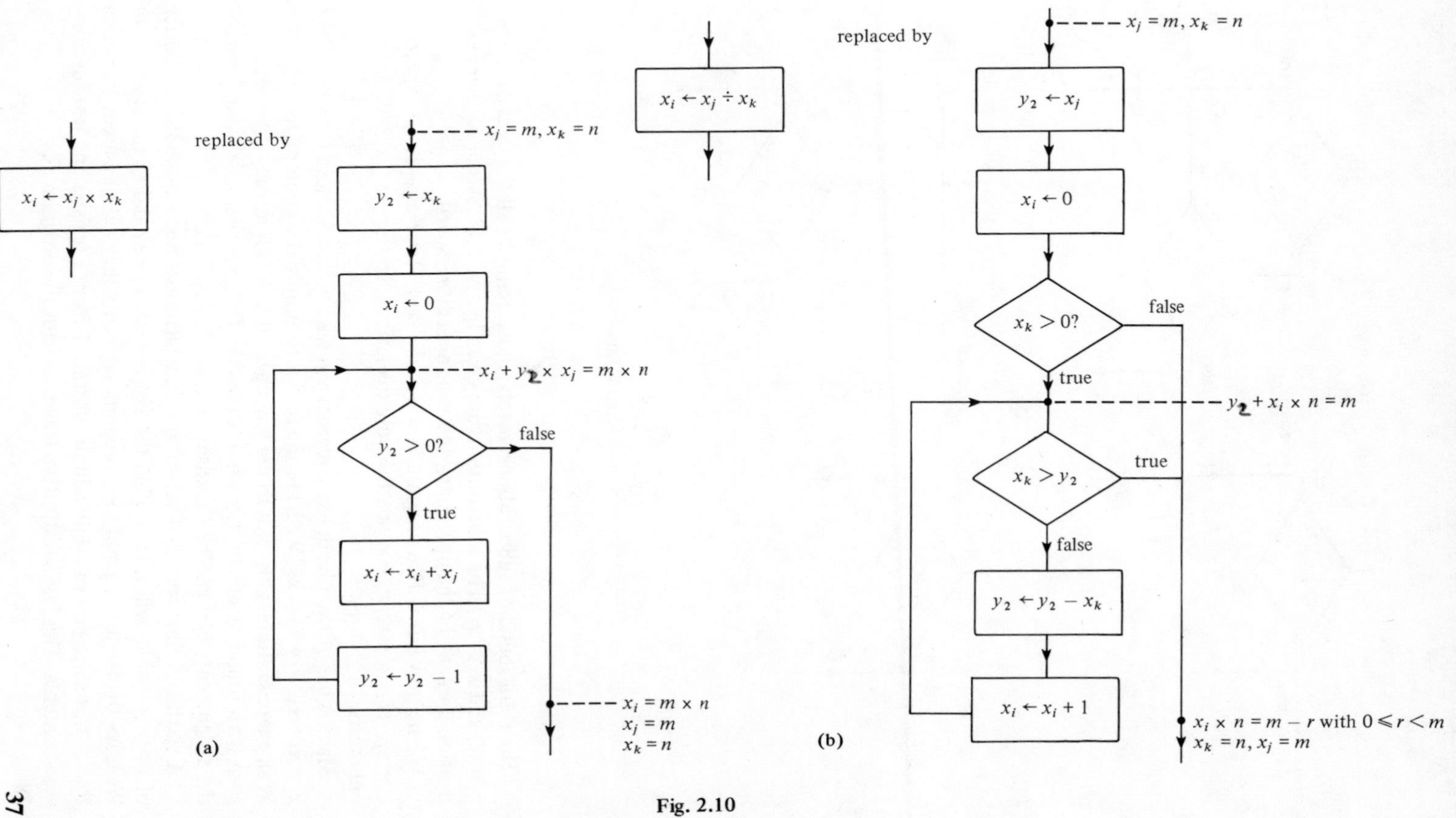

xᵢ ← xⱼ × xₖ
replaced by
xⱼ = m, xₖ = n
y₂ ← xₖ
xᵢ ← 0
xᵢ + y₂ × xⱼ = m × n
y₂ > 0?
false
true
xᵢ ← xᵢ + xⱼ
y₂ ← y₂ − 1
xᵢ = m × n
xⱼ = m
xₖ = n
(a)
xᵢ ← xⱼ ÷ xₖ
replaced by
xⱼ = m, xₖ = n
y₂ ← xⱼ
xᵢ ← 0
xₖ > 0?
false
true
y₂ + xᵢ × n = m
xₖ > y₂
true
false
y₂ ← y₂ − xₖ
xᵢ ← xᵢ + 1
xᵢ × n = m − r with 0 ≤ r < m
xₖ = n, xⱼ = m
(b)

Fig. 2.10

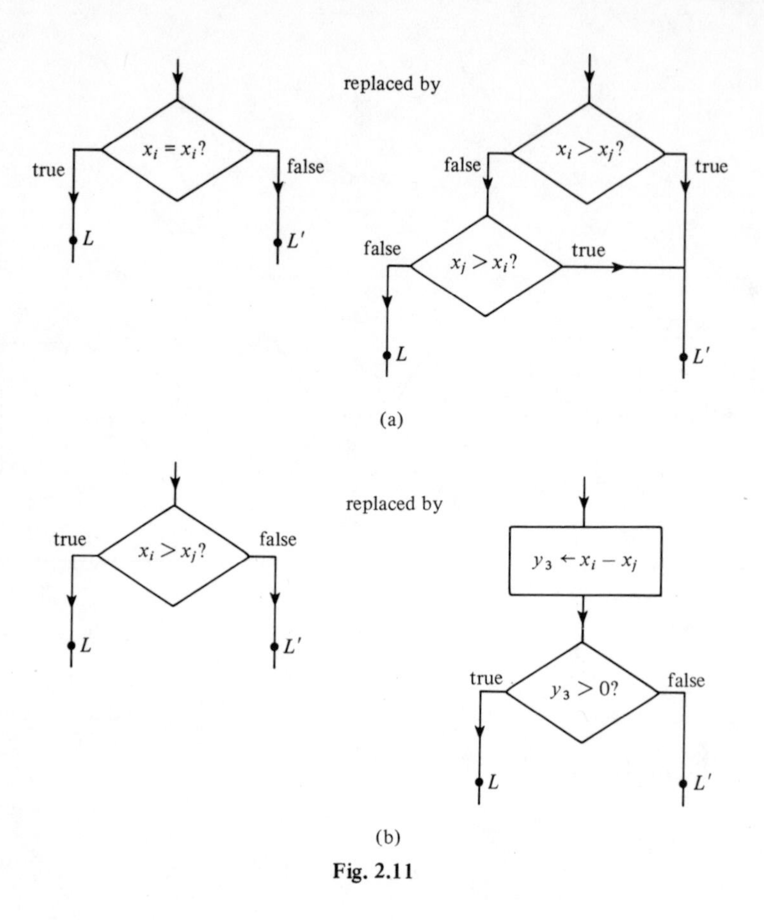

Fig. 2.11

The third round of substitutions, involving y_3, removes all the tests of the form $x_i = x_j?$ and $x_i > x_j?$ The substitutions are given in Fig. 2.11. Again neither expansion uses any of the operations and tests already removed.

We are now left with a program in which $x_i \leftarrow x_i + 1, x_i \leftarrow x_i - 1, x_i \leftarrow x_j + x_k$, $x_i \leftarrow x_j - x_k, x_i \leftarrow m, x_i \leftarrow x_j$, are the only operations, and $x_i = m?, x_i > 0?$ are the only tests.

Making use of the fourth extra register y_4, we can now remove the operations $x_i \leftarrow x_j + x_k, x_i \leftarrow x_j - x_k$. We leave the reader to supply the appropriate substitutions as an exercise. Remember not to use any operation or test already discarded.

A fifth round of substitutions introduces the fifth new variable y_5 and removes the assignments $x_i \leftarrow x_j$. The expansion is given in Fig. 2.12.

A sixth and final round of substitutions, which does not require the introduction of a new variable, will get rid of all the assignments $x_i \leftarrow m$ and all the tests $x_i = m?$ We leave the reader to supply the program segments that must be used. Remember that at this stage you can only add or subtract 1 from a register and test for non-zero contents. This last substitution leaves us with the program π'.

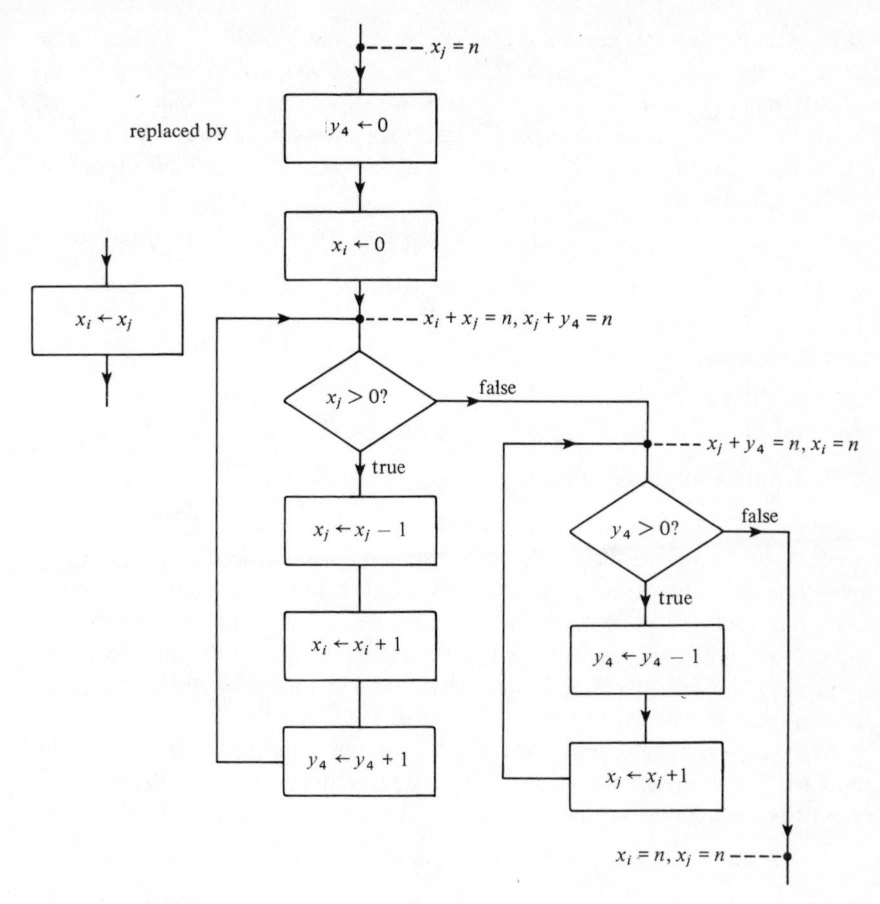

Fig. 2.12

2.2.5 DEFINITION

A register program that only uses operations of the form $x_i \leftarrow x_i - 1, x_i \leftarrow x_i + 1$ and tests of the form $x_i > 0$? is a *simple program.* ▮

2.2.6 THEOREM

Every register function is an associated function of a simple program.

Proof. Let f be a k-adic register function for some $k \geqslant 1$. It is therefore computed by some register program π with $x_1, x_2, \ldots, x_k$ as input registers, and, say, x_i as output register. Applying the above transformation to π, with $y_1, \ldots, y_5$ variables other than $x_1, x_2, \ldots, x_k$, produces a simple program π' which computes f using the same input and output registers. ▮

We can interpret this result as a machine simulation. Consider the machine **SR**, which has the same memory set as **R**, but which can only add or subtract 1 from each register and test for non-zero contents. We take some program π, replace each variable x_i by x_{i+5}, and then apply the transformation described above using x_1, x_2, x_3, x_4, x_5 as the newly introduced variables. The result will be a program π' for **SR** such that

$$\mathbf{R}_\pi = g^{-1} \circ \mathbf{SR}_{\pi'} \circ g,$$

where g: $\{n_i\}_{i=1}^{\infty} \mapsto 0, 0, 0, 0, 0, \{n_i\}_{i=1}^{\infty}$. Therefore,

2.2.7 THEOREM

SR simulates **R**. ▮

2.3 Limited-register machines

There are two ways that we can restrict the memory capacity of **R**. We can either put an upper bound on the number of registers that can be used, or we can put an upper bound on the capacity of each of the infinite number of registers. The first restriction turns out to be no restriction at all. We can prove that **R** is equivalent to the two register machine **SR2**. However, restricting each of the infinite number of memory registers to a bounded capacity results in a machine **BR** which is much 'weaker' than **R**.

To see this, remember that a program for **BR**, being finite, can reference only a finite number of different registers. Thus the program computes on **BR** what is essentially a function over the finite set:

$$\{\langle n_1, n_2, \ldots, n_K \rangle \mid 0 \leqslant n_i \leqslant M \text{ for each } n_i\},$$

where M is the largest number that can be stored in the registers of **BR**, and K is the highest subscript of a variable that appears in the program. Hence there is no program for this machine that can be used to compute the function

$$n \mapsto n + 1, \quad n \in \mathcal{N},$$

as this is a function over an infinite set. Since we can compute this function on **R**, **BR** *cannot* simulate **R**. In chapters 5 and 6, we shall deal with other machines that have essentially finite memories. We shall then see that a modified version of **BR**, a version which has input and output streams that can be used for the encoding and decoding of arbitrarily large numbers, still cannot compute every function that we can compute on **R**. In fact it is equivalent to a machine that only has an input stream and an output stream and no register memory at all!

2.3.1 THE TWO REGISTER MACHINE, **SR2**

We have already implicitly defined **SR2** in exercise 2.1.4. It has two registers, x and y, each capable of recording any non-negative integer. It can add and subtract 1 from each register (as with **R** an attempt to subtract 1 from zero leaves the contents unchanged), and test each register for non-zero contents. More formally its memory set is $\mathcal{N} \times \mathcal{N}$, and it supplies the appropriate interpretation to function names,

$$x \leftarrow x+1 \quad x \leftarrow x-1 \quad y \leftarrow y+1 \quad y \leftarrow y-1$$

and predicate names,

$$x > 0? \quad y > 0?$$

All other names are assigned the totally undefined function.

***Stepwise simulation of* SR *on* SR2** The first task is to find a memory encoding function which enables us to represent the unlimited register memory of **SR** in the two-register memory of **SR2**. To do this we must make use of the unbounded capacity of the **SR2** registers.

First of all each sequence $\{n_i\}_{i=1}^{\infty}$ representing a memory element of **SR** is uniquely recorded by the k-tuple,

$$\langle n_1, n_2, \ldots, n_k \rangle,$$

where n_k is the last non-zero value in the sequence. But by the uniqueness of prime factorization any k-tuple is uniquely recorded by the product,

$$2^{n_1} \times 3^{n_2} \times \cdots \times p_k^{n_k} = \prod_{i=1}^{k} p_i^{n_i}, \quad p_i \text{ the } i\text{th prime number.}$$

Therefore as memory encoding function we can use

$$g: \{n_i\}_{i=1}^{\infty} \mapsto \left\langle \prod_{i=1}^{k} p_i^{n_i}, 0 \right\rangle.$$

Intuitively g records the contents of the x_i-register of **SR** by the exponent of p_i in the prime factorization of the contents of the x-register of **SR2**. The y-register of **SR2** is free for use as working store. Consequently to simulate the operation $x_i \leftarrow x_i + 1$ of **SR** we need to increase the p_i exponent by 1. This is achieved by multiplying x by p_i, that is multiplying x by some constant integer value which happens to be the ith prime number. Figure 2.13 gives the form of a program for **SR2** which will multiply x by any constant n. $\Pi_{x_i \leftarrow x_i+1}$, the program to simulate the operation $x_i \leftarrow x_i + 1$ on **SR2**, is the version of the program for $n = p_i$. Thus when $i = 4$, $p_i = 7$, so we take the version of program that has a sequence of seven $y \leftarrow y + 1$ operations as the simulating program $\Pi_{x_4 \leftarrow x_4+1}$.

To simulate the test $x_i > 0?$, we need to determine whether or not the exponent of p_i is zero, that is whether or not p_i exactly divides x. Figure 2.14 gives the form of a program for **SR2** that tests whether or not any constant n exactly divides x. Again we just take the version of this program with $n = p_i$ to get $\Pi_{x_i > 0?}$.

We leave the reader to supply a program for **SR2** that divides the contents of x by a constant n that exactly divides x. The version of this program, for $n = p_i$, tagged on to the TRUE exit of $\Pi_{x_i > 0?}$, gives the simulating program $\Pi_{x_i \leftarrow x_i - 1}$. The FALSE exit of $\Pi_{x_i > 0?}$ remains as a halt.

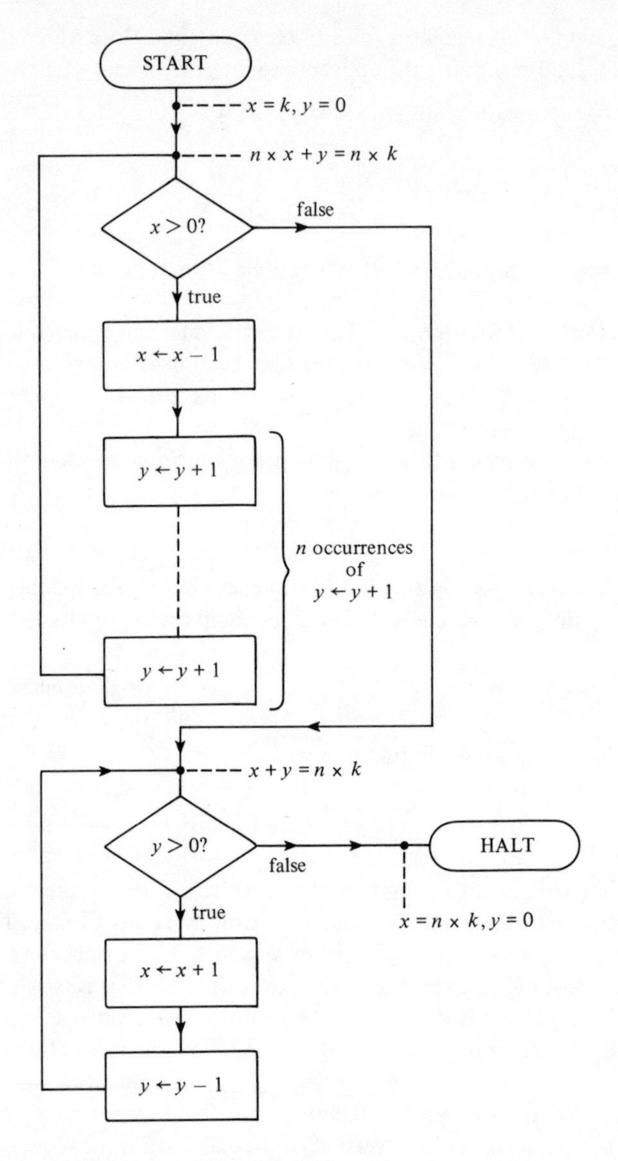

Fig. 2.13

We have proved that **SR2** stepwise simulates **SR**. Hence any function that can be computed using **R** can also be computed on this rudimentary two-register machine. The penalty, of course, is a vastly increased computation time.

2.3.2 EXERCISES*

(1) **SR2** is not the 'smallest' machine that simulates **R**. At the expense of even longer computation time we can make do with just one register. Devise a machine

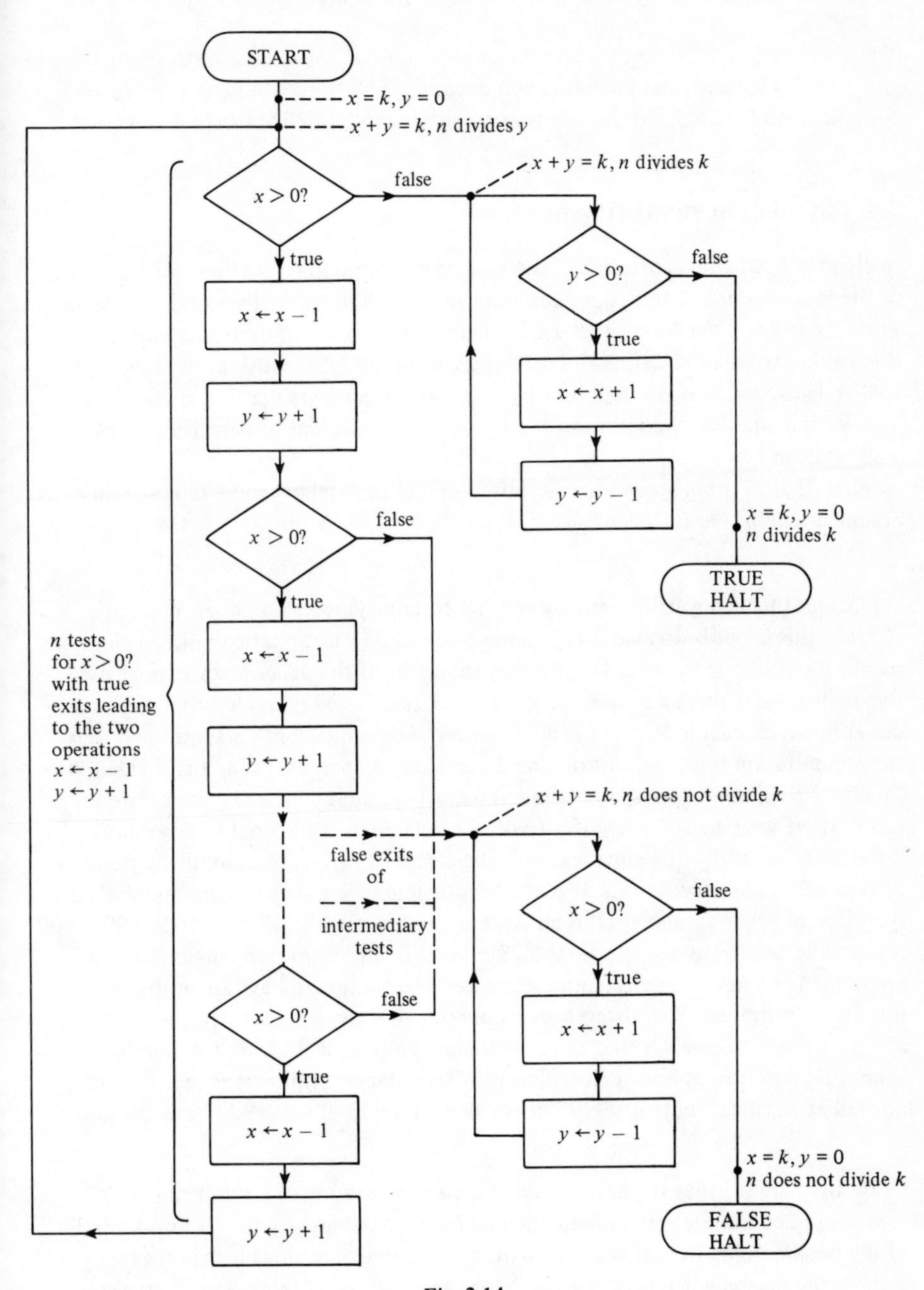
START
$x = k, y = 0$
$x + y = k, n$ divides y
$x > 0?$
false
$x + y = k, n$ divides k
true
$x \leftarrow x - 1$
$y \leftarrow y + 1$
$y > 0?$
false
true
$x \leftarrow x + 1$
$y \leftarrow y - 1$
$x = k, y = 0$
n divides k
TRUE
HALT
$x > 0?$
false
true
$x \leftarrow x - 1$
$y \leftarrow y + 1$
n tests
for $x > 0?$
with true
exits leading
to the two
operations
$x \leftarrow x - 1$
$y \leftarrow y + 1$
$x + y = k, n$ does not divide k
false exits
of
intermediary
tests
$x > 0?$
false
true
$x \leftarrow x + 1$
$y \leftarrow y - 1$
$x > 0?$
false
true
$x \leftarrow x - 1$
$y \leftarrow y + 1$
$x = k, y = 0$
n does not divide k
FALSE
HALT

Fig. 2.14

whose memory set is $\mathcal{N}$ and prove that it stepwise simulates **SR2**. [*Hint*: memory configuration $\langle m,n \rangle$ of **SR2** is uniquely recorded by the single integer $2^n \times 3^m$.]
(2) If a function $f: \mathcal{N} \to \mathcal{N}$ can be computed on **SR** using x_1 as both input and output register, what encoding and decoding functions would be used to compute f on (a) **SR2**, (b) the one register machine you defined in (1)? ∎

2.4 Symbol manipulating machines

In chapter 1, when we introduced the idea of a computable function, we made use of the idea of a pencil-and-paper computation. In 1936 an English mathematician, Turing, defined a machine which he argued was a formalization of this idea[9]. In this section we shall re-define the machine within our framework as the machine **TM(α)**. However, first we shall briefly review the arguments that Turing used to justify his claim that the machine was the formal equivalent of pencil-and-paper computation.

First of all, Turing argued that a finite number of symbols and a tape (of unbounded length) are sufficient:

'Computing is normally done by writing certain symbols on paper. We may suppose this paper is divided into squares like a child's arithmetic book. In elementary arithmetic the two-dimensional character of the paper is sometimes used. But such a use is always avoidable, and I think that it will be agreed that the two-dimensional character of paper is no essential of computation. I assume then that the computation is carried out on one-dimensional paper, i.e. on a tape divided into squares. I shall also suppose that the number of symbols which may be printed is finite. If we were to allow an infinity of symbols, then there would be symbols differing to an arbitrarily small extent. The effect of this restriction of the number of symbols is not very serious. It is always possible to use sequences of symbols in the place of single symbols. Thus an Arabic numeral such as 17 or 99999999999999 is normally treated as a single symbol. Similarly in any European language words are treated as single symbols (Chinese, however, attempts to have an enumerable infinity of symbols). The differences from our point of view between the single and compound symbols is that the compound symbols, if they are too lengthy, cannot be observed at one glance. This is in accordance with experience. We cannot tell at a glance whether 99999999999999 and 99999999999999 are the same.'

He then argued that the action to be taken at any moment is determined by some bounded number of symbols then being observed and by the 'state of mind' of the person doing the calculation. Within our framework this means that the tests of the machine can be restricted to the recognition of sequences of symbols of bounded length. In fact we shall restrict the tests to the recognition of a single symbol under a scanning head that looks at one square at a time. We can always program the test for a fixed-length sequence of symbols. The different 'states of mind' correspond to the different control points of the program.

Finally he argued that the operations of the computer can be restricted to the alteration of symbols on the observed squares and a change in the squares that are observed:

'Let us imagine the operations performed by the computer to be split up into "simple operations" which are so elementary that it is not easy to imagine them further divided. Every such operation consists of some change of the physical system consisting of the computer and his tape. We know the state of the system if we know the sequence of symbols on the tape, which of these are observed by the computer (possibly with a special order), and the state of mind of the computer. We may suppose that in a simple operation not more than one symbol is altered. Any other changes can be split up into simple changes of this kind. The situation in regard to the squares whose symbols may be altered in this way is the same as in regard to the observed squares. We may, therefore, without loss of generality, assume that the squares whose symbols are changed are always "observed squares".

'Besides these changes of symbols, the simple operations must include changes of distribution of observed squares. The new observed squares must be immediately recognisable by the computer. I think it is reasonable to suppose that they can only be squares whose distance from the closest of the immediately previously observed squares does not exceed a certain fixed amount. Let us say that each of the new observed squares is within L squares of an immediately previously observed square . . .

'The simple operations must therefore include:

(a) Changes of the symbol on one of the observed squares.
(b) Changes of one of the squares observed to another square within L squares of one of the previously observed squares.

'It may be that some of these changes necessarily involve a change of state of mind. The most general single operation must therefore be taken to be one of the following:

(A) A possible change (a) of symbol together with a possible change of state of mind.
(B) A possible change (b) of observed squares, together with a possible change of state of mind.'

In our formulation we shall restrict the operations to a change or erasure of the currently scanned symbol and moves left or right of the scanning head to an immediately adjacent square. Changes of fixed length sequences of symbols and moves of the scanning head to more distant squares can be readily programmed. Transferring to a new instruction is the analogue of a change of 'state of mind'.

2.4.1 THE TURING MACHINE TM(α)

The information environment of **TM(α)** is depicted in Fig. 2.15. It comprises a two-way infinitely extendable tape on which is printed a finite string of symbols from a finite alphabet α, the alphabet of tape symbols. To the left and right of this tape string the tape is completely blank. The scanning head is always positioned over one of the non-blank squares except when the tape is completely blank.

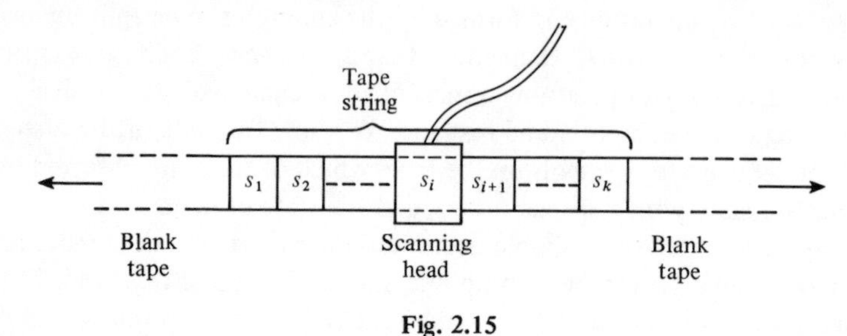

Fig. 2.15

Notation Before we formally define **TM(α)** we need to introduce some notation relating to strings. The empty string (the string recorded on the tape when it is completely blank) we shall denote by Λ. The set of all finite strings of symbols, each of which is contained in the alphabet α, we shall denote by α^*. The empty string is an element of α^*. Thus when $\alpha = \{0, 1\}$,

$$\alpha^* = \{\Lambda, 0, 1, 00, 01, 10, 11, 000, \ldots\}$$

The concatenation of two strings σ_1, σ_2 will be denoted by $\sigma_1\sigma_2$ and is the string σ_1 immediately followed by the string σ_2. For example, if $\sigma_1 = 001$, $\sigma_2 = 101$ then $\sigma_1\sigma_2 = 001101$. Finally $|\sigma|$ denotes the number of symbols in the string σ. Thus $|\Lambda| = 0$. ∎

We can now give the formal definition of **TM(α)**. Its memory set is

$$\{\langle\sigma, i\rangle \mid \sigma \in \alpha^* \text{ and } 0 \leqslant i \leqslant |\sigma|;\ i = 0 \text{ iff } \sigma = \Lambda\},$$

where σ is the tape string and i gives the position of the scanning head from the left end of the string. Thus the configuration of Fig. 2.15 would be recorded by memory set element $\langle s_1 s_2 \cdots s_k, i\rangle$. A completely blank tape is recorded by $\langle\Lambda, 0\rangle$. The set α is any finite alphabet containing *at least two symbols.* In future we shall simply assume this restriction. By alphabet we shall mean a finite set of at least two symbols.

The operations and tests of **TM(α)**, all totally defined, are listed in Table 2.1 together with an informal description and a formal specification. The symbol s_0, which is printed whenever the scanning head moves from a printed square to a blank square, is some designated *initializing symbol* from α. We use $s_1 \cdots \hat{s}_i \cdots s_k$ as an abbreviation for $\langle s_1 s_2 \cdots s_i \cdots s_k, i\rangle$, and $\hat{\Lambda}$ as an abbreviation for $\langle\Lambda, 0\rangle$.

Table 2.1

Operations	Informal description	Formal specification
For each symbol $s \in \alpha$ PRINT s	Changes the scanned symbol to s without moving the scanning head	$\begin{cases} \hat{\Lambda} \mapsto \langle s, 1\rangle \\ s_1 \cdots \hat{s}_i \cdots s_k \mapsto s_1 \cdots \hat{s} \cdots s_k \end{cases}$
MOVE LEFT	Scanning head is moved left one square. If this takes it from a printed square to a blank square s_0 is printed on new square	$\begin{cases} \hat{\Lambda} \mapsto \hat{\Lambda} \\ \langle \sigma, 1\rangle \mapsto \langle s_0 \sigma, 1\rangle \\ \langle \sigma, i\rangle \mapsto \langle \sigma, i-1\rangle \text{ if } i > 0 \end{cases}$
MOVE RIGHT	Analogous to MOVE LEFT	$\begin{cases} \hat{\Lambda} \mapsto \hat{\Lambda} \\ \langle \sigma, \lvert\sigma\rvert\rangle \mapsto \langle \sigma s_0, \lvert\sigma s_0\rvert\rangle \\ \langle \sigma, i\rangle \mapsto \langle \sigma, i+1\rangle \text{ if } 1 \leqslant i < \lvert\sigma\rvert \end{cases}$
ERASE	Only has an effect when scanning head is positioned at the left or right end of the tape string. It erases the scanned symbol and if a symbol is printed on an adjacent square moves the head to that square	$\begin{cases} \hat{\Lambda} \mapsto \hat{\Lambda} \\ \langle \sigma, i\rangle \mapsto \langle \sigma, i\rangle \text{ if } 1 < i < \lvert\sigma\rvert \\ \hat{s}_1 s_2 \cdots s_k \mapsto \hat{s}_2 \cdots s_k \\ s_1 s_2 \cdots \hat{s}_k \mapsto s_1 s_2 \cdots \hat{s}_{k-1} \\ \hat{s} \mapsto \hat{\Lambda} \end{cases}$
Tests		
For each $s \in \alpha$ s?	Tests whether scanning head is over a square on which s is printed. All the tests return false if the tape is completely blank.	$\begin{cases} \hat{\Lambda} \mapsto \text{false} \\ s_1 \cdots \hat{s}_i \cdots s_k \mapsto \begin{cases} \text{true if } s_i = s \\ \text{false if } s_i \neq s \end{cases} \end{cases}$
LEFT END?	Tests whether scanning head is positioned over leftmost symbol of tape string. It returns true if tape is completely blank	$\begin{cases} \hat{\Lambda} \mapsto \text{true} \\ \langle \sigma, i\rangle \mapsto \begin{cases} \text{true if } i = 1 \\ \text{false if } 1 < i \leqslant \lvert\sigma\rvert \end{cases} \end{cases}$
RIGHT END?	Analogous to LEFT END?	$\langle \sigma, i\rangle \mapsto \begin{cases} \text{true if } i = \lvert\sigma\rvert \\ \text{false if } 1 \leqslant i < \lvert\sigma\rvert \end{cases}$

We shall be particularly interested in the version of the Turing machine with $\alpha = \{0, 1\}$ and 0 as the initializing symbol. We use Σ as the conventional name for the two-symbol alphabet $\{0, 1\}$. We shall also drop the reference to the tape alphabet when $\alpha = \Sigma$, and use **TM** as the name for **TM(Σ)**.

Standard encoder and decoder The most obvious use of **TM**(α) is to compute functions with arguments and values that are strings. We therefore take α^* to be the standard input/output set of **TM**(α), and as the standard encoder and decoder we take the functions:

$$\text{instring}: \sigma \mapsto \begin{cases} \langle \sigma, 1 \rangle & \text{if } \sigma \neq \Lambda \\ \langle \Lambda, 0 \rangle & \text{if } \sigma = \Lambda \end{cases}$$

$$\text{outstring}: \langle \sigma, i \rangle \mapsto \sigma$$

respectively. Intuitively we encode a non-empty σ by printing it on a completely blank tape and positioning the head at the left end of σ. If $\sigma = \Lambda$ the tape is left blank with the head positioned anywhere along the blank tape. We decode by taking the result as the entire string printed on the tape, irrespective of the position of the head.

Thus for any program π,

$$\text{outstring} \circ \mathbf{TM}(\alpha)_\pi \circ \text{instring}$$

is a partial function over α^*.

2.4.2 EXAMPLE PROGRAM FOR TM

Figure 2.16 gives the overall form of a program Π_{pal} to test whether or not the input string is a palindrome. A palindrome is a string which comprises the same sequence of symbols read forwards or backwards, for example 'able was I ere I saw elba'. Formally we can define a palindrome over the alphabet Σ as either:

(a) the empty string, or
(b) a string of length one, or
(c) a string of the form $0\,\sigma'\,0$ or $1\,\sigma'\,1$ where σ' is a palindrome.

The program Π_{pal} contains some 'high-level' operations and tests. The reader should satisfy himself that programs can be written to implement these using only the machine level facilities of **TM**. We also ask the reader to check that the attached assertions satisfy the requirements of a correctness proof. The computation of the program is always completed, since all the operations and tests are totally defined and each execution of the loop reduces the number of symbols in the tape string by two. Control must leave the loop when the length of the tape string has been reduced to zero or one.

Thus Π_{pal} is such that

$$\text{outstring} \circ \mathbf{TM}_{\Pi_{\text{pal}}} \circ \text{instring}(\sigma) = \begin{cases} 0 & \text{if } \sigma \text{ is a palindrome} \\ 1 & \text{otherwise.} \end{cases}$$

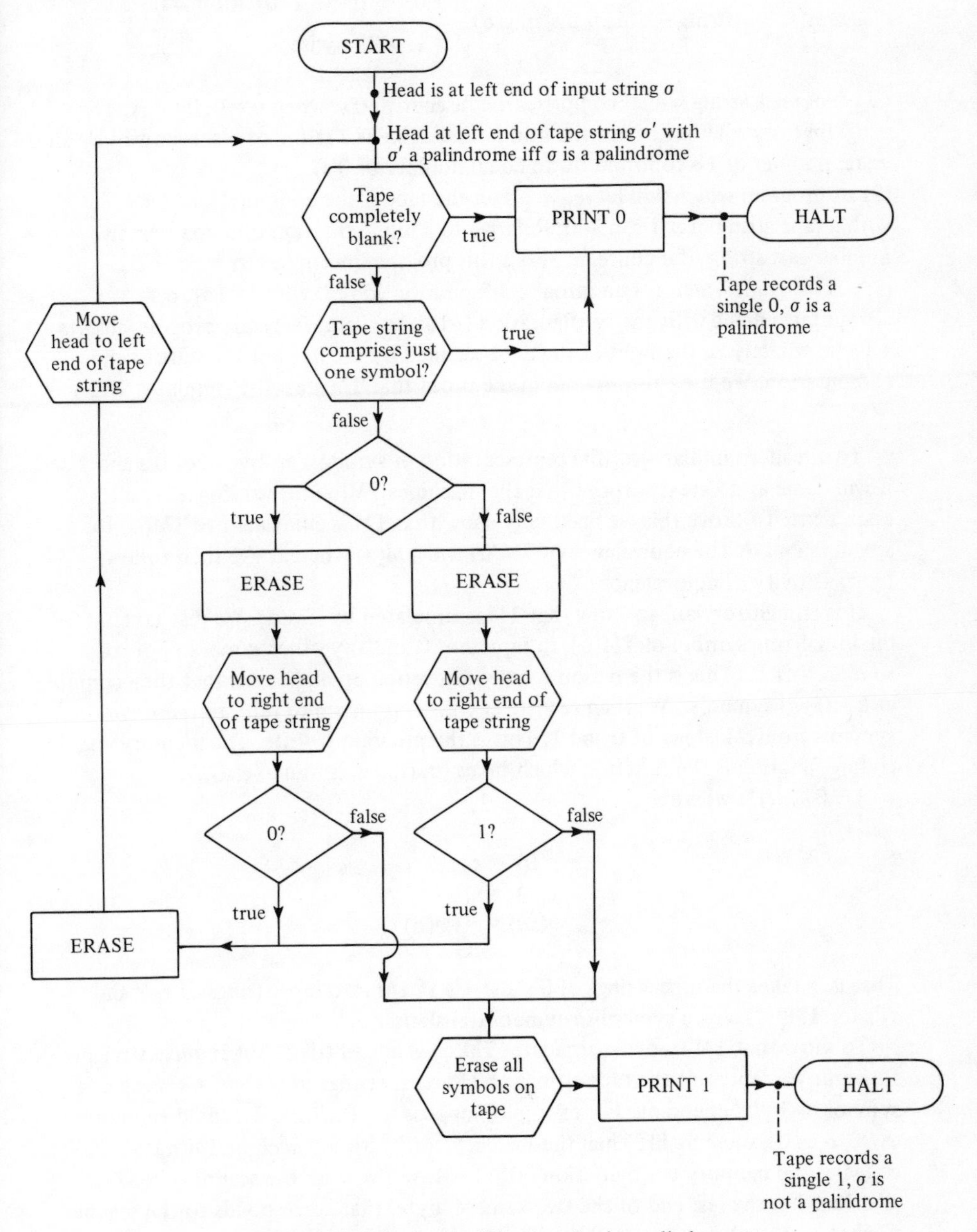

Fig. 2.16 Program to test if input string is a palindrome

2.4.3 EXERCISE

Write and prove correct the following programs for **TM**:

(1) A program π such that,

$$\text{outstring} \circ \mathbf{TM}_\pi \circ \text{instring}(\sigma) = \begin{cases} 0 & \text{if } \sigma = 0^n 1^n 0^n \text{ for } n \geqslant 0 \\ 1 & \text{otherwise} \end{cases}$$

(0^n denotes a string which comprises n consecutive 0's; when $n = 0$, $0^n = \Lambda$. The program tests whether or not the initial tape string is a string of 0's, followed by an equal number of 1's followed by an equal number of 0's).

(2) A program which will leave $2n$ 1's on the tape if the computation starts with a tape string of n 1's, $n \geqslant 0$. Relative to a representation of a non-negative number as a string of n consecutive 1's this program multiplies its input by 2.

(3)* A program which for an initial configuration $\langle \sigma\sigma', i \rangle$ with $i = |\sigma|$, $\sigma \neq \Lambda$, always terminates with the configuration $\langle \sigma 1 \sigma', 1 \rangle$. (Intuitively the program inserts a 1 immediately to the right of the digit scanned by the head at the start of the computation. We use this program in the proof that **TM** stepwise simulates **SR2**.) ∎

To a reader familiar with the representation of symbols as 'bytes' of 0's and 1's it will come as no great surprise that the machines **TM**(α) for varying α are all equivalent. To prove this we need only show that **TM** is equivalent to **TM**(α) for any alphabet α. The equivalence of **TM**(α) and **TM**(β) where $\alpha \neq \beta$ then follows by transitivity of equivalence.

It is straightforward to show that **TM** is simulated by **TM**(α). We just take s_0, the initializing symbol of **TM**(α), to represent 0 and any other symbol s_1 of α to represent 1. (This is the reason for the restriction on alphabets, that they contain at least two symbols.) We then rewrite any given program to refer to these two symbols from α instead of 0 and 1. This is the program rewrite. The memory encoding function is the function which takes $\langle \sigma, i \rangle$, $\sigma \in \Sigma^*$ into $\langle g(\sigma), i \rangle$, $g(\sigma) \in \{s_0, s_1\}^*$, where

$$\begin{aligned} g(0) &= s_0, \\ g(1) &= s_1, \\ g(s\sigma) &= g(s)g(\sigma). \end{aligned}$$

That is, g takes the tape strings of 0's and 1's of **TM** into tape strings of s_0's and s_1's for **TM**(α) using a symbol-to-symbol translation.

To show that **TM** stepwise simulates **TM**(α) is not so trivial but is quite straightforward. We represent the tape strings of **TM**(α) as strings of 0's and 1's using a symbol-to-'byte' encoding. For example, suppose $\alpha = \{a, b, c\}$. We could represent a as 00, b as 01 and c as 11. Then the memory configuration $a\hat{c}cb$ of **TM**(α) is encoded as the memory configuration $00\hat{1}11101$ of **TM**, with the scanning head positioned at the left end of the two-symbol 'byte' that corresponds to the scanned symbol of **TM**(α). In general if α contains n symbols $s_0, s_1, \ldots, s_{n-1}$ and

$2^{k-1} < n \leqslant 2^k$, we can uniquely represent each symbol in α as a *k-byte* of 0's and 1's. Then the memory encoding function for the stepwise simulation is

$$g: \langle \sigma, i \rangle \mapsto \langle h(\sigma), (i-1) \times k + 1 \rangle,$$

where for each $s \in \alpha$, $h(s)$ is the k-byte representing s and $h(s\sigma) = h(s)h(\sigma)$.

The programs for **TM** that simulate the operations and tests of **TM**(α) must update and examine the k-bytes. For example, the program to simulate PRINT s must overprint the k-byte whose left-most symbol is currently under the scanning head of **TM** with the k-byte that represents s. It then repositions the scanning head over the left-most symbol of the new k-byte. We leave the reader to complete the proof of stepwise simulation as an exercise.

We have proved:

2.4.4 THEOREM

The machines **TM**(α), for varying alphabets α, constitute a family of equivalent machines. ∎

We have proposed the Turing machine as a formalization of the idea of pencil-and-paper computation. However, the computation of any program on any machine can be followed using pencil and paper. This is because we require each of the operations and tests of a machine to be defined by functions that can be hand computed (given enough paper and time). Thus the Turing machine should be able to simulate any machine. In particular it should be able to simulate any of the register machines that we have considered so far.

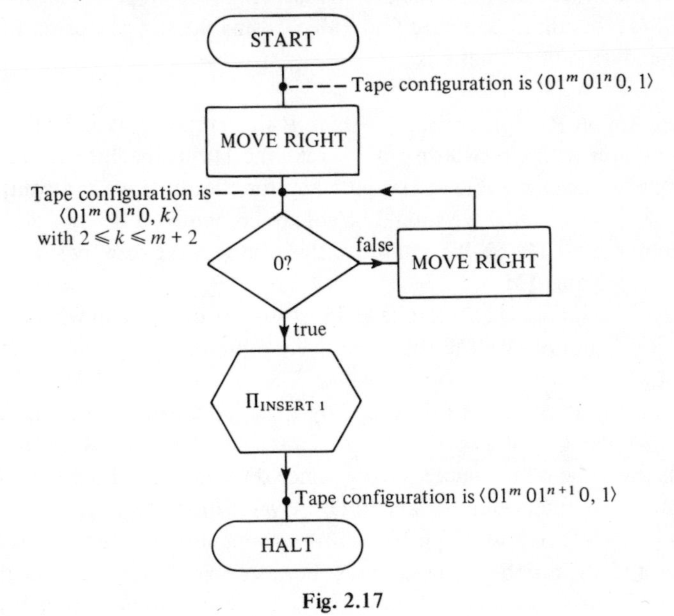

Fig. 2.17

***Stepwise simulation of* SR2 *by* TM** To represent the memory configurations of **SR2** as configurations for **TM**, we use the encoding function

$$g: \langle m,n \rangle \mapsto \langle 01^m 01^n 0, 1 \rangle,$$

which records the contents of the two registers of **SR2** by substrings of the corresponding number of 1's. The 0's mark the ends of the two substrings.

Relative to this memory encoding, Fig. 2.17 is the program for **TM** that simulates the **SR2** operation $y \leftarrow y + 1$. $\Pi_{\text{INSERT 1}}$ is the program of exercise 2.4.3(3). That program on its own simulates the operation $x \leftarrow x + 1$. We leave it to the reader to give the programs that simulate each of the other operations and tests of **SR2**. All this should be very straightforward by now.

Since **SR2** simulates **R**, it follows that the Turing machine simulates **R**. Thus every function that we can compute using **R**, we can compute using **TM**(α). In particular we can compute any register function. However, we can prove this fact more directly. We already know that every register function is the associated function of some simple program for **R**. Thus let us suppose that $f: \mathcal{N}^k \rightarrow \mathcal{N}$ is a register function. There is a simple program π for **R** that computes f using $x_1, x_2, \ldots, x_k$ as input registers and, say, x_i as output register. Let N be the highest subscript of a variable used by π. We rewrite π so that it manipulates memory configurations of $TM(\alpha)$, $\alpha = \{0, 1, x_1, x_2, \ldots, x_N\}$, of the form

$$\hat{x}_1 11 \ldots 1 x_2 11 \ldots 1 x_3 1 \ldots x_{N-1} 111 \ldots x_N 111 \ldots 10,$$

with the number of consecutive 1's immediately following the symbol x_i giving the contents of the x_i register. For example, the operation $x_i \leftarrow x_i + 1$ of π is replaced by a sub-program for **TM** that moves the scanning head right until it finds x_i. It then inserts a 1 and moves the head back to the left end of the tape string. We can now use the resulting program to compute f on **TM**(α), using the straightforward (and obvious) encoding and decoding functions.

***Simulating* TM *on* R** The register machine **R** was proposed as a idealization of a digital computer with a register memory. Like the Turing machine it should be a general-purpose machine able to compute any function that we can compute on any machine. In particular we should be able to compute on **R** any function that we can compute on **TM**(α). We can prove this is in fact the case by showing that **R** stepwise simulates **TM**.

We leave the details as an exercise and just suggest one way in which the memory configurations of **TM** can be uniquely represented as memory configurations of **R**.

Each configuration of **TM** is recorded by an ordered pair $\langle \sigma, i \rangle$ comprising a string from Σ^* and a non-negative integer. In the simulation on **R**, i can simply be held as the value of a variable, say x_1. Since σ is a string of binary digits we could read it as a binary number and hold the value in another variable x_2. However, this is just a little too simple. It will not distinguish between strings that differ with respect to the number of leading 0's. For example, 0011 and 11 both represent the number 3 but are different strings. We can achieve a unique representation if we also record the length of the tape string as the value of a third variable x_3. Then the memory configuration $0\hat{0}11$ is recorded by $x_1 = 2, x_2 = 3, x_3 = 4$, whereas the configuration $1\hat{1}$ is recorded by $x_1 = 2, x_2 = 3, x_3 = 2$. There are many other ways of uniquely recording the memory configurations of **TM** as non-negative integers. The more redundant the encoding, the easier it should be to write the programs for **R** that simulate the operations and tests of **TM**. For example, we might also use a fourth variable that has the value 0 or 1 and indicates which symbol is currently being scanned. This must be updated by the programs that simulate the PRINTs and MOVEs of **TM** but makes the symbol test programs trivial.

2.4.5 EXERCISES

(1) Complete the proof that **TM** stepwise simulates **TM**(α).
(2) Relative to any chosen representation of the memory set of **TM** in the memory set of **R**, prove that **R** stepwise simulates **TM**.
(3) Complete the proof that **TM** stepwise simulates **SR2**.
(4) Suppose that the Turing machine tape is only infinitely extendable to the right and that the scanning head cannot move to the left of the tape string σ. Modify the definition of the MOVE LEFT operation to take into account this restriction and show that the new version of the machine stepwise simulates **TM**.
(5)* If we give the Turing machine some extra tapes, each with its own scanning head, we may be able to compute some extra functions. Define a variant of the Turing machine which has k two-way infinitely extendable tapes, each with its own scanning head. Function and predicate names must now indicate the tape as well as the operation or test. For example, MOVE LEFT 2 will name the operation to move the head on the second tape one place to the left. Prove that the machine will not compute any function that we cannot already compute on **TM**(α).
(6)* The Post machine **PM** is a machine with an information environment that comprises an infinitely long tape with a read head and a write head (see Fig. 2.18). The non-blank portion of the tape is the slack between the read and write heads and it records a string $\sigma \in \Sigma^*$. The read head is always positioned just to the left

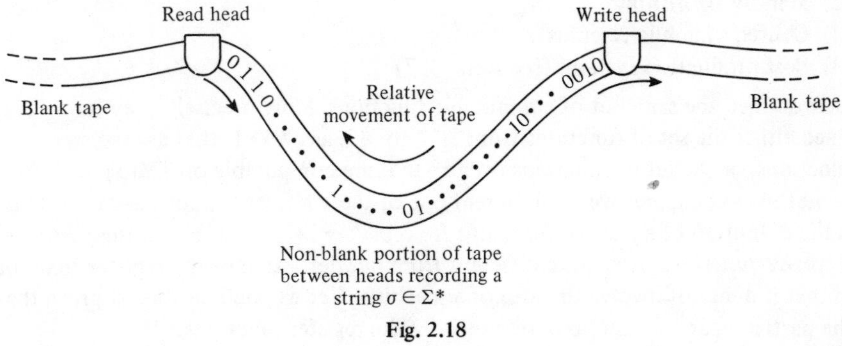

Fig. 2.18

of the first symbol of σ, and the write head just to the right of the last symbol of σ. The two heads can move independently along the tape. However, each can move only to the right. The move operation of the read head erases the first symbol of σ as the head takes up its new position. A print of 0 or 1 by the write head also moves the head one position to the right, and so its effect is to add a 0 or a 1 at the back end of σ. The read head can test whether the symbol at the front of σ is 0 or 1. When both tests return false, there is no slack and the tape string is Λ. There are no tests for the write head.

Define **PM** as an abstract machine. Prove that it is equivalent to **TM**. [*Hint*: Make use of **SR2** to prove that **PM** simulates **TM**.]

(7)** Sketch a proof that the Turing machine is universal in the following sense. Show that there is a single program π for **TM**, which given a suitable encoding of any **TM** program π' and any **TM** memory configuration $\langle \sigma, i \rangle$ as data, will compute the value of $\mathbf{TM}_{\pi'}(\langle \sigma, i \rangle)$ if the result is defined.

Make use of the result of (5) above. Just indicate the overall form of the interpreting program π. ∎

2.5 Church's thesis

The results of the preceding sections have shown that **R**, **SR**, **SR2**, **TM**(α) and **PM** are equivalent machines. Thus the classes of functions that can be computed using these various machines are identical. We claim that this single class of functions is precisely the class of partial functions that are computable in an intuitive sense. More explicitly we claim that each function we can compute using these machines is intuitively a computable function, and that whenever the mapping between the source set and target set of a function can be algorithmically specified, then that function can be computed using a flowchart program on any of these machines. This claim is generally referred to as *Church's thesis*, or as the *Church–Turing thesis.*

We cannot prove the thesis, for it equates an intuitive concept with a mathematical explication. In its favour, there is Turing's argument that his machine is an appropriate formalization of pencil-and-paper computation. Moreover all other attempts to formalize the notion of a computable function, including for example:

(1) Kleene recursion equations[4],
(2) Markov algorithms[5],
(3) Church's lambda calculus[1],
(4) Post production systems (see Refs. 3, 7)

have defined the same set of computable functions. More precisely they have defined either the set of functions from $\mathcal{N}^k$ to $\mathcal{N}$, any $k \geqslant 1$, that are register functions, or the set of functions over α^* that are computable on **TM**(α).

In the next chapter we shall present one of these alternative formulations. This is the definition of a class of functions from $\mathcal{N}^k \to \mathcal{N}$, $k \geqslant 1$, called the *partial recursive functions.* It is quite different from our definition of the register functions in that it does not involve the idea of a machine. Yet we shall be able to prove that the partial recursive functions are precisely the register functions.

Adopting Church's thesis as a working hypothesis has the following consequences. It means that we can show that a function is computable on any of the above machines simply by describing an informal algorithm to compute the function. More importantly it means that we can show that a function is *not computable* by showing that it cannot be computed by one of these machines. In chapter 4 we shall use Church's thesis in just this way.

2.6 Notes and references

The Turing machine was first defined in 1936[9]. The machine as defined here is much closer to Wang's programmable Turing machine[10]. A programmable register machine is defined by Sheperdson and Sturgis[8]. The machine **SR2** is usually referred to as a two-counter machine. The proof that it is equivalent to the Turing machine was first given by Minsky[7] (see also Ref. 6).

Jones[3] gives several different formalizations of the concept of a computable function and proves their equivalence. A survey of the evidence for Church's Thesis appears in Kleene[4].

The chief advocate of structured programming is Dijkstra[2]. As commonly used, the term 'structured programming' implies not only a hierarchical development of the program but a restriction on the control structure of each program in the hierarchy. Thus, overlapping or multi-exit loops are not allowed. We shall study this type of program structure in the next chapter. The 'structured programming' that is simply a progression of stepwise simulations is generally referred to as 'stepwise refinement'[11].

References

1. Church, A., *The Calculi of Lambda-Conversion*, *Ann. Math. Studies*, **6**, Princeton (1943)
2. Dijkstra, E. W., 'Notes on structured programming', in *Structured Programming*, (O. J. Dahl, E. W. Dijkstra, and C. A. R. Hoare, eds.) Academic Press, New York (1972)
3. Jones, N. D., *Computability Theory*, Academic Press, London (1973)
4. Kleene, S. C., *Introduction to Metamathematics*, Van Nostrand, Princeton, USA (1952)
5. Markov, A. A., *The Theory of Algorithms* (English translation) National Science Foundation, Washington, D.C. (1961)
6. Minsky, M. L., *Computation: Finite and Infinite Machines*, Prentice-Hall, Englewood Cliffs, New Jersey (1967)
7. Minsky, M. L., 'Recursive unsolvability of Post's problem of "Tag" and other topics in theory of Turing machines', *Ann. Math.*, **74**, 437–454 (1961)
8. Sheperdson, J. C. and R. E. Sturgis, 'The computability of partial recursive functions', *J. Assoc. Comp. Mach.*, **10**, 217–255 (1963)
9. Turing, A. M., 'On computable numbers, with an application to the Entscheidungsproblem', *Proc. London Math. Soc.* (2)**42**, 230–265 (1936)
10. Wang, H., 'A variant to Turing's theory of computing machines', *J. Assoc. Comp. Mach.*, **4**, 63–92 (1957).
11. Wirth, N., 'Program development by stepwise refinement', *Comm. Assoc. Comp. Mach.*, **14**(4), 221–227 (April 1971)

3 Count programs, while programs and recursively defined functions

In this chapter we examine more closely the class of register functions. We do this by looking at the associated functions of certain restricted classes of programs. We shall discover that one class of programs, the class of while programs, is such that every register function is the associated function of some program in the class. By devising methods for 'reading-off' the associated functions of a while program from its sub-program structure, we shall arrive at an alternative characterization of the register functions. This is a direct characterization as a set of functions closed under various forms of function definition. By showing that these same functions can be defined using somewhat different forms of function definition, we prove that the register functions are the *partial recursive functions.*

3.1 Count programs and while programs

Count programs and while programs are subsets of the set of register programs. We shall define these subsets inductively. That is, we shall first specify a set of register programs as basic programs. We shall then give methods for combining programs so as to construct new programs. The classes of programs in which we are interested will then be defined as just those programs that can be constructed from the basic programs using selected methods of program construction. More mathematically, we shall define each class as the smallest class that includes the basic programs and is closed under certain specified methods of program construction.

We choose inductive definitions for the classes of programs for two reasons. Firstly, the inductive definition gives each non-basic program an implicit overall structure corresponding to the program construction that finally constructs the program. (If there are several such constructions, then the program will have several different overall structures.) More importantly, it enables us to prove properties of all the programs in the class by *structural induction.* To show that something is true of every object in an inductively defined class of objects, we merely need to show that it is true of all the basic objects and that its truth is preserved by the various methods for constructing new objects. Note that this corresponds to doing an induction on the overall structure of each object in the class. Hence the name *structural* induction.

Basic programs As basic programs, we take the empty program and all register programs that have one operation instruction and no test instructions:

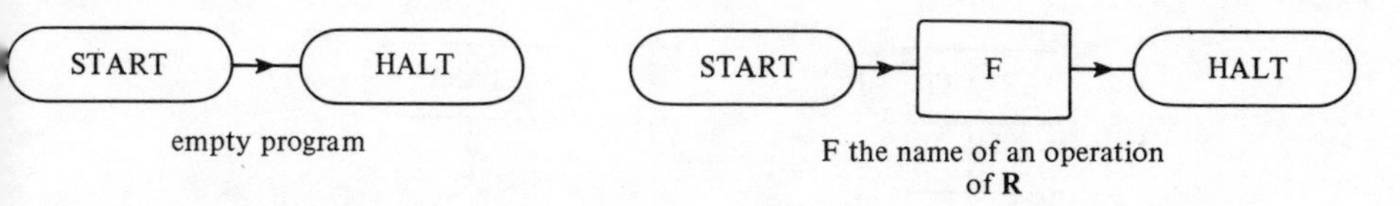

empty program

F the name of an operation of **R**

Methods of program construction In all we shall make use of four methods of program construction which we call *linear concatenation, conditional branching, count loop* and *while loop*. The constructions are depicted in Fig. 3.1. Linear concatenation and conditional branching each construct a new program from two given programs π and π'. The count and while constructions construct a new program using just one program π. The programs used in the constructions are assumed to have exactly one halt instruction.

3.1.1 DEFINITIONS

(1) The *conditional programs* comprise the smallest class of programs that includes all the basic programs and is closed under linear concatenation and conditional branching.
(2) The *count programs* comprise the smallest of programs that includes all the basic programs and is closed under linear concatenation, conditional branching and the count loop construction.
(3) The *while programs* comprise the smallest class of programs that includes all the basic programs and is closed under linear concatenation, conditional branching and the while loop construction. ∎

Figure 3.2 shows a while program partly decomposed into its sub-program structure.

Note that every count program is a while program. This is because the count loop construction is equivalent to a linear concatenation followed by a while construction. There are of course while programs that are not count programs. The count programs are of interest because:

(1) they are a subset of the while programs,
(2) whether or not a program is a count program can be determined by a fairly straightforward algorithmic check,
(3) every program in the subset computes a total function on **R**.

We leave the reader to satisfy himself regarding (2). We prove (3) by structural induction:

3.1.2 THEOREM

If π is a count program then $\mathbf{R}_\pi$ is a total function.

Proof. First we check that each of the basic programs computes a total function on **R**. The empty program computes the totally defined identity function, and since each operation of **R** is totally defined, each one operation instruction program computes a total function.

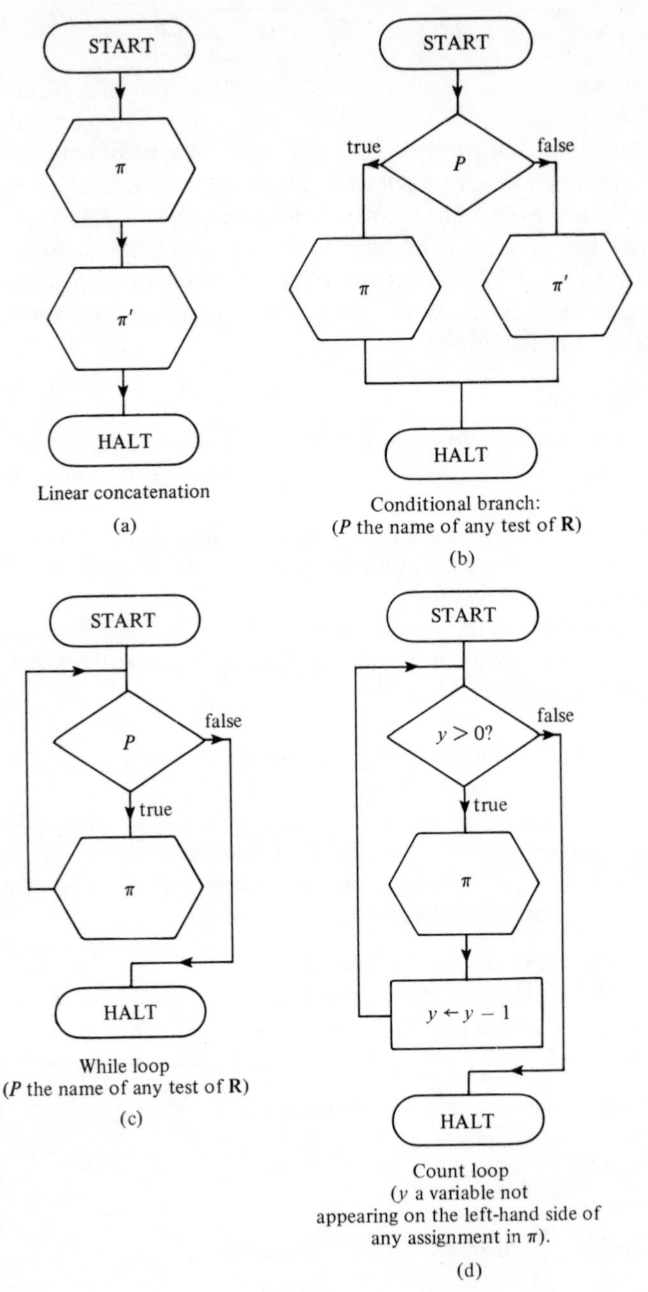

Fig. 3.1

Next we show that the property of computing a total function is preserved by linear concatenation, conditional branching and the count loop construction. For linear concatenation it is obvious. It is preserved by conditional branching since

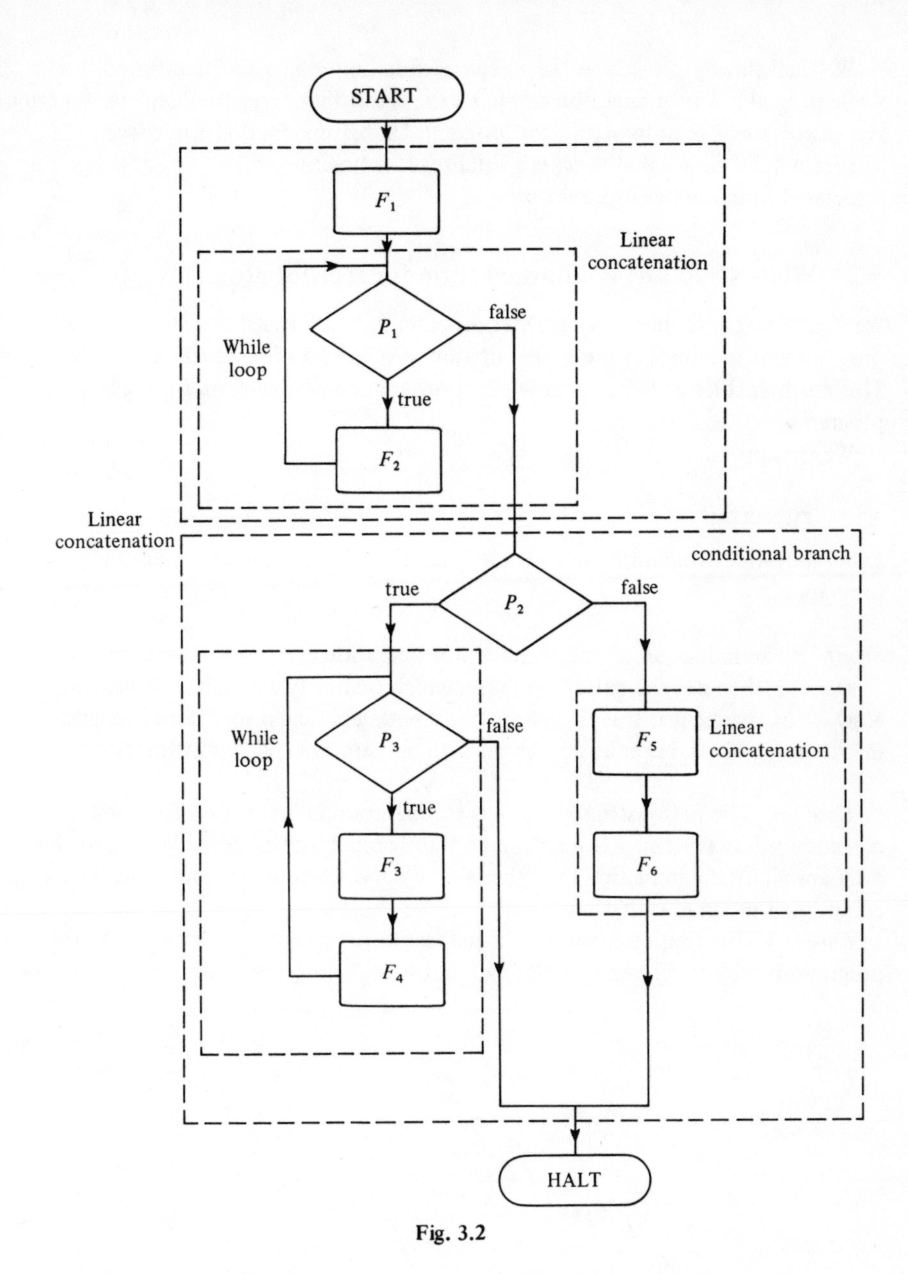

Fig. 3.2

each **R** test is totally defined. Finally it is preserved by the count loop construction since the non-negative value of count variable y is reduced by one each time round the loop (the condition that y does not appear on the left-hand side of any assignment in π ensures this), and execution of the loop terminates when it is reduced to zero. ∎

We shall shortly prove that every register function is an associated function of a while program. A neat analogue would be the result that every total register function is an associated function of a count program. Unfortunately this is not true. Theorem 4.3.2 shows that there is a total register function which cannot be an associated function of any count program.

3.2 While structure as a normal form for register programs

We shall now prove that every register program π can be transformed into a while program which computes the same function over the set of registers used by π. This result enables us to consider while structure as a normal form for register programs.

We first prove:

3.2.1 THEOREM

Every loop-free program π can be transformed into an equivalent conditional program π'.

Proof. By an induction on the number n of operation and test instructions in π.

If $n = 0$, then π is the empty program, which is already a conditional program. Now let us assume it is true for all programs with less than n operation and test instructions, $n > 0$. Let π be a program with n operation and test instructions.

Case (a). The first instruction of π is an operation instruction I. The program π_0 produced by deleting I from π can be transformed into an equivalent conditional program π_0' by the induction hypothesis. The concatenation of I and π_0' is then a conditional program equivalent to π.

Case (b). The first instruction of π is a test instruction I. Let π_t and π_f be the programs produced from π by deleting I and substituting, respectively, its true

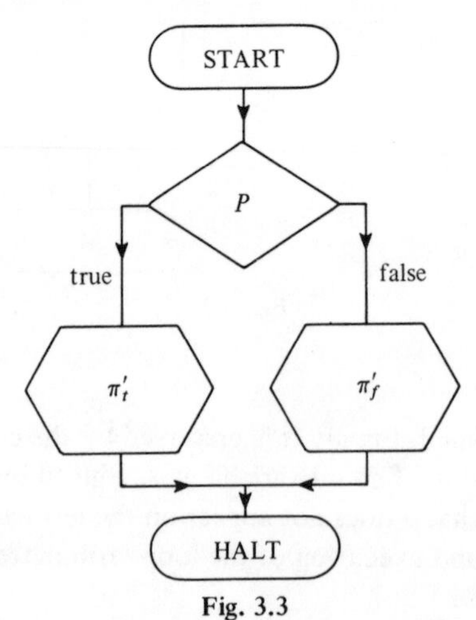

Fig. 3.3

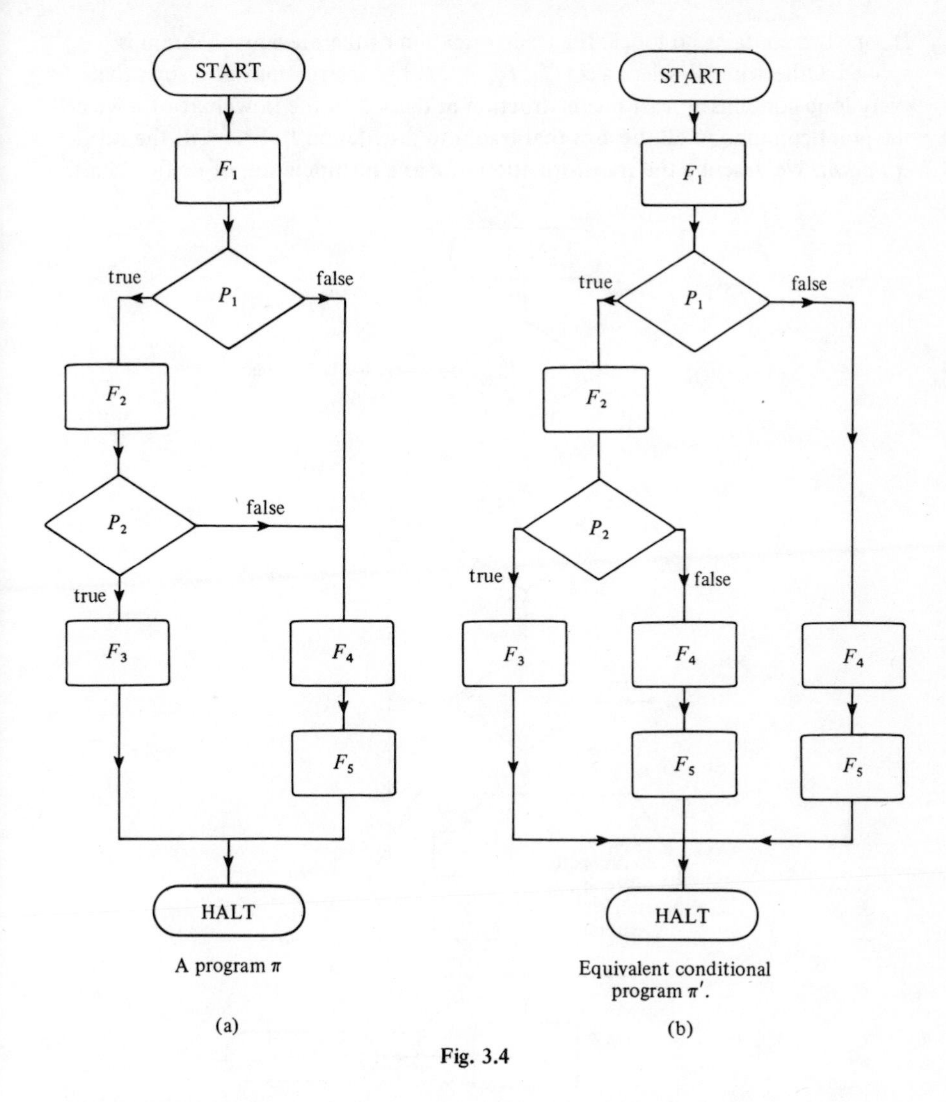

A program π

(a)

Equivalent conditional program π'.

(b)

Fig. 3.4

exit label and its false exit label in the start instruction. By induction hypothesis π_t and π_f each can be transformed into equivalent conditional programs π'_t and π'_f. Then the program of Fig. 3.3, where P is the test name of I, is a conditional program equivalent to π. ∎

The transformation implicit in the above proof is illustrated in Fig. 3.4.

3.2.2 THEOREM

By making use of at most one extra variable, every register program π can be transformed into a while program which computes the same function over the set of registers used by π.

Proof. If π contains no loops, the transformation of the previous theorem is applied. Otherwise we select a set $\{I_1, I_2, \ldots, I_n\}$ of instructions of π such that every loop contains at least one instruction in the set. In the flowchart of π we call the point common to all the arcs that lead into instruction I_i, $1 \leqslant i \leqslant n$, the ith *cut-point.* We describe the transformation of π as a manipulation of its flowchart.

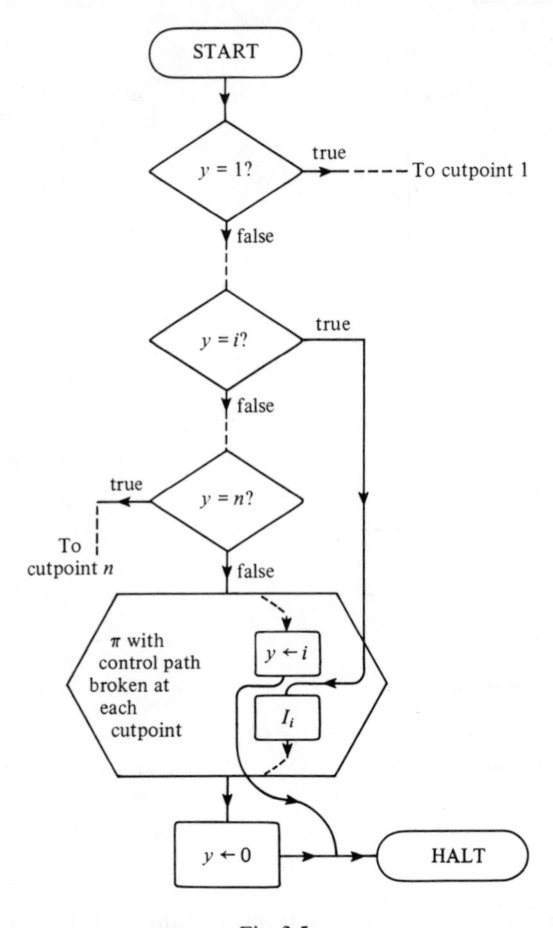

Fig. 3.5

First we transform π into a loop-free program π' as follows. We break the control path of each loop by inserting at the ith cutpoint, $1 \leqslant i \leqslant n$, an assignment $y \leftarrow i$, where y is a variable not appearing in π, with the exit path of the assignment leading immediately to the halt. Just before the halt we insert the assignment $y \leftarrow 0$. Finally, immediately after the start, we insert a sequence of tests on the value of y such that when the value of y is i, $1 \leqslant i \leqslant n$, the program will be entered at the ith cutpoint instruction, and for any other value of y the program is entered at its normal first instruction. Figure 3.5 illustrates the form of this loop-free program π'.

Note that π' is such that if its computation commences with y having a value greater than n, then the computation follows exactly that of π until a cut-point is reached. If it is the ith cut-point, i is assigned to y to record the fact that control had reached this point. If the computation is made to proceed by re-entering the program π' it will recommence at the ith cut-point, and continue until control reaches another cut-point. Thus π' can be used to re-produce the computation of π in spurts. In each spurt, control moves from one cut-point to the next. Note that if on re-entering π' control would have reached the halt, then y is assigned a zero value.

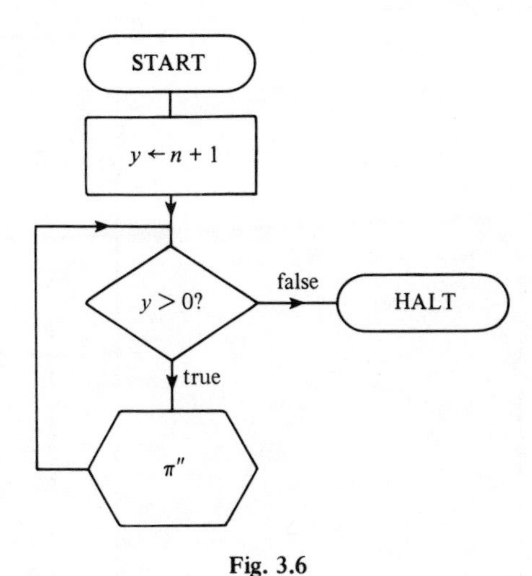

Fig. 3.6

π' is a loop-free program. By theorem 3.2.1 it can be transformed into an equivalent conditional program π''. Since π'' is a conditional program the program of Fig. 3.6 is a while program. Moreover since π'' is equivalent to π', the foregoing discussion concerning the possible computations of π' applies equally to π''. Consequently the computation of the while program lurches from cut-point to cut-point through the entire computation of π. (This correspondence can be established formally by an induction on the number of cut-points traversed during the computation of π.) ∎

COROLLARY

Every register function is an associated function of a while program. ∎

The while transformation is illustrated in Fig. 3.7. Only one cut-point is needed, just before the P_1 test, since this instruction is contained in both loops of the program.

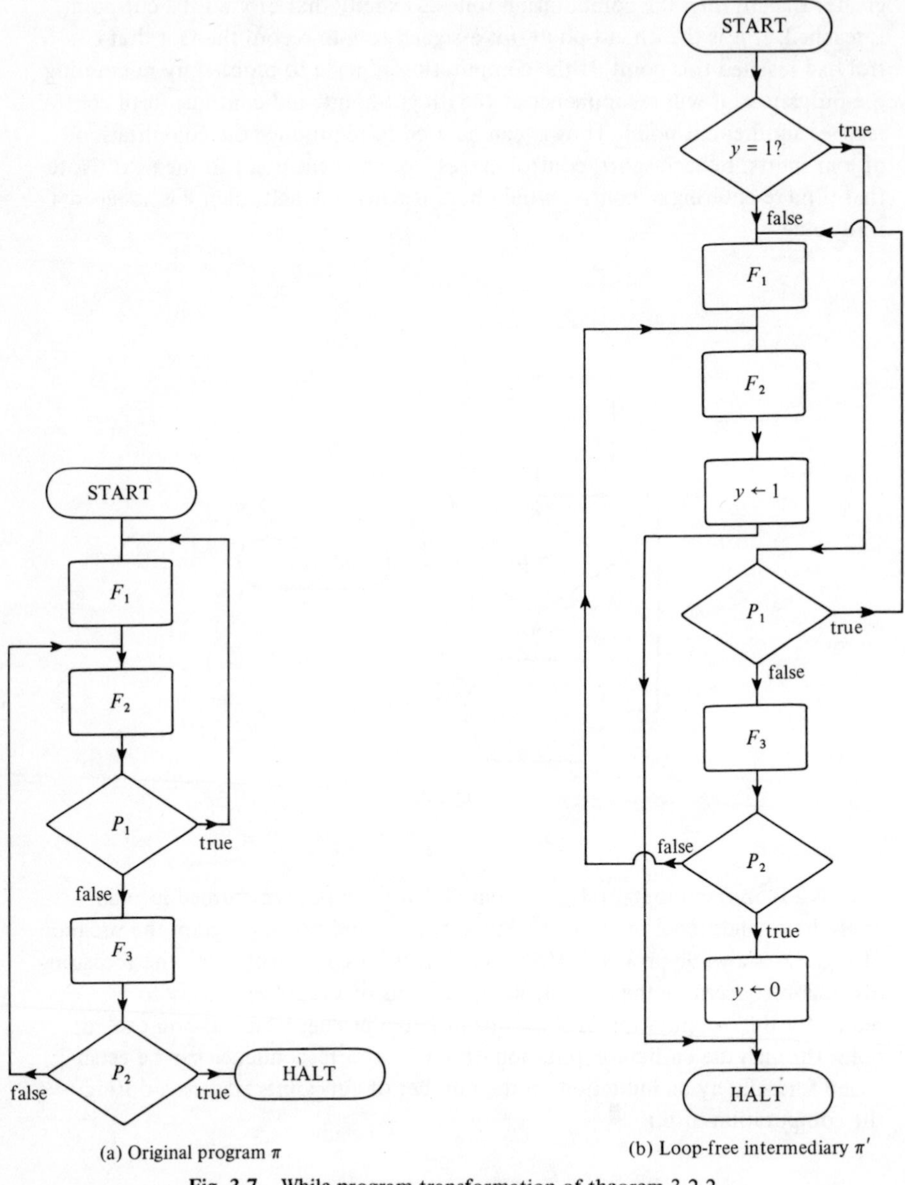

(a) Original program π

(b) Loop-free intermediary π'

Fig. 3.7 While program transformation of theorem 3.2.2

3.2.3 EXERCISES

(1) Transform the program of Fig. 3.8 into a while program.

(2)* The reader has probably noticed the similarity between cut-points as used in a while transformation and assertion points as used in a proof of program

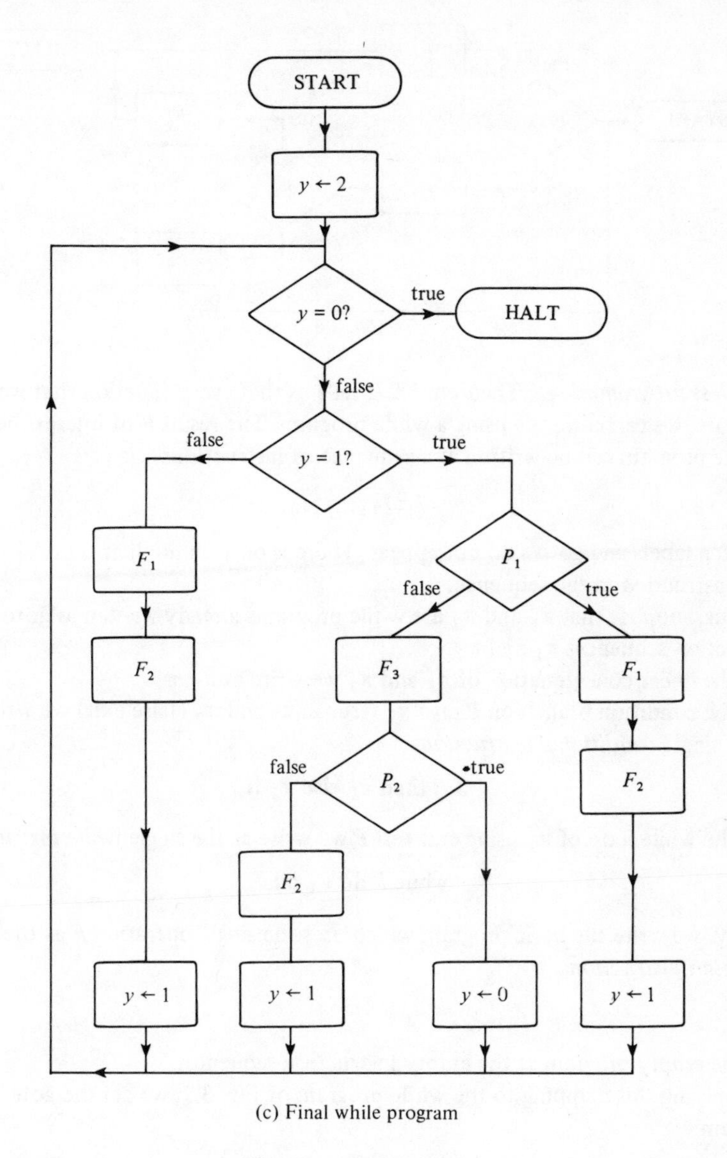

(c) Final while program

Fig. 3.7. (continued)

correctness. Suppose that some non-while program π is proved correct relative to start assertion S and halt assertion H by attaching assertions $A_1, A_2, \ldots, A_n$ to n cut-points in the body of the program. If these cut-points are used to transform π into a while program, what assertion would you attach to the loop entry of the resulting while program to prove its correctness? Assume that y is the newly introduced variable. ∎

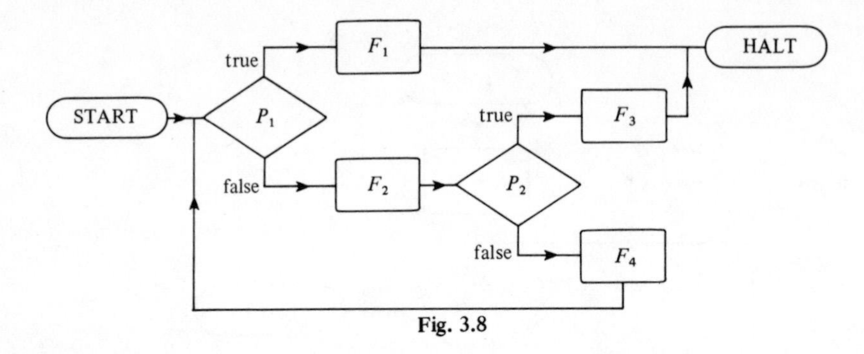

Fig. 3.8

Goto-less programming Theorem 3.2.2 tells us that every function that we can compute, we can compute using a while program. The result is of interest because a while program can be written as a sequence of instructions

$$I_1; I_2; \ldots; I_n$$

in which labels and goto's do not appear. There is only an implicit transfer to the next instruction in the sequence.

Thus, suppose that π_1 and π_2 are while programs already written as goto-less instruction sequences $\hat{\pi}_1$ and $\hat{\pi}_2$.

(1) The linear concatenation of π_1 and π_2 we write as $\hat{\pi}_1; \hat{\pi}_2$.

(2) The condition branch on P into π_1 (true exit) and π_2 (false exit) we write as the single *conditional instruction*

$$\textbf{if } P \textbf{ then } \hat{\pi}_1 \textbf{ else } \hat{\pi}_2 \textbf{ fi}$$

(3) The while loop of π_2 using exit test P we write as the single *while instruction*

$$\textbf{while } P \textbf{ do } \hat{\pi}_1 \textbf{ od}$$

Finally, we write the basic program which uses the single operation F as the single *operation instruction*

$$F$$

and the empty program as the empty instruction sequence.

Applying this mapping to the while program of Fig. 3.2, we get the goto-less program:

```
F1;
while P1 do F2 od;
if P2 then
          while P3 do F3; F4 od
else F5; F6 fi
```

There is controversy concerning the advantages and disadvantages of goto-less programming. Basically those who oppose the use of the goto argue that programs which use only conditional branching and standard forms of iterative control are easier to understand and prove correct. Those who wish to retain the use of the goto argue that many algorithms are most naturally expressed using, for example, loops with several exits or even partially overlapping loops. They argue that when these are reformulated to avoid the use of explicit goto's, they become much less transparent. A thorough investigation of the debate is outside the scope of this book. We leave the interested reader to consult the references given at the end of the chapter.

Simple while programs and simple count programs In chapter 2 we established (theorem 2.2.6) that by introducing extra variables any register program π can be transformed into a simple program that computes the same function over the set of registers used by π. This was achieved by a stepwise expansion of the program with individual instructions replaced by program segments. With slight modifications that series of substitutions will transform a count program into a simple count program. We shall think of these substitutions as being applied to the label-free instruction sequence that represents the count program.

We ask the reader to check that, with the exception of the sub-program that replaces $x_i \leftarrow x_j \div x_k$, each of the substitutions for an operation instruction is a count program. If we can find a count program to substitute for $x_i \leftarrow x_j \div x_k$ then every one of these substitutions transforms a count program instruction sequence into a count program instruction sequence. We leave the reader to find such a substitution. (Use two extra variables.)

In a count program instruction sequence the only tests that need replacing are those of the conditional instructions, all the tests of while instructions already being of the allowed form for a simple program. Again with one exception, the substitution for the test for equality $x_i = x_j$?, each of the test substitutions when applied to the test of a conditional instruction transforms a count program into a count program. The reader should check this. The substitution, as given, for $x_i = x_j$? does not preserve count program structure. (Try it!) We must instead replace the conditional instruction

$$\textbf{if } x_i = x_j \textbf{ then } \hat{\pi}_1 \textbf{ else } \hat{\pi}_2 \textbf{ fi}$$

by the equivalent nested conditional

$$\textbf{if } x_i > x_j \textbf{ then } \hat{\pi}_2 \textbf{ else if } x_j < x_i \textbf{ then } \hat{\pi}_2 \textbf{ else } \hat{\pi}_1 \textbf{ fi fi}$$

Using the modified series of substitutions we shall again produce a program that computes the same function over the set of registers used by the original program. However, the new program will be a simple count program if the original program was a count program. Hence we obtain the following theorem.

3.2.4 THEOREM

Every associated function of a count program is an associated function of a simple count program. ∎

To get the corresponding result for while programs it is easier to make use of theorem 3.2.2. Although this introduces assignments of integer constants to y these assignments may be replaced by simple count programs. Thus modified, it will transform a simple program into a simple while program. Now we already know that every register function is an associated function of a simple program. Hence we obtain the following theorem.

3.2.5 THEOREM

Every register function is an associated function of a simple while program. ∎

Invoking Church's thesis, the upshot of theorem 3.2.5 is that every computable function can be computed using a simple while program. It gives us a characterization of the computable functions in terms of a very restricted class of programs.

3.3 The while recursive functions

We have already remarked that the inductive definition of the while programs gives each non-basic program an implicit structure as a linear concatenation, a conditional branch, or a while loop. For conditional branches and while loops, the sub-program structure is uniquely determined. For linear concatenation it is uniquely determined if we adopt the decomposition that gives the first program the maximum number of instructions when there is a choice. That each program can be assigned a unique sub-program structure suggests that we might be able to define the functions it computes in terms of the functions computed by its sub-programs.

Structure-related function definition Suppose π is a while program. π has one of the sub-program structures depicted in Fig. 3.9. In each case we can define its ith associated function in terms of the associated functions of its sub-programs. We assume that $h_1, h_2, \ldots, h_k$ are the k-adic associated functions of π_1 and that $g_1, g_2, \ldots, g_k$ are the k-adic associated functions of π_2.

(1) π is the linear concatenation of π_1 and π_2. As indicated in Fig. 3.9 if the initial values of $x_1, x_2, \ldots, x_k$ are $j_1, j_2, \ldots, j_k$, then their values just before entering π_2 will be $h_1(j_1, \ldots, j_k), \ldots, h_k(j_1, \ldots, j_k)$. The value of x_i at the end of the computation will therefore be

$$g_1(h_1(j_1, \ldots, j_k), \ldots, h_k(j_1, \ldots, j_k)).$$

Thus the ith associated function of π is

$$f_i : \langle x_1, \ldots, x_k \rangle \mapsto g_i(h_1(x_1, \ldots, x_k), \ldots, h_k(x_1, \ldots, x_k)).$$

(2) π is a conditional branch. Again referring to Fig. 3.9 we can see that the final value of x_i is $h_i(j_1, \ldots, j_k)$ if the result of P is true and $g_i(j_1, \ldots, j_k)$ if the result is false. Thus the ith associated function of π is

$$f_i : \langle x_1, \ldots, x_k \rangle \mapsto \begin{cases} h_i(x_1, \ldots, x_k) & \text{if } P \\ g_i(x_1, \ldots, x_k) & \text{if not } P. \end{cases}$$

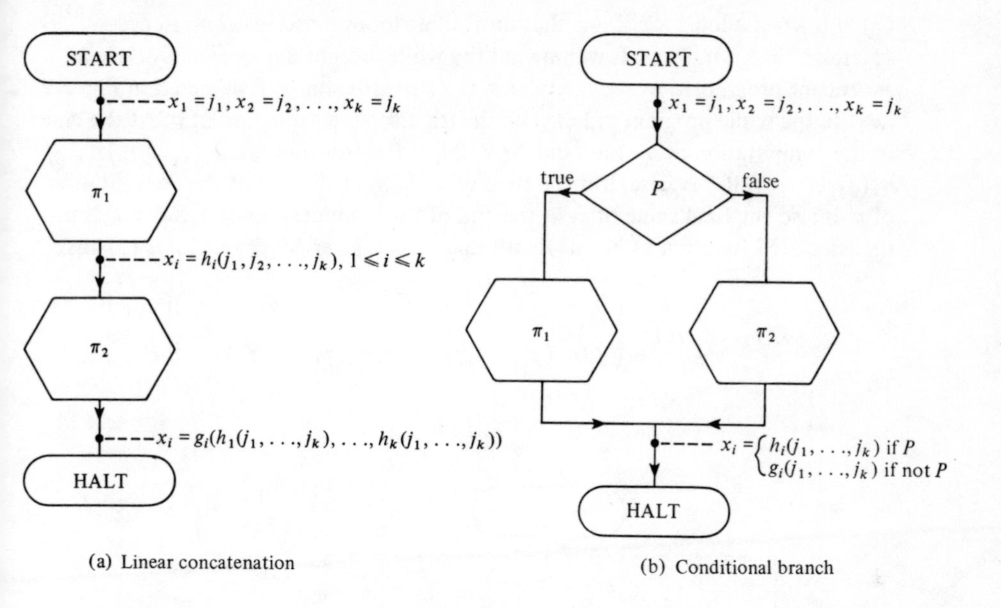

(a) Linear concatenation

(b) Conditional branch

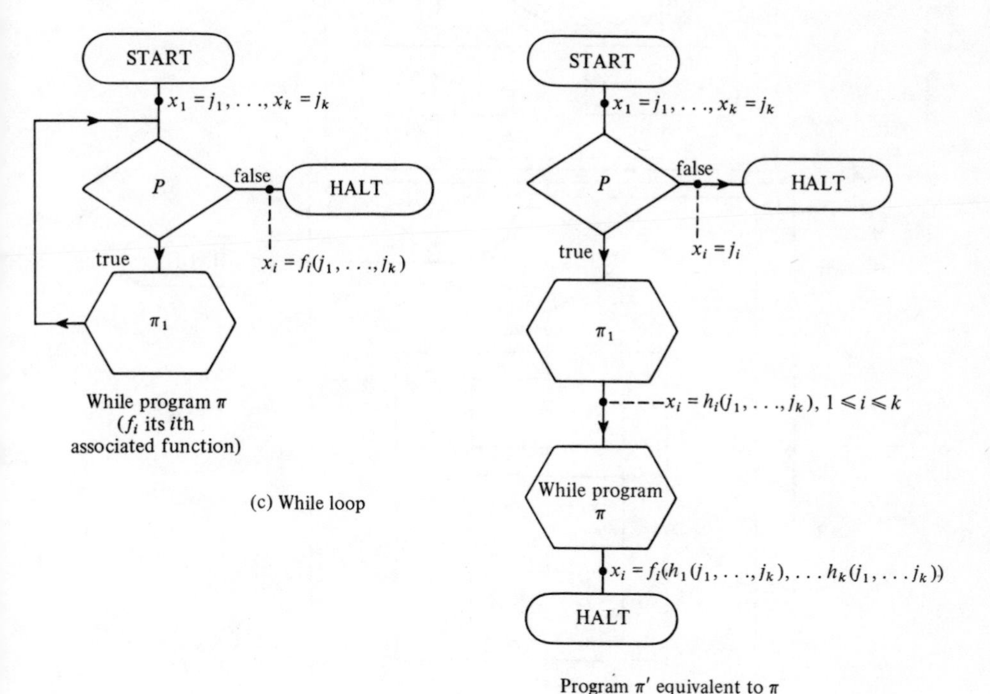

(c) While loop

Fig. 3.9

(3) π is a while loop. We know that unwinding loops preserves equivalence (exercise 1.6.5(1)). Thus, if we unwind the while loop of π once, we produce an equivalent program π' which contains π as a sub-program. π' is depicted in Fig. 3.9 next to the while program π. Let f_i be the ith associated function of π. At the end of the computation of π', the value of x_i is j_i if P is true and $f_i(h_1(j_1,\ldots,j_k),\ldots, h_k(j_1,\ldots j_k))$ if P is false. But the final value of x_i at the end of the computation of π' is also the final value of x_i at the end of the computation of π. Since f_i is the ith associated function of π, this final value of x_i is given by $f_i(j_1,\ldots,j_k)$. Thus

$$f_i(j_1,\ldots,j_k) = \begin{cases} j_i & \text{if not } P \\ f_i(h_1(j_1,\ldots,j_k),\ldots,h_k(j_1,\ldots,j_k)) & \text{if } P. \end{cases}$$

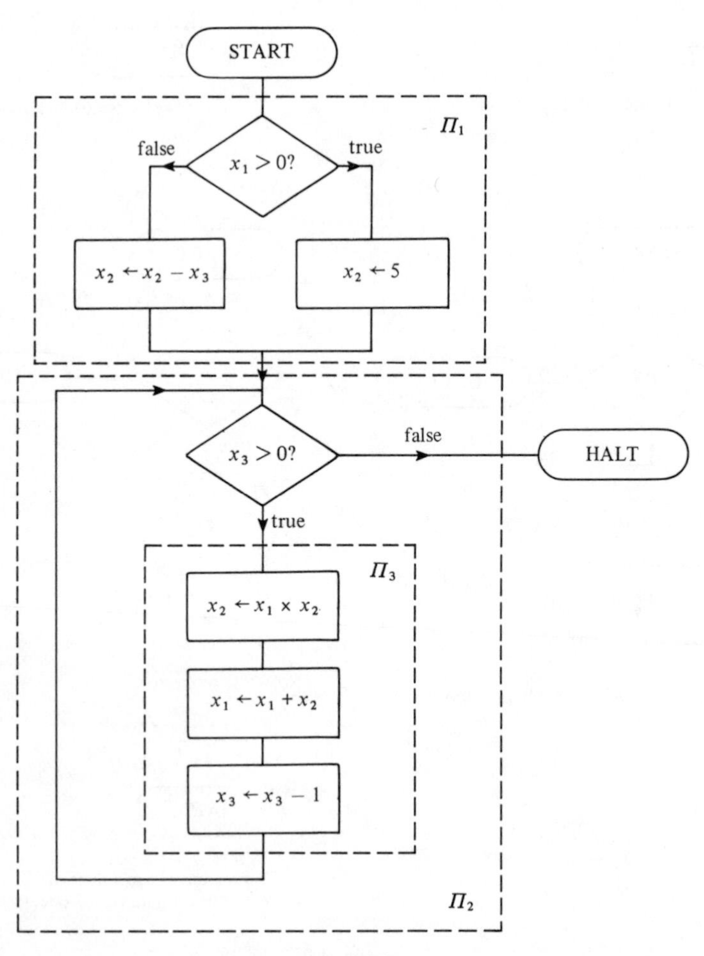

Fig. 3.10

In other words the ith associated function of π is the recursively defined function

$$f_i: \langle x_1, \ldots, x_k \rangle \mapsto \begin{cases} x_i & \text{if not } P \\ f_i(h_1(x_1, \ldots, x_k), \ldots, h_k(x_1, \ldots, x_k)) & \text{if } P \end{cases}$$

Consider now the actual while program of Fig. 3.10. Using the above structure related forms of function definition we can 'read-off' the definitions for its triadic associated functions f_1, f_2, f_3.

At the top level, the program is a linear concatenation of two sub-programs Π_1 and Π_2. Thus for $i = 1, 2, 3$,

$$f_i : \langle x_1, x_2, x_3 \rangle \mapsto g_i(h_1(x_1, x_2, x_3), \ldots, h_3(x_1, x_2, x_3))$$

if h_1, h_2, h_3 are the triadic associated functions of Π_1 and g_1, g_2, g_3 are the triadic associated functions of Π_2. It remains to define these functions by identifying the structures of Π_1 and Π_2.

Π_1 is a conditional branch of basic programs. So its associated functions are conditionally defined using test $x_1 > 0$?:

$$h_1: \langle x_1, x_2, x_3 \rangle \mapsto \begin{cases} x_1 & \text{if } x_1 > 0 \\ x_1 & \text{if not } x_1 > 0 \end{cases} \quad \text{i.e., } x_1$$

$$h_2: \langle x_1, x_2, x_3 \rangle \mapsto \begin{cases} x_2 - x_3 & \text{if } x_1 > 0 \\ 5 & \text{if not } x_1 > 0 \end{cases}$$

$$h_3: \langle x_1, x_2, x_3 \rangle \mapsto \begin{cases} x_3 & \text{if } x_1 > 0 \\ x_3 & \text{if not } x_1 > 0 \end{cases} \quad \text{i.e., } x_3.$$

Π_2 is a while loop with sub-program Π_3 comprising the body of the loop. Without further decomposition it is easy to see that Π_3 takes $\langle x_1, x_2, x_3 \rangle$ into $\langle x_1 + x_1 x_2, x_1 x_2, x_3 - 1 \rangle$. Thus the ith associated function of Π_2 is

$$g_i: \langle x_1, x_2, x_3 \rangle \mapsto \begin{cases} x_i & \text{if } x_3 = 0 \\ g_i(x_1 + x_1 x_2, x_1 x_2, x_3 - 1) & \text{if } x_3 \neq 0. \end{cases}$$

This completes the specification of the associated functions. In particular the function f_2 which gives the final value of x_2 as a function of the initial values of x_1, x_2, x_3 is

$$f_2: \langle x_1, x_2, x_3 \rangle \mapsto g_2(x_1, h_2(x_1, x_2, x_3), x_3),$$

where

$$g_2: \langle x_1, x_2, x_3 \rangle \mapsto \begin{cases} x_2 & \text{if } x_3 = 0 \\ g_2(x_1 + x_1 x_2, x_1 x_2, x_3 - 1) & \text{if } x_3 > 0 \end{cases}$$

and

$$h_2: \langle x_1, x_2, x_3 \rangle \mapsto \begin{cases} x_2 - x_3 & \text{if } x_1 > 0 \\ 5 & \text{if } x_1 \geqslant 0. \end{cases}$$

3.3.1 EXERCISE

Define the associated function of the while program

$$
\begin{aligned}
&x_1 \leftarrow 0;\\
&\textbf{while } x_3 > 0 \textbf{ do}\\
&\qquad x_1 \leftarrow x_1 + x_2;\\
&\qquad x_3 \leftarrow x_3 - 1\\
&\textbf{od}
\end{aligned}
$$

which gives the final value of x_1 as a function of x_1, x_2 and x_3. Note that this amounts to a recursive definition of $x_2 \times x_3$. ∎

Essentially, what we have done in devising a method for 'reading-off' the associated functions from the program structure, is to relate each program constructor of the inductive definition of the while programs to a particular form of function definition. This suggests that we can parallel the inductive definition of, say, the class of simple while programs, with an inductive definition of their associated functions; the basic functions being essentially those functions we can compute using the basic programs, and the ways in which new functions can be defined being essentially the forms of function definition that correspond to the program constructors.

Basic functions

The *successor* function $S : x \mapsto x + 1$

The *predecessor* function $P : x \mapsto \begin{cases} x - 1 & \text{if } x > 0 \\ 0 & \text{if } x = 0 \end{cases}$

For each $k \geqslant 1$ and each i in $1 \leqslant i \leqslant k$, a *projection* function

$$p_k^i : \langle x_1, x_2, \ldots, x_k \rangle \mapsto x_i$$

Forms of function definition

(1) *Generalized composition*
If g is an m-adic function and $h_1, h_2, \ldots, h_m$ are k-adic functions, then

$$f : \langle x_1, x_2, \ldots, x_k \rangle \mapsto g(h_1(x_1, \ldots, x_k), \ldots, h_m(x_1, \ldots, x_k))$$

is the *generalized composition* of g with $h_1, h_2, \ldots, h_m$. $f(x_1, x_2, \ldots, x_k)$ is undefined if any of

$$h_1(x_1, \ldots, x_k), \ldots, h_m(x_1, \ldots, x_k)$$

are undefined.

(2) *Conditional definition*
If g and h are both k-adic functions, then

$$f: \langle x_1, x_2, \ldots, x_k \rangle \mapsto \begin{cases} g(x_1, x_2, \ldots, x_k) & \text{if } x_i = 0 \\ h(x_1, x_2, \ldots, x_k) & \text{if } x_i > 0, \end{cases}$$

where $1 \leqslant i \leqslant k$, is *conditionally defined* from g and h.

(3) *While recursion*
If g and $h_1, h_2, \ldots, h_k$ are k-adic functions, then

$$f: \langle x_1, x_2, \ldots, x_k \rangle \mapsto \begin{cases} g(x_1, \ldots, x_k) & \text{if } x_i = 0 \\ f(h_1(x_1, \ldots, x_k), \ldots, h_k(x_1, \ldots, x_k)) & \text{if } x_i > 0, \end{cases}$$

where $1 \leqslant i \leqslant k$, is a function defined by *while recursion* from g and $h_1, h_2, \ldots, h_k$. The function f is undefined if any of

$$h_1(x_1, \ldots, x_k), \ldots, h_k(x_1, \ldots, x_k)$$

are undefined.

3.3.2 DEFINITION

The while recursive functions comprise the smallest class of functions which includes all the basic functions and is closed under generalized composition, conditional definition and while recursion. ▮

3.3.3 THEOREM

The register functions are precisely the while recursive functions.

Proof. We just give the outline of the proof, leaving the reader to fill in the details. We must show that every register function is a while recursive function and that every while recursive function is a register function.

Since we know (theorem 3.2.5) that every register function is an associated function of a simple while program, we need only prove that the associated functions of the simple while programs are while recursive. Simple while programs use only

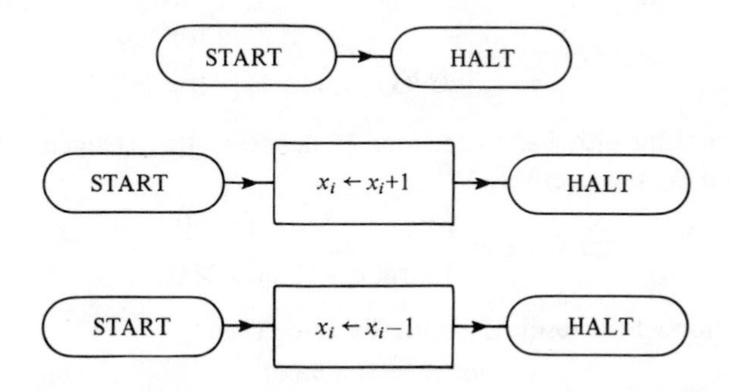

as basic programs. It is quite easy to check that every k-adic associated function of one of these basic programs is while recursive. For example, if $i \leqslant k$, then the ith associated function of the $x_i \leftarrow x_i + 1$ program is

$$f_i : \langle x_1, x_2, \ldots, x_k \rangle \mapsto S(p_k^i(x_1, x_2, \ldots, x_k)),$$

the generalized composition of the successor function and a projection function. All the other associated functions of this program are projection functions. Now note that for a simple while program our structure-related methods for defining associated functions are just special cases of generalized composition, conditional definition and while recursion. The function definition associated with linear concatenation is generalized composition with $m = k$, that associated with conditional branching is precisely conditional definition since all tests of a simple program must be of the form $x_i > 0$?, and finally that associated with a simple while loop is a special case of while recursion with $g = p_k^i$. It follows that every associated function of a simple while program can be defined as a while recursive function. Hence every register function is while recursive.

We prove the converse by structural induction on the class of while recursive functions. Trivially every basic function is an associated function of some register program. It remains to prove that if each of the functions used in a generalized composition, conditional definition or while recursion is an associated function of a register program, then so is the defined function. We leave the reader to fill in the details (exercise below). This proves that every while recursive function is a register function. ∎

3.3.4 EXERCISE

Complete the proof of the above theorem by showing how to construct the program with the defined function as an associated function, from programs which have the functions used in the definition as associated functions. Note that in each case the new program is a while program if the old programs are while programs. ∎

Defining while recursive functions It is interesting to try to establish directly that certain functions are while recursive. To do this we must define each function using only basic functions or functions we have already defined, and of course each definition must be a generalized composition, a conditional definition or a while recursion. For example,

$$add : \langle x, y \rangle \mapsto \begin{cases} x & \text{if } y = 0 \\ add(x+1, y-1) & \text{if } y > 0 \end{cases}$$

defines addition using only basic functions. (x denotes $p_2^1(x, y)$ and $x + 1$ and $y - 1$ denote $S(x)$ and $P(y)$ respectively.)

$$zero : x \mapsto \begin{cases} x & \text{if } x = 0 \\ zero(x-1) & \text{if } x > 0 \end{cases}$$

defines a function whose result is identically zero. Then

$$one : x \mapsto S(zero(x))$$

defines a function which always returns 1,

$$two : x \mapsto S(one(x))$$

defines a function which always returns 2, and so on.

$$sub : \langle x, y \rangle \mapsto \begin{cases} y & \text{if } x = 0 \\ sub(x-1, y-1) & \text{if } x > 0 \end{cases}$$

subtracts x from y. Note that if $x > y$ it returns zero. Using *sub* and the conditionally defined

$$pos : x \mapsto \begin{cases} zero(x) & \text{if } x > 0 \\ one(x) & \text{if } x = 0, \end{cases}$$

we may define

$$less : \langle x, y \rangle \mapsto pos(sub(x, y)),$$

a function which returns 0 if $x < y$ and 1 if $x \geqslant y$. Like *pos* this is a test function with 0 representing true and 1 representing false. Then

$$div : \langle x, y \rangle \mapsto div'(x, y, 0, less(y, x)),$$

where

$$div' : \langle x, y, z, w \rangle \mapsto \begin{cases} z & \text{if } w = 0 \\ div'(x, sub(x,y), z+1, less(sub(x,y),x)) & \text{if } w > 0 \end{cases}$$

returns the whole number of times x divides into y with undefined result when $x = 0$. The fourth argument of div' indicates whether or not $x > y$, the condition that terminates the recursion. The third argument is the count of the number of recursions and hence the number of times that x is subtracted from y before the remainder has become less than x.

The watchful reader may have noticed that the definitions of *div* and div' are not strictly a generalized composition and a while recursion as specified. However, we can easily 'dress up' the definitions so that they do conform. A legitimate generalized composition for *div* would be

$$div : \langle x, y \rangle \mapsto div'(p_2^1(x, y), p_2^2(x, y), zero_2(x,y), not\text{-}less(x,y))$$

where

$$zero_2 : \langle x, y \rangle \mapsto zero(p_2^1(x, y))$$

and

$$not\text{-}less : \langle y, x \rangle \mapsto less(p_2^2(y, x), p_2^1(y, x)).$$

We leave the reader to do a similar 'dressing-up' operation on the definition of div'.

We could proceed to define all the register functions. At each stage the sequence of definitions culminating in a particular defined function can be thought of as a 'program' for that function. It is a 'program' that we know can be 'compiled' into a while program. Indeed the proof of this (exercise 3.3.4) indirectly specifies a 'compiler'. We leave the reader to define a few more functions as an exercise.

Theorem 3.3.3 and Church's thesis should be enough to convince us that every intuitively computable k-adic function over the non-negative integers can be defined as a while recursive function.

3.3.5 EXERCISE

Define the following as while recursive functions.

(1) $mult\,(x,y) = xy$ (see exercise 3.3.1)

(2) $exp\,(x,y) = x^y$

(3) $$log\,(x,z) = \begin{cases} \text{the } y \text{ such that } x^y = z, \text{ if it exists} \\ \Omega \text{ otherwise} \end{cases}$$

(4) $$rem\,(x,y) = \begin{cases} \text{the remainder on division of } y \text{ by } x, \text{ if } x > 0 \\ \Omega \text{ otherwise} \end{cases}$$

(5) $$divides\,(x,y) = \begin{cases} \Omega \text{ if } x = 0 \\ 0 \text{ if } x > 0 \text{ and } x \text{ divides } y \\ 1 \text{ if } x > 0 \text{ and } x \text{ does not divide } y \end{cases}$$

(6) $$isprime\,(x) = \begin{cases} 0 \text{ if } x \text{ is a prime number} \\ 1 \text{ otherwise.} \end{cases}$$ ∎

3.4 Primitive recursive and partial recursive functions*

In this section we give inductive definitions for two more classes of functions, the *primitive recursive* and the *partial recursive* functions. The definitions of these functions are historically important. They derive from an early attempt to provide a precise mathematical characterization of the intuitive concept of a computable function. (See the notes at the end of the chapter.) We shall prove that the partial recursive functions are precisely the register functions. As a corollary of that proof we shall be able to identify the primitive recursive functions with the associated functions of the count programs.

Basic functions The basic functions are the same as for the inductive definition of the while recursive functions. That is, we start with the successor function, the predecessor function and all the projection functions.

Forms of function definition

(1) *Generalized composition*
This is the same as the generalized composition for the while recursive functions.

(2) *Primitive recursion*
If g is a k-adic function and h a $(k + 2)$-adic function, then

$$f : \langle x_1, \ldots, x_k, y \rangle \mapsto \begin{cases} g(x_1, \ldots, x_k) & \text{if } y = 0 \\ h(x_1, \ldots, x_k, y - 1, f(x_1, \ldots, x_k, y - 1)) & \text{if } y > 0 \end{cases}$$

is defined from g and h by *primitive recursion.* If $k = 0$, that is we are defining a new monadic function, the value for $y = 0$ can be given as any non-negative integer. $f(x_1, \ldots, x_k, y)$ is undefined if $f(x_1, \ldots, x_k, y - 1)$ is undefined. (Note the differences between this and definition by while recursion. In the primitive recursive evaluation of f only the last argument is changed and it is always reduced by one. Moreover the result of the evaluation is used as an argument to the function h before the final value is returned.)

(3) *The μ-operator*
If h is a function with $k+1$ arguments then

$$f : \langle x_1, \ldots, x_k \rangle \mapsto \mu z : h(x_1, \ldots, x_k, z) = 0$$

is defined from h by the *μ-operator.* The value of $f(x_1, \ldots, x_k)$ is the *least value* of z such that $h(x_1, \ldots, x_k, z) = 0$ and for all $z' < z$, $h(x_1, \ldots, x_k, z') \neq \mathbf{\Omega}$. The value is undefined if there is no such z.

3.4.1 DEFINITION

The *primitive recursive functions* comprise the smallest class of functions which includes all the basic functions and is closed under generalized composition and primitive recursion.

The *partial recursive functions* comprise the smallest class of functions which includes all the basic functions and is closed under generalized composition, primitive recursion and the μ-operator. ∎

It is quite easy to show, by structural induction, that every primitive recursive function is total. Since there are non-total partial recursive functions, for example the totally undefined

$$\mu z : S(z) = 0,$$

the primitive recursive functions form a proper subset of the partial recursive functions. As we shall see they even form a proper subset of the partial recursive functions that are total functions.

As with the while recursive functions we can establish that certain functions are primitive or partial recursive by actually defining them:

$$add : \langle x, y \rangle \mapsto \begin{cases} x & \text{if } y = 0 \\ add(x, y-1) + 1 & \text{if } y > 0 \end{cases}$$

is a primitive recursive definition of addition. Actually a strict primitive recursive definition would be

$$add : \langle x, y \rangle \mapsto \begin{cases} p_1^1(x) & \text{if } y = 0 \\ h(x, y-1, \mathrm{add}(x, y-1)) & \text{if } y > 0, \end{cases}$$

where

$$h : \langle x, y, z \rangle \mapsto S(p_3^3(x, y, z)),$$

which is 'dressed-up' with projection functions and an auxiliary function defined by composition. Each of the following definitions can be similarly 'dressed-up'. They are definitions for the functions defined earlier as while recursive functions. The reader should compare these definitions, which are mainly primitive recursive, with the earlier definitions.

$$mult : \langle x, y \rangle \mapsto \begin{cases} 0 & \text{if } y = 0 \\ add(x, mult(x, y-1)) & \text{if } y > 0 \end{cases}$$

$$zero : x \mapsto \begin{cases} 0 & \text{if } x = 0 \\ zero(x-1) & \text{if } x > 0 \end{cases}$$

$$sub' : \langle x, y \rangle \mapsto \begin{cases} x & \text{if } y = 0 \\ sub'(x, y-1) - 1 & \text{if } y > 0 \end{cases}$$

$$sub : \langle x, y \rangle \mapsto sub'(y, x).$$

$$pos : x \mapsto \begin{cases} 1 & \text{if } x = 0 \\ zero\,(pos(x-1)) & \text{if } x > 0 \end{cases}$$

$$less : \langle x, y \rangle \mapsto pos(sub(x, y))$$

$$div : \langle x, y \rangle \mapsto \mu z : less(y, mult(x, z+1)) = 0.$$

Notice that only *div* is defined using the μ-operator. *div* is also the only non-total function. When $x = 0$, there is no z such that $y < x(z+1)$. When $x > 0$, the least z satisfying the inequality is always less than $y + 1$. Thus if we put an upper bound on z and redefine *div* as

$$\text{div} : \langle x, y \rangle \mapsto \mu z < y + 1 : less(y, mult\ (x, z + 1)) = 0$$

we would be defining essentially the same function.

The bounded μ-operator If h is a $(k + 1)$-adic function and g a k-adic function the function

$$f : \langle x_1, \ldots, x_k \rangle \mapsto \mu z < g(x_1, \ldots, x_k) : h(x_1, \ldots, x_k, z) = 0$$

is defined from g and h by the *bounded μ-operator.* The value of $f(x_1, \ldots, x_k)$ is the *least value* of z *less than* the value of $g(x_1, \ldots, x_k)$ such that $h(x_1, \ldots, x_k, z) = 0$ and for all $z' < z, h(x_1, \ldots, x_k) \neq \Omega$. The value is zero if no z satisfies the condition.

The bounded μ-operator puts an upper bound on the iterative search for a z. Moreover the upper bound can be expressed as any function of the arguments $x_1, \ldots, x_k$ of the function being defined. The question arises: Is it always possible to define an upper bound function g such that when a z does exist satisfying $h(x_1, \ldots, x_k, z) = 0$ and for all $z' < z, h(x_1, \ldots, x_k, z') \neq \Omega$, then z is less than $g(x_1, \ldots, x_k)$? The answer is no. In other words there are some computations which will eventually terminate, but for which we cannot compute in advance an estimate of the length of the computation. The answer is no because, as we shall see, there are partial recursive total functions which are not primitive recursive, and the bounded μ-operator does not extend the class of primitive recursive functions.

3.4.2 THEOREM

The function

$$f : \langle x_1, \ldots, x_k \rangle \mapsto \mu z < g(x_1, \ldots, x_k) : h(x_1, \ldots, x_k, z) = 0$$

is primitive recursive if both g and h are.

Proof. We show how to redefine f using only composition and primitive recursion.

$$cond : \langle x, y, z \rangle \mapsto \begin{cases} p_3^1(x, y, z) & \text{if } z = 0 \\ p_4^2(x, y, z-1, cond(x, y, z-1)) & \text{if } z > 0 \end{cases}$$

is a primitive recursive function which returns x if $z = 0$, y if $z > 0$. With a little 'dressing-up',

$$f' : \langle x_1, \ldots, x_k, z, w \rangle \mapsto \begin{cases} 0 & \text{if } w = 0 \\ cond(z - w, f'(x_1, \ldots, x_k, z, w-1), h(x_1, \ldots, \\ \qquad x_k, z - w)) & \text{if } w > 0 \end{cases}$$

is a primitive recursive definition of a function which returns the least number y between $z - w$ and z which satisfies $h(x_1, \ldots, x_k, y) = 0$. Since

$$f(x_1, \ldots, x_k) = f'(x_1, \ldots, x_k, g(x_1, \ldots, x_k), g(x_1, \ldots, x_k)),$$

f is primitive recursive. ∎

3.4.3 EXERCISES

(1) Making use of the bounded μ-operator where necessary, show that the following functions are primitive recursive:

(a) $exp(x, y) = x^y$.

(b) $log(x, z) = \begin{cases} \text{the } y \text{ such that } x^y = z, & \text{if it exists} \\ 0 & \text{otherwise} \end{cases}$

(c) $rem(x, y) = \begin{cases} \text{the remainder on division of } y \text{ by } x, & \text{if } x > 0 \\ 0 & \text{otherwise} \end{cases}$

(d) $divides(x, y) = \begin{cases} 0 & \text{if } x \text{ divides } y \\ 1 & \text{if } x = 0 \text{ or } x \text{ does not divide } y \end{cases}$

(e) $isprime(x) = \begin{cases} 0 & \text{if } x \text{ is a prime number} \\ 1 & \text{otherwise.} \end{cases}$

(2) Show that there are primitive recursive functions *cons*, *hd* and *tl* such that

$$hd(cons(x, y)) = x$$
$$tl(cons(x, y)) = y$$

for all arguments x and y. (There are many primitive recursive functions satisfying these conditions. One group makes use of prime factorization.) ∎

We leave the reader to prove the following by structural induction:

3.4.4 THEOREM

(1) Every primitive recursive function is an associated function of a count program
(2) Every partial recursive function is an associated function of a while program

Proof. As exercise.** ∎

To get the converse results, we shall look again at the problem of defining the associated functions of a simple while program π in terms of the associated functions of its sub-programs.

When π is a linear concatenation or a conditional branch, it is quite easy to show that its associated functions are primitive recursive (partial recursive) if the associated functions of its sub-programs are primitive recursive (partial recursive). Indeed for linear concatenation the result is immediate, since generalized composition is an allowed form of function definition. For the conditional branch we simply use the already defined primitive recursive function

$$cond : \langle x, y, z \rangle \mapsto \begin{cases} x & \text{if } z = 0 \\ y & \text{if } z > 0 \end{cases}$$

to define the associated functions of π as generalized compositions. It is the loops that present problems.

Thus let π have the while structure depicted by Fig. 3.11 with $g_1, \ldots, g_k$ the associated functions of the sub-program π_1. Let g be the function

$$g : \langle x_1, \ldots, x_k \rangle \mapsto \langle g_1(x_1, \ldots, x_k), \ldots, g_k(x_1, \ldots, x_k) \rangle.$$

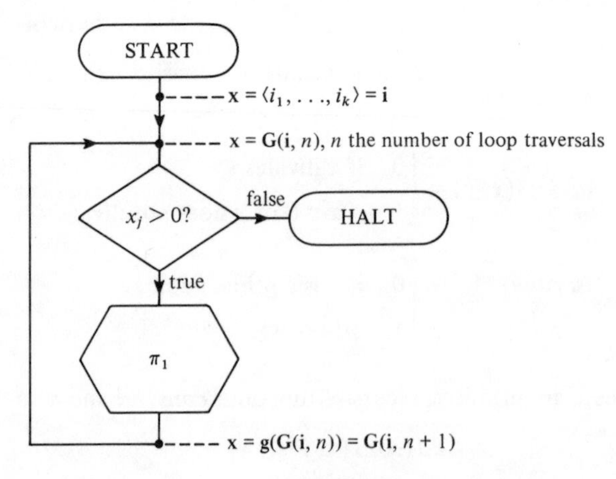

Fig. 3.11

This takes any vector of initial values of $x_1, \ldots, x_k$ into the vector (if defined) of values that they have after the computation of π_1.

Let $\mathbf{x}$ denote $\langle x_1, \ldots, x_k \rangle$. Suppose that for the computation of π the initial value of $\mathbf{x}$ is $\mathbf{i} = \langle i_1, \ldots, i_k \rangle$. After one iteration of the loop $\mathbf{x} = \mathbf{g}(\mathbf{i})$, after two iterations it will be $\mathbf{g}(\mathbf{g}(\mathbf{i}))$ and after n iterations it will be $\mathbf{G}(\mathbf{i}, n)$, where

$$\mathbf{G} : \langle \mathbf{x}, n \rangle \mapsto \begin{cases} \mathbf{x} & \text{if } n = 0 \\ \mathbf{g}(\mathbf{G}(\mathbf{x}, n-1)) & \text{if } n > 0. \end{cases}$$

Now suppose that there are primitive recursive functions $c_k, d_k^1, \ldots, d_k^k$ such that

$$\begin{aligned} d_k^1(c_k(x_1, \ldots, x_k)) &= x_1 \\ d_k^2(c_k(x_1, \ldots, x_k)) &= x_2 \\ &\vdots \\ d_k^k(c_k(x_1, \ldots, x_k)) &= x_k \end{aligned}$$

(For the case $k = 2$, c_k is *cons*, d_k^1 is *hd* and d_k^2 is *tl* of exercise 3.4.3(2).) With c_k we can encode the vector $\mathbf{x}$ as a single integer x and with d_k^i we can retrieve the component x_i from the encoding. Using these functions we can define the equivalent of the vector function $\mathbf{g}$, namely

$$g : x \mapsto c_k(g_1(d_k^1(x), \ldots, d_k^k(x)), \ldots, g_k(d_k^1(x), \ldots, d_k^k(x)))$$

This takes the integer encoding of vector $\mathbf{x}$ into the integer encoding of $\mathbf{g}(\mathbf{x})$. The equivalent of the vector function $\mathbf{G}(\mathbf{x}, n)$ is simply

$$G : \langle x, n \rangle \mapsto \begin{cases} x & \text{if } n = 0 \\ g(G(x, n-1)) & \text{if } n > 0, \end{cases}$$

which takes the integer encoding of the vector of initial values of $x_1, \ldots, x_k$ into the integer encoding of the vector of values after n iterations of the loop. Since g is defined by generalized composition and G by primitive recursion, G is primitive recursive (partial recursive) if $g_1, \ldots, g_k$, the associated functions of π_1, are primitive recursive (partial recursive). This is of course conditional on our being able to show that $c_k, d_k^1, \ldots, d_k^k$ are primitive recursive.

The integer encoding of the initial values $i_1, \ldots, i_k$ of variables $x_1, \ldots, x_k$ is $c_k(i_1, \ldots, i_k)$. Thus the integer encoding of their values after n iterations of the loop is $G(c_k(i_1, \ldots, i_k), n)$. The value of x_i after n iterations of the loop is therefore $F_i(i_1, \ldots, i_k, n)$, where

$$F_i : \langle x_1, \ldots, x_k, n \rangle \mapsto d_k^i(G(c_k(x_1, \ldots, x_k), n)).$$

F_i is the ith associated function of π parameterized with the number of iterations of the loop.

When the loop in π is a count loop, substituting i_j for n gives the value of x_i when control leaves the loop. i_j is the initial value of x_j, the count variable of the loop. Since the value of this variable is reduced by one each time round the loop its initial value is the number of times that control traverses the loop. Hence the ith associated function of π is given by

$$f_i : \langle x_1, \ldots, x_k \rangle \mapsto F_i(x_1, \ldots, x_k, x_j).$$

We conclude that if the associated functions of π_1 are primitive recursive then so are the associated functions of π.

3.4.5 THEOREM

Every associated function of a count program is primitive recursive.

Proof. The functions computed by the basic programs are primitive recursive and we have shown that the associated functions of a linear concatenation, a conditional branch and a count loop of a simple program are primitive recursive if the associated functions of its sub-programs are. The result for arbitrary count programs now follows from theorem 3.2.4. ∎

Returning to the general case, the number of times that the control traverses the loop is simply the least value of n which makes $F_j(i_1, \ldots, i_k, n)$, the value of exit test variable x_j after n iterations of the loop, equal to zero. In other words the number of iterations of the loop is given by $complength(i_1, \ldots, i_k)$ where

$$complength : \langle x_1, \ldots, x_k \rangle \mapsto \mu z : F_j(x_1, \ldots, x_k, z) = 0.$$

Using *complength* we can define the ith associated function of π by the generalized composition

$$f_i : \langle x_1, \ldots, x_k \rangle \mapsto F_i(x_1, \ldots, x_k, complength(x_1, \ldots, x_k)).$$

We conclude that when π is a simple while program its associated functions are partial recursive if the associated functions of π_1 are.

3.4.6 THEOREM

Every associated function of a while program is partial recursive.

Proof. Exercise. Similar to the proof of theorem 3.4.5. ∎

It remains to show that the functions $c_k, d_k^1, \ldots, d_k^k$ are primitive recursive. Exercise 3.4.3(2) provides these functions for $k = 2$ (*cons*, *hd* and *tl*). Using these we can define

$$c_3 : \langle x_1, x_2, x_3 \rangle \mapsto cons(x_1, cons(x_2, x_3))$$
$$d_3^1 : x \mapsto hd(x)$$
$$d_3^2 : x \mapsto hd(tl(x))$$
$$d_3^3 : x \mapsto tl(tl(tl(x)));$$

then

$$c_4 : \langle x_1, x_2, x_3\, x_4\rangle \mapsto cons(x_1, c_3(x_2, x_3, x_4))$$
$$d_4^1 : x \mapsto hd(x)$$
$$d_4^2 : x \mapsto d_3^1(tl(x))$$
$$d_4^3 : x \mapsto d_3^2(tl(x))$$
$$d_4^4 : x \mapsto d_3^3(tl(x));$$

and so on until we can eventually define

$$c_k : \langle x_1, \ldots, x_k\rangle \mapsto cons(x_1, c_{k-1}(x_2, \ldots, x_k))$$
$$d_k^1 : x \mapsto hd(x)$$
$$d_k^2 : x \mapsto d_{k-1}^1(tl(x))$$
$$\vdots$$
$$d_k^k : x \mapsto d_{k-1}^{k-1}(tl(x)).$$

Note also that for the case $k = 1$, c_k and d_k^k are simply the monadic projection p_1^1. We leave the reader to check (a simple induction on k will do it) that $c_k, d_k^1, \ldots, d_k^k$ are such that $d_k^i(c_k(x_1, \ldots, x_k)) = x_i$ for all i in $1 \leqslant i \leqslant k$.

3.4.7 THEOREM

There is a partial recursive function which is total but not primitive recursive.

Proof. We make use of a result from the next chapter. This is theorem 4.3.2 which states that there is a total register function which is not the associated function of any count program. Since every register function is partial recursive by a corollary of theorem 3.4.6, and every primitive recursive function is an associated function of a count program by theorem 3.4.4, this total register function satisfies the conditions of the theorem. ∎

Finally the while transformation theorem 3.2.2 has its echo in a normal form result for partial recursive functions:

3.4.8 THEOREM

Every partial recursive function can be defined by using the μ-operator at most once.

Proof. Every partial recursive function f is the ith associated function, say, of some register program π. Applying the while loop transformation of theorem 3.2.2 to π produces a while program π' that contains at most one while loop. Transforming this into a simple while program π'' only introduces count loops. (See proof of theorem 3.2.4.) The definition of the ith associated function of π' is an alternative definition of f. Since π has at most one while loop, this alternative definition uses the μ-operator at most once. ∎

3.5 Notes and references

Bohm and Jacopini[2] were the first to prove that an arbitrary program can be transformed to while form by introducing 'control' variables. Ashcroft and Manna[1] describe an algorithm for achieving the transformation which, unlike ours, preserves most of the loop structure of the original program. They also prove that in general the transformation cannot be achieved without the introduction of extra 'control' variables, i.e. variables that remember where the control should be.

Sheperdson and Sturgis[8] were the first to relate the partial recursive functions with the functions computable on a register machine. Like us, Engeler[4] gives methods for 'reading-off' the partial recursive functions from sub-program structure. However, he treats a quite different class of inductively defined programs.

The primitive recursive functions were first defined by Gödel in his investigations into provability in formal mathematical systems. Kleene's attempt to formalize a more general notion of computability suggested by Herbrand and Gödel[5] led to the concept of a partial recursive function[6].

On the 'goto' programming controversy, the reader should consult Dijkstra[3] and Knuth[7]. Knuth gives an excellent account of the history of the campaign against the 'goto' as well as his own assessment of its usefulness.

References

1. Ashcroft, E., and Z. Manna, 'The translation of 'goto' programs into 'while' programs', *Proc. IFIP Congress 1971,* Vol. 1, North-Holland, Amsterdam, pp. 250–255 (1972)
2. Bohm, C., and G. Jacopini, 'Flow diagrams, Turing machines, and languages with only two formation rules', *Comm. Assoc. Comp. Mach.*, **9**(5), 366–371 (1966)
3. Dijkstra, E. W., 'Go To statements considered harmful', *Comm. Assoc. Comp. Mach.*, **11**(3), 147–148, 538, 541 (March 1968)
4. Engeler, E., *Introduction to the Theory of Computation*, Academic Press, London (1973)
5. Gödel, K., *On Undecidable Propositions of Formal Mathematical Systems*, lecture notes, Inst. Advanced Study, Princeton, N.J. (1934)
6. Kleene, S. C., 'General recursive functions of natural numbers', *Mathematisch Ann.*, **122**, 727–747 (1936)
7. Knuth, D. E., 'Structured programming with go to statements', *ACM Comp. Surveys*, **6**(4), 261–302 (December 1974)
8. Sheperdson, J. C., and R. E. Sturgis, 'The computability of partial recursive functions', *J. Assoc. Comp. Mach.*, **10**, 217–255 (1963)

4 Unsolvable problems

In this chapter we shall prove that certain tasks are not mechanizable. For example, we shall show that the problem of whether or not any two programs are **TM**-equivalent cannot be subjected to an algorithmic test. We shall prove these negative results making frequent use of Church's thesis.

4.1 Generable and decidable sets

The set of strings α^* is an infinite set. We shall be interested in those infinite subsets of α^* membership of which can be confirmed, or better still decided, in an algorithmic fashion.

First let us note that for every subset A of α^* there is sequence containing all and only those strings that are members of A. This is because there is an infinite sequence

$$\Lambda, \text{all strings of length one, all strings of length two}, \ldots$$

of all the strings in α^*. (We choose some lexicographical order for the symbols in α^* and list the strings of equal length in lexicographical order.) Now imagine all the strings that are not members of A deleted from the sequence. If A is an infinite subset we end up with an infinite sequence

$$\sigma_0, \sigma_1, \ldots, \sigma_n, \ldots.$$

If A is a finite subset we end up with a finite sequence

$$\sigma_0, \sigma_1, \ldots, \sigma_{k-1},$$

where k is the number of strings in A.

Now suppose the sequence of strings of the subset A is *algorithmically generable.* That is, suppose that there is some pencil-and-paper algorithm which we can use to compute first σ_0, then σ_1, then σ_2, and so on. We can use such an algorithm to confirm that some string σ is a member of A. This is because any string that is a member of A must appear at some point in the sequence, say at σ_N. All we need do is to keep on generating the strings in the sequence until we reach σ_N. At this point we know that σ is indeed a member of A and we have confirmed the membership algorithmically.

We can generate the sequence if we have an algorithm which given n will produce σ_n. If the sequence is infinite, the algorithm will compute a total function from $\mathcal{N}$ to α^*. If the sequence is finite it will compute a partial function from $\mathcal{N}$ to α^* defined only for $n = 0, 1, \ldots, k-1$, where k is the length of the sequence. In either case, since the sequence includes all and only the strings of the subset A, the range of the function is A.

4.1.1 DEFINITION

A subset A of α^* is (*algorithmically*) *generable* if it is the range of a computable function $g : \mathcal{N} \to \alpha^*$ which, if not a total function, has as its domain a finite subset $\{0, 1, \ldots, k-1\}$ of the non-negative integers. We call g a generating function for A. ∎

We have already remarked that if a set A is generable with generating function g we can confirm membership by generating the sequence $g(0), g(1), \ldots g(n), \ldots$ until the given string appears. Let us call this the *membership* algorithm. We can of course apply the membership algorithm to any string $\sigma \in \alpha^*$. When $\sigma \in A$ the algorithm eventually terminates. But when $\sigma \notin A$ the algorithm does not terminate since σ does not appear anywhere in the sequence. Thus our membership algorithm computes a partial function whose domain is the generable set. We conclude that every generable set is the domain of some computable function.

Surprisingly the converse is also true. Every subset of α^*, if it is the domain of a computable function, is an algorithmically generable set. Thus suppose f is some computable function with domain the subset A of α^*. By Church's thesis f is computable on $\mathbf{TM}(\alpha)$ using some program π. We hand simulate the computations of π on $\mathbf{TM}(\alpha)$ to compute the kth string in A as follows:

(1) Set n to 1
(2) List the first n strings $\sigma_0, \sigma_1, \ldots, \sigma_{n-1}$ of α^*
(3) Hand simulate n steps of the computation of π on $\mathbf{TM}(\alpha)$ for each of $\sigma_0, \sigma_1, \ldots, \sigma_{n-1}$ as input string, running the computations in parallel. As and when a computation is completed record its input string. If at least k of those computations are completed then the kth recorded input string is the kth string in A. Otherwise repeat from step 2 increasing n by 1.

If there are less than k strings in A, the above algorithm does not terminate. Otherwise, let N be such that exactly k of the input strings $\sigma_0, \sigma_1, \ldots, \sigma_{N-1}$ are in the domain of $\mathbf{TM}(\alpha)_\pi$. Let M be the length of the longest computation for any of these k strings as input. The above algorithm will terminate for some n in the range $N \leqslant n \leqslant M$.

Note that every string in A is computed as the kth string for some k.

4.1.2 THEOREM

A subset A of α^* is algorithmically generable if and only if it is the domain of a computable function. ∎

We have already noted that membership of a generable set can only be confirmed. However, if a generable subset A of α^* is such that its complement set

$$A' = \{\sigma \mid \sigma \in \alpha^* \text{ and } \sigma \notin A\},$$

is also generable, then we can algorithmically determine whether or not any string $\sigma \in \alpha^*$ is a member of A. To do this we generate the sets A and A' in parallel. The string σ *must* eventually appear either in the listing of A or the listing of A'. When it appears we have the yes or no answer to the membership question. A is a *decidable set*:

4.1.3 DEFINITION

A subset of α^* is (*algorithmically*) *decidable* if the function

$$M : \sigma \mapsto \begin{cases} \text{true} & \text{if } \sigma \in A \\ \text{false} & \text{if } \sigma \notin A \end{cases}$$

is computable. ∎

Trivially, the complement of a decidable set is also decidable. Moreover every decidable set is the domain of a computable function. (We simply modify the membership-deciding algorithm so that it loops whenever it would otherwise have halted with the false result.) Thus:

4.1.4 THEOREM

A subset of α^* is decidable if and only if both it and its complement are generable. ∎

We shall discover that there are generable sets which are not also decidable sets. That is there are generable sets whose complements are *not* generable. One such set is the set of strings of 0's and 1's which, under a specified symbol-to-byte encoding, represent programs for **TM** that have a completed computation when started with a blank tape. This set is generable but not decidable. In other words, given any program π for **TM**, if it is a program that halts when started with a blank tape, we can discover this fact by applying an algorithm to π. However, there is no other algorithm which we can simultaneously apply to π which will *always* tell us that π is not a blank-tape halting program when indeed it is not.

4.1.5 EXERCISE

Using informally described algorithms, show that a subset of α^* is the domain of a computable function if and only if it is the range of a computable function. ∎

4.2 Algorithmic solvability

In chapter 1, we introduced the idea of an (*algorithmically*) *solvable* problem. We said that the problem of **M**-equivalence of programs was solvable if there is some algorithm which can be applied to *any* pair of programs and which will determine *whether or not* the two programs are **M**-equivalent. By recording a program π as a string σ_π, which is just the concatenation of its instructions beginning with the start instruction, the issue of whether **M**-equivalence of programs is solvable becomes the issue of whether

$$A = \{\sigma \mid \sigma = \sigma_\pi \, \sigma_{\pi'} \quad \text{where } \pi \text{ and } \pi' \text{ are } \mathbf{M}\text{-equivalent}\}$$

is a decidable subset of α^*; assuming that α includes all the symbols that can appear in a program (see section 1.2).

The problem is solvable if and only if A is a decidable set. But suppose that A is just a generable set. In that case the best we can do is an algorithm that is guaranteed to terminate only when the answer is yes. For let π_1 and π_2 be two programs that are **M**-equivalent. We can confirm this by generating the set A. Eventually the string that represents this equivalent pair of programs will appear.

Finally we must allow for the possibility that A is not even generable. When this is the case there is no algorithm which will always terminate with the yes answer when presented with a pair of **M**-equivalent programs. For if there were, it could be used to confirm membership of A, and hence to generate A. This means that every algorithm that we devise for confirming **M**-equivalence of programs must have a blind spot; for every algorithm, there will be at least one pair of **M**-equivalent programs for which the algorithm does not terminate with the yes answer.

Problem solvability The problem of **M**-equivalence of programs is really an infinite set of questions of the form

'Is π_1 **M**-equivalent to π_2?'

with yes/no answers. The form of the question defines the problem. We shall consider any infinite set of questions, providing they have a specified form and have yes/no answers, to constitute a problem. As with the **M**-equivalence of programs we shall distinguish three possibilities with respect to its algorithmic solvability:

(1) There is a single algorithm which, when applied to any question in the class will always eventually terminate with the correct yes/no answer. The problem is *(algorithmically) solvable.*
(2) There is a single algorithm which, when applied to any question in the class will always eventually terminate with the correct answer when the answer is yes. When the answer is no the algorithm may or may not terminate. However, when it does terminate it gives the correct no answer. The problem is *(algorithmically) semi-solvable.*
(3) The problem is not semi-solvable. There is no algorithm which, when applied to any question in the class always eventually terminates when the answer is yes. The problem is *(algorithmically) totally unsolvable.*

Note that we are assuming that the yes answers are of primary interest. A problem P may be such that there is an algorithm that always terminates with the correct *no* answer but no algorithm that always terminates with the correct *yes* answer. We still say that the problem is totally unsolvable. However, the *complement* problem, $\overline{P}$, comprising the infinite set of questions

{'Is the answer to q no?' | q is a question of problem P}

is semi-solvable. This is because the algorithm that always gives a correct no answer for the problem P will be an algorithm that always gives a correct yes answer for the problem $\bar{P}$. That this situation can arise should not surprise us unduly. We already know that a set may be generable even when its complement is not. This occurs whenever the generable set is not also a decidable set. For problems the analogous result is:

4.2.1 THEOREM

A problem is solvable if and only if both it and its complement problem are semi-solvable.

Corollary The complement of a problem that is semi-solvable, but not solvable, is totally unsolvable.

Proof. The theorem and its corollary are almost immediate consequences of the definitions. ∎

We now examine several problems to do with the computation of programs on **TM** and **R**. None of these problems are solvable. We begin with the *halting problem.*

The halting problem The halting problem for a machine **M** is the question

'Does the computation of $\mathbf{M}_\pi(m)$ eventually terminate?'

for any program π and any memory configuration m.

4.2.2 THEOREM

The halting problem for **TM** is not solvable.

Proof. The proof is a *reductio ad absurdum.* We assume that the problem is solvable. Making use of Church's thesis, we then show that there must be some program for **TM** that both halts and does not halt for a particular input. This is a contradiction. Hence the original assumption must be false. The halting problem for **TM** is not solvable.

Let us assume the halting problem is solvable, that there is some algorithm which can be applied to any program π and any **TM** memory configuration $\langle\sigma, k\rangle$ to determine whether or not $\mathbf{TM}_\pi\ (\langle\sigma, k\rangle) \neq \mathbf{\Omega}$. Certainly then the specialization of the halting problem, where we only consider memory configurations of the form $\langle\sigma, 1\rangle$, is solvable. Let σ_π be the representation of the program π as a string of 0's and 1's such that any string $\sigma' \in \Sigma^*$ which is of the form $\sigma_\pi\sigma$ can be uniquely decomposed into the substrings σ_π and σ. (Without loss of generality we can assume that π has exactly one halt instruction and that σ_π is the string that results from a symbol to byte expansion of the concatenation of the instructions of π which ends with the halt instruction. We can then uniquely decompose σ' by looking for the first occurrence of the byte that represents the special halt symbol.)

Then the set

$$A = \{\sigma' \mid \sigma' \text{ is of the form } \sigma_\pi \sigma \text{ where } \mathbf{TM}_\pi(\langle \sigma, 1\rangle) \neq \Omega\}$$

is a decidable subset of Σ^*.

By Church's thesis there is a program for **TM** that tests for membership of this set. Without loss of generality we can assume that this program, Π_{test}, has a TRUE halt and a FALSE halt and is such that it halts at the TRUE halt for input strings in A and at the FALSE halt for all input strings not in A.

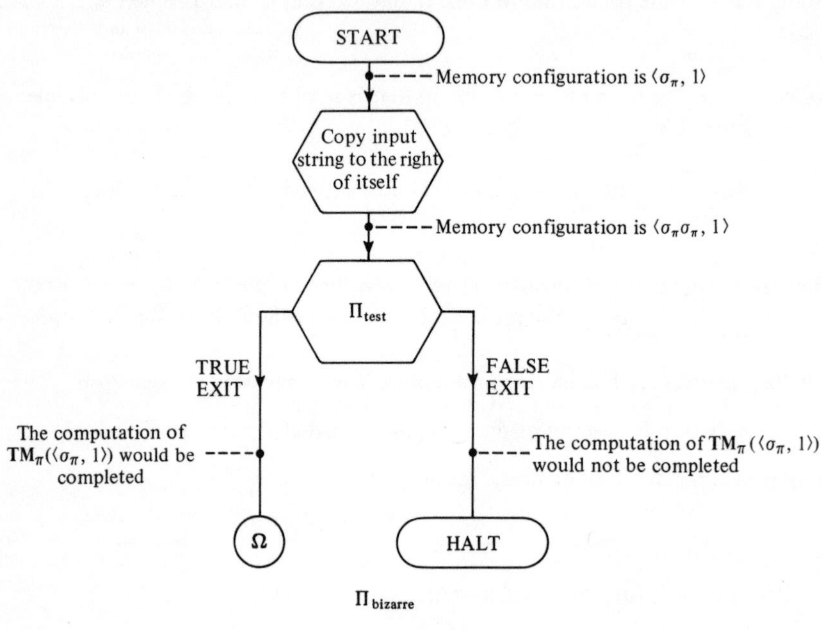

Fig. 4.1

Given such a program we can use it to construct the program Π_{bizarre} for **TM** depicted in Fig. 4.1. From the assertions attached to the program we can see that Π_{bizarre} is such that for all input strings σ_π representing a program π

$$\mathbf{TM}_{\Pi_{\text{bizarre}}}(\langle \sigma_\pi, 1\rangle) = \Omega \text{ if and only if } \mathbf{TM}_\pi(\langle \sigma_\pi, 1\rangle) \neq \Omega.$$

When the input string is $\sigma_{\Pi_{\text{bizarre}}}$, that is the string representation of Π_{bizarre} itself, we have

$$\mathbf{TM}_{\Pi_{\text{bizarre}}}(\langle \sigma_{\Pi_{\text{bizarre}}}, 1\rangle) = \Omega \quad \text{if and only if} \quad \mathbf{TM}_{\Pi_{\text{bizarre}}}(\langle \sigma_{\Pi_{\text{bizarre}}}, 1\rangle) \neq \Omega$$

This is a contradiction, for it requires the computation to be completed if and only if it is not completed. The conclusion must be that there can be no program Π_{test}. Hence the halting problem for **TM** is not solvable. ∎

Note that the very least that the above theorem proves is that if there is an algorithm for solving the **TM** halting problem then it cannot be formulated as a program for **TM**. Yet in order for something to be an algorithm, it must surely be such that it can be given a precise formulation in some computational formalism. However, every proposed computational formalism, no matter how superficially different, has turned out to be equivalent to computability on the Turing machine. It is this fact that so strongly supports Church's thesis and justifies our conclusion that there is no way of solving the **TM** halting problem that we would call algorithmic. However:

4.2.3 THEOREM

The halting problem for **TM** is semi-solvable.

Proof. Given a program π and a memory configuration $\langle \sigma, k \rangle$ we simply hand simulate the computation of $\mathbf{TM}_\pi(\langle \sigma, k \rangle)$. We give a yes answer to the question

'Does the computation of $\mathbf{TM}_\pi(\langle \sigma, k \rangle)$ eventually halt?'

if this hand simulation does indeed halt. ∎

An immediate consequence of theorems 4.2.1, 4.2.2 and 4.2.3 is that the non-halting problem for **TM**, namely the question

'Does the computation of $\mathbf{TM}_\pi(\langle \sigma, k \rangle)$ fail to halt?'

is totally unsolvable. The non-halting problem is the complement of the halting problem.

4.2.4 THEOREM

The non-halting problem for **TM** is totally unsolvable. ∎

From these two unsolvability results we can show that many other problems are not solvable. We show that a problem is not solvable by showing that another problem known to be not solvable *reduces* to that problem.

Problem reduction Let P and P' be problems. If there is an algorithm which will map any particular question q of the problem P into some question q' of the problem P', such that the answer to q is yes if and only if the answer to q' is yes, then we say that problem P *reduces* to problem P'.

In the solvability hierarchy

solvable
↓
semi-solvable
↓
totally unsolvable

P is *at least* as solvable as P', the problem to which it reduces. This is because we can use any algorithm we have for P' to answer questions of the problem P. Thus, given a particular question q of P, we first apply the algorithm that gives us the equivalent question q' of P'. The answer to q is then whatever answer we get by applying the algorithm for P' to q'.

Of course if P is *at least* as solvable as P' then P' is *no more* solvable than P. Thus if we already know that P is only semi-solvable then we may conclude that P' is at most semi-solvable. If we already know that P is totally unsolvable, we may conclude that P' is also totally unsolvable. In particular, any problem to which the **TM** halting problem reduces is at most semi-solvable, and any problem to which the **TM** non-halting problem reduces is totally unsolvable.

Consider the halting problem for **R**. The halting problem for **TM** reduces to that for **R**. This is because the proof that **R** simulates **TM** provides us with an algorithm for mapping any memory configuration $\langle \sigma, k \rangle$ and program π into a memory configuration $\{n_i\}_{i=1}^{\infty}$ and program π' such that

$$\mathbf{TM}_{\pi}(\langle \alpha, k \rangle) \neq \Omega \text{ if and only if } \mathbf{R}_{\pi'}(\{n_i\}_{i=1}^{\infty}) \neq \Omega.$$

It follows that the halting problem for **R** is at most semi-solvable. In this case we can also prove the converse reduction. The proof that **TM** simulates **R** provides the algorithm for reducing the halting problem for **R** to the halting problem for **TM**. Thus the **R** halting problem is at least semi-solvable. We conclude that the halting problem for **R** is semi-solvable but not solvable. An exactly similar argument applied to each of the other machines we defined in chapter 2 gives us:

4.2.5 THEOREM

The halting problems for **TM**(α), **R**, **SR**, **SR2** and **PM** are semi-solvable but not solvable. ∎

From now on we shall assume without proof that a solvability or unsolvability result for any one of these machines applies to the corresponding problem for each of the others. A two-way reduction is always possible via program compilation and memory encoding.

4.2.6 THEOREM

The problem of **TM** equivalence of programs is totally unsolvable.

Proof. We show that the non-halting problem for **TM** reduces to the problem of **TM** program equivalence.

To prove the reduction we need to specify an algorithm for mapping any given question of the form 'Is $\mathbf{TM}_{\pi}(\langle \sigma, k \rangle) = \Omega$?' into a question of the form 'Is $\mathbf{TM}_{\pi'} = \mathbf{TM}_{\pi''}$?'. Clearly π' and π'' are programs related to π and the initial configuration $\langle \sigma, k \rangle$. The relationship must be such that the answer to the program equivalence question is the answer to the program termination question. Our problem then is to find the programs π' and π'' which give us the equivalent question.

Suppose π' is a program whose computations on **TM** go undefined except for the particular initial configuration $\langle \sigma, k \rangle$ mentioned in the termination question for π. For initial configuration $\langle \sigma, k \rangle, \pi'$ follows the computation of π. Given π and $\langle \sigma, k \rangle$, it is quite easy to construct the program π'. We add a segment of code to the front end of π which tests whether or not the initial configuration is $\langle \sigma, k \rangle$. (Remember that in a particular termination question, $\langle \sigma, k \rangle$ would be specified as an explicit string and integer.) The TRUE exit of this code leads into the program π and the FALSE exit into an Ω-loop.

Now note that π' is a program that computes the totally undefined function on **TM** if and only if $\mathbf{TM}_\pi(\langle \sigma, k \rangle) = \Omega$. So we can find the answer to the termination question if we can find whether or not π' computes the totally undefined function. We can discover this by asking whether π' is equivalent to a program that does compute the totally undefined function. The program

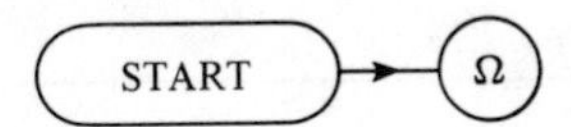

is such a program. This is the program π'' of the equivalent program equivalence question. Note that we have informally specified an algorithm for producing the programs π' and π'' given π and $\langle \sigma, k \rangle$. Moreover the answer to the question 'Is $\mathbf{TM}_\pi(\langle \sigma, k \rangle) = \Omega$?' is yes if and only if the answer to the question 'Is $\mathbf{TM}_{\pi'} = \mathbf{TM}_{\pi''}$?' is yes. ∎

Observe that in proving the above theorem we have incidentally established another unsolvability result. The non-halting question 'Is $\mathbf{TM}_\pi(\langle \sigma, k \rangle) = \Omega$?' was first transformed into the question 'Is $\mathbf{TM}_{\pi'}$ totally undefined?'. The set of all questions of this form constitute the problem of whether an arbitrary program computes the totally undefined function on **TM**. Hence this problem is also totally unsolvable.

4.2.7 EXERCISE

Using the problem reduction technique,
(1) show that the blank-tape halting problem for **TM** is not solvable. This is the question

> 'Will the computation of π on **TM** which starts with the tape completely blank, eventually halt?'

for an arbitrary program π;
(2)* show that the problem of whether an arbitrary program computes a total function on **R** is at most semi-solvable. ∎

4.3 Diagonalization

In the proof of the unsolvability of the halting problem for **TM** we made use of a bit string representation σ_π of a program π produced by applying a symbol-to-byte expansion to the concatenation of the instructions of π. Let

$$\sigma_{\pi_0}, \sigma_{\pi_1}, \sigma_{\pi_2}, \ldots, \sigma_{\pi_n}, \ldots$$

be any sequence that includes all and only those bit strings that represent programs. Let

$$\pi_0, \pi_1, \pi_2, \ldots, \pi_n, \ldots$$

be the corresponding sequence of programs (π_i is the program with bit string representation σ_{π_i}). Then Table 4.1 represents an infinite table which gives the termination record for each program π_i for initial tape strings that are bit-string representations of programs. A 0 in the ith row and jth column means that the computation of $\mathbf{TM}_{\pi_i}(\langle \sigma_{\pi_j}, 1 \rangle)$ is completed, a 1 in that position indicates that it is not completed.

Table 4.1

Bit strings representing programs

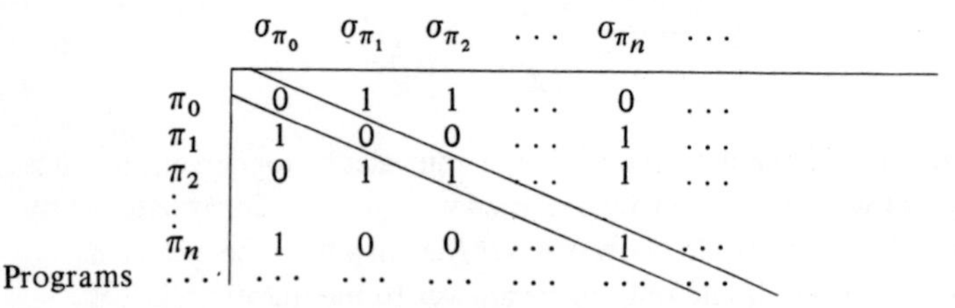

Programs	σ_{π_0}	σ_{π_1}	σ_{π_2}	...	σ_{π_n}	...
π_0	0	1	1	...	0	...
π_1	1	0	0	...	1	...
π_2	0	1	1	...	1	...
$\vdots$						
π_n	1	0	0	...	1	...
...	...	...	...	...	...	...

The table entries along the diagonal, i.e., those that lie in the ith row and ith column for all $i \geqslant 1$, give the termination record when the program has its own bit-string representation as initial tape string. If the reader refers back to the proof of theorem 4.2.2 he can check that the program Π_{bizarre} is a program whose termination record is given by the diagonal sequence but with 0 replaced by 1 and 1 replaced by 0. This is because for all $j \geqslant 1$,

$$\mathbf{TM}_{\Pi_{\text{bizarre}}}(\langle \sigma_{\pi_j}, 1 \rangle) = \mathbf{\Omega} \quad \text{if and only if } \mathbf{TM}_{\pi_j}(\langle \sigma_{\pi_j}, 1 \rangle) \neq \mathbf{\Omega}.$$

But Π_{bizarre} has its own bit-string representation which appears somewhere in the sequence

$$\sigma_{\pi_0}, \sigma_{\pi_1}, \ldots, \sigma_{\pi_n}, \ldots.$$

Suppose it is the string σ_{π_N}. In that case the termination record of Π_{bizarre} is the termination record of π_N and is given by the Nth row of the table. Consider the entry in the Nth column of that row, that is the point where the row intersects the diagonal. Since it is the row that gives the termination record of Π_{bizarre}, the entry is 0 if and only if it is 1, a blatant contradiction. However, the program Π_{bizarre} could be constructed if the halting problem for **TM** were solvable; we conclude that the halting problem for **TM** is not solvable.

The essential structure of the above *reductio ad absurdum* is as follows. On the assumption that some conjecture is true, we show that there is, at least conceptually, an infinite table with a row entry that differs from the diagonal entry in each column. Since this is impossible the conjecture must be false. We call this form of argument *diagonalization*.

Exercise 4.2.7(2) established the fact that the problem of whether an arbitrary register program computes a total function is at most semi-solvable. If this problem were semi-solvable, the set $\{\sigma_\pi \mid \mathbf{R}_\pi \text{ total}\}$ of bit-string representations of programs would be generable. By generating the set we are, in effect, algorithmically generating a sequence of programs

$$\pi_0, \pi_1, \ldots, \pi_n, \ldots$$

which includes all and only those register programs which compute total functions. We use a diagonal argument to prove that this is impossible. The problem is therefore totally unsolvable.

4.3.1 THEOREM

There is no algorithmically generable sequence

$$\pi_0, \pi_1, \ldots, \pi_n, \ldots$$

which includes all and only those register programs that compute total functions.

Proof. If π computes a total function on $\mathbf{R}$ then its monadic associated function f over the non-negative integers, the function computed using x_1 as input and output register and all other registers as working registers, will be total. Table 4.2 is a table of these monadic associated functions. The nth row has all the values of the monadic associated function f_n of some program π_n, where $\mathbf{R}_{\pi_n}$ is total.

Table 4.2

	0	1	2	...	n	...
f_0	$f_0(0)$	$f_0(1)$	$f_0(2)$	...	$f_0(n)$	...
f_1	$f_1(0)$	$f_1(1)$	$f_1(2)$	...	$f_1(n)$	...
f_2	$f_2(0)$	$f_2(1)$	$f_2(2)$	...	$f_2(n)$	...
$\vdots$						
f_n	$f_n(0)$	$f_n(1)$	$f_n(2)$	...	$f_n(n)$	...
...	...	...	...	...	...	...

Consider the function

$$g : n \mapsto f_n(n) + 1.$$

There can be no row entry for this function.

Now let us suppose that some sequence

$$\pi_0, \pi_1, \ldots, \pi_n, \ldots$$

of all and only those programs which compute total functions on $\mathbf{R}$ is algorithmically generable. We show that g is then the monadic associated function of some program in the sequence. It must therefore have a row entry in the table. This is our diagonal contradiction.

g is total and computable: Given n we use the algorithm for generating the sequence of programs to find π_n. We now hand simulate the computation of π_n on **R** with $x_1 = n$ and all other registers initialized to zero. We add one to the final value of $x_1 = f_n(n)$ to get the value of $g(n)$. By Church's thesis, since g is computable it must be a register function. In other words it is the monadic associated function of some register program. By adding instructions to π which explicitly initialize all of its variables except x_1 to zero, we ensure that it computes a total function on **R**. This means that π occurs somewhere in the sequence $\pi_0, \pi_1, \ldots \pi_n, \ldots$, say as π_N. But then g is the function f_N, giving us the contradiction that

$$f_N(N) = g(N) = f_N(N) + 1. \quad \blacksquare$$

Note that no diagonal contradiction arises in the proof if we do not insist that every program that computes a total function on **R** appears in the algorithmically generable sequence of programs. In that case, we merely conclude that g is a register function that is not the associated function of any program in the sequence.

In chapter 3 we asked the reader to satisfy himself that there is an algorithm for testing whether or not a program is a count program. Using this algorithm we could generate the set of count programs. Thus we have:

4.3.2 THEOREM

There is a total register function that is not the associated function of any count program. $\blacksquare$

Another way in which we can escape the diagonal contradiction is to drop the requirement that the generable sequence includes only register programs that compute total functions. Thus, for example, the set of all register programs is algorithmically generable. (Again this is because there is an algorithm for testing whether or not a program is a register program.) Suppose that

$$\pi_0, \pi_1, \ldots, \pi_n, \ldots$$

is a generable sequence of all the register programs. The monadic associated function f_n of π_n is now a partial function. The appropriate definition of g is therefore

$$g : n \mapsto \begin{cases} f_n(n) + 1 & \text{when } f_n(n) \neq \Omega \\ \Omega & \text{when } f_n(n) = \Omega. \end{cases}$$

The reader should convince himself that g is computable. Again then, by Church's thesis, g is a register function and therefore the monadic associated function of some register program π. Since the sequence includes all register programs, π is the program π_N for some N. This time we must conclude that $g(N) = f_N(N) = \Omega$ to avoid the contradiction that $f_N(N) = f_N(N) + 1$. In other words, we avoid the diagonal contradiction only if g is not a total function.

Actually, g is an example of a computable function which is *inherently* partial. There is no way of extending g to a total function which is also computable. For instance, the function

$$g' : n \mapsto \begin{cases} f_n(n) + 1 & \text{when } f_n(n) \neq \Omega \\ 0 & \text{when } f_n(n) = \Omega \end{cases}$$

certainly cannot be computable. The assumption of computability leads directly to the diagonal contradiction again.

We call the function g' the *completion* of g.

4.3.3 THEOREM

There is a non-total computable function over the non-negative integers whose completion is not computable. ∎

The upshot of the above result is that the concept of a partial function is an essential one when dealing with computable functions.

4.4 Notes and references

The (algorithmically) decidable and (algorithmically) generable sets are often referred to as the recursive and recursively enumerable sets respectively.

The first proof of the unsolvability of the Turing machine halting problem was given by Turing[2].

Although we have grouped together all the problems that are not semi-solvable as the totally unsolvable problems we can in fact distinguish *degrees of unsolvability* within this grouping. Thus if a totally unsolvable problem P reduces to a problem P', but not vice versa, then P' is even less solvable than P. For a detailed treatment of problem reduction, diagonalization, and degrees of unsolvability see Rogers[1].

References

1. Rogers, H., *Theory of Recursive Functions and Effective Computability*, McGraw-Hill, New York (1967)
2. Turing, A. M., 'On computable numbers, with an application to the Entscheidungsproblem', *Proc. London Math. Soc.* (2) 42, 230–265 (1936)

5 Machines with input and output streams

5.1 Defining a machine with input and output streams

Any reader with practical experience of computers knows that they invariably have input and output devices. Even the smallest computers usually have something like a paper-tape reader and a paper-tape punch. Moreover the internal memory, or 'core storage', is not normally used for the encoding of data and the decoding of results. Indeed, from the point of view of the user (not the programmer) the computer is a black box. The user represents his data as a string of characters punched on a paper tape and mounted in the tape reader of the machine. The computation then proceeds with the data on the tape being read in, in a piece-meal fashion, as and when required. At the same time, the results are usually being punched out on the output tape as and when their values are computed. At the end of the computation the user reads off the results from the string of characters that have been punched on the output tape.

Because the machine does not need to read in the whole of the data at the start of the computation, the input tape acts as an extension of the internal memory. In fact it can record more information than can be held in the internal memory all at once. Then the machine just reads in the data in chunks of a size that it can handle. Likewise the output tape is an extension of the internal memory, since the computer can punch out the results piecemeal in order to free its internal memory for the processing of more input.

However, the input and output tape are merely a source of data and a depository for results, respectively, and the information being processed flows through the machine in one direction–from the input stream, to the internal memory, to the output stream. The input and output tapes are therefore just *weak* extensions of the internal memory, used only for the encoding of data and the decoding of results. This idea is illustrated by Fig. 5.1.

There is a very good reason why we should try to formalize this type of information environment and its use. It enables us to study machines with essentially

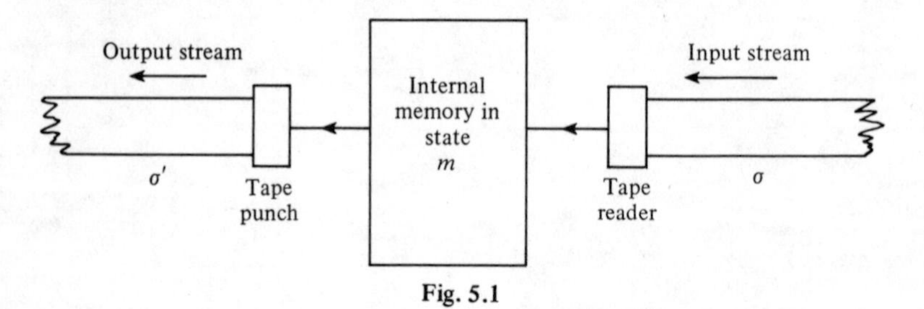

Fig. 5.1

finite memories which can still be used to compute functions with arbitrarily large arguments and values. Such a machine has a finite internal memory, but input and output streams which can hold strings of symbols of unbounded length. Nor does this commit us to assuming that there is an unlimited amount of paper tape available, for the input and output streams do not need to be permanently recorded. We can think of them as sequences of signals that arrive at and depart from the machine, the incoming signals being generated by an external source and the outgoing signals being absorbed by an external sink. From this standpoint the machine just transforms one signal sequence into another and the functions it computes are functions over the *set of signal sequences.*

Can we formalize the idea of a machine with input and output streams within our existing framework?

Each configuration of the information environment of Fig. 5.1 is uniquely recorded if we know the contents of the output stream σ', the state m of the internal memory and the contents of the input stream σ. That is, we can uniquely record the configuration by the triple $\langle \sigma', m, \sigma \rangle$. So the memory set of the machine is $\alpha^* \times M \times \alpha^*$, where α is the alphabet of input and output symbols and M is some set defining the range of configurations of the internal memory. During a computation information must be transferred from the input stream to the internal memory and from the internal memory to the output stream. To do this the machine must at least be able to recognize any symbol from α when it appears at the head of the input stream, be able to erase the symbol at the head of the input stream, and be able to print any of the symbols in α onto the output stream. Any attendant changes in the internal memory can then be produced by explicit instructions in the program immediately following or preceding these 'input/output' instructions. This leads us to:

5.1.1 DEFINITION

A machine **M** has *standard input/output* (*standard I/O*) *over the alphabet* α if the following conditions are satisfied:

(1) The memory set of **M** takes the form $\alpha^* \times M \times \alpha^*$, i.e., the set of all ordered triples $\langle \sigma', m, \sigma \rangle$ where $m \in M$ and $\sigma, \sigma' \in \alpha^*$. The set M is the *internal memory* of **M** and the third and first components are the *input stream* and the *output stream* respectively. Some $m_0 \in M$ is designated as the *initial state* of the internal memory.

(2) The operations and tests of **M** include the following *pseudo I/O instructions.* Here, if $\sigma \in \alpha^*$, $(\sigma]$ denotes the string obtained from it by erasing its leftmost symbol, being undefined if $\sigma = \Lambda$, and for each $s \in \alpha$, $s\sigma$ (respectively σs) denotes the string obtained by concatenating s onto the left-hand (respectively right-hand) end of σ. For each interpretation, we assume the function or predicate to be applied to the memory state $\langle \sigma', m, \sigma \rangle$:

ERASE INPUT
This is interpreted as the partial function with value $\langle \sigma', m, (\sigma] \rangle$.

PRINT s

For each $s \in \alpha$, this is interpreted as the total function with value $\langle \sigma' s, m, \sigma \rangle$.

INPUT $s?$

For each $s \in \alpha$ this is interpreted as the total predicate with value true if $\sigma = s(\sigma]$, false otherwise. Note that this allows us to test for end of input as then the test returns false for all $s \in \alpha$.

(3) All other function or predicate names are either interpreted as the totally undefined function or as partially defined functions and predicates acting co-ordinatewise on the internal memory M. These latter are the *internal* operations and tests of **M**. ∎

We have still to capture the idea that only the input stream is used for the encoding of data, and only the output stream for the decoding of results. The simplest way to do this is to incorporate a standard encoder and decoder into the definition of a standard machine. Thus we shall assume that every computation on a standard machine starts with the configuration,

$$\langle \Lambda, m_0, \sigma \rangle,$$

where m_0 is the designated initial state of the internal memory. Since the internal memory always starts in state m_0 and the output stream is initially empty, only the input stream can be used to encode data via the input string σ. A completed computation terminates with some configuration,

$$\langle \sigma', m, \sigma'' \rangle,$$

and we assume that only the contents of the output stream σ' carries information concerning the result. We therefore take the function computed by a program π on a standard machine to be the set of all ordered pairs $\langle \sigma, \sigma' \rangle$ such that when σ is the initial contents of the input stream the computation halts with σ' being the final contents of the output stream.

In terms of our earlier formulation this is really the function

$$d \circ \mathbf{M}_\pi \circ e : \alpha^* \mapsto \alpha^*,$$

where e and d are the *standard* encoder and decoder given respectively by

$$e : \sigma \mapsto \langle \Lambda, m_0, \sigma \rangle$$

and

$$d : \langle \sigma', m, \sigma'' \rangle \mapsto \sigma',$$

since strictly speaking $\mathbf{M}_\pi$ is the function over the entire memory set of the machine. However, from now on, we shall be dealing almost exclusively with standard machines so we use $\mathbf{M}_\pi$ to denote the function $d \circ \mathbf{M}_\pi \circ e$ as a notational convenience.

Finally, we must modify our definitions of machine simulation and machine equivalence for standard machines. We shall say that one standard machine can simulate another if it can be programmed to compute any function over strings that can be computed on the other machine. Since the I/O alphabets of the machines may be different, we allow some symbol-to-byte representation to take strings of symbols from one alphabet into strings of symbols from the other. More formally, we have:

5.1.2 DEFINITION

A standard machine $\mathbf{M}'$ over alphabet β can *I/O simulate* a standard machine $\mathbf{M}$ over alphabet α if, for some symbol-to-byte representation function $g : \alpha^* \to \beta^*$, we can specify an algorithm which given any program π produces a program π' such that

$$\mathbf{M}_\pi = g^{-1} \circ \mathbf{M}'_{\pi'} \circ g.$$

(Remember that $\mathbf{M}_\pi$ is now the function $d \circ \mathbf{M}_\pi \circ e$ over α^*, where e and d are the standard encoder and decoder for the machine $\mathbf{M}$. Likewise for $\mathbf{M}'_{\pi'}$.)

Two standard machines are *I/O equivalent* if each I/O simulates the other. ∎

Clearly this is no radical departure from our earlier definitions of machine simulation and equivalence.

5.1.3 EXERCISE*

Give a formal definition of the standard Turing machine **STM**(α, β) over the arbitrary alphabet α with tape symbols from the arbitrary alphabet β and a blank tape as the initial state of the internal memory. Satisfy yourself that this machine is equivalent (in the old sense) to **TM**. ∎

We denote **STM**(Σ, Σ) simply by **STM**.

5.2 Finite memory modification

The reader who has attempted exercise 2.4.3(3) knows that we can use the structure of a program to record a finite amount of information. That problem required a program for the Turing machine to shift a portion of the tape string one place to the left. As the scanning head moves left it prints on the next square the symbol that was on the immediately preceding square. What this symbol was must be remembered by the program, in effect by having two branches with almost identical code, one of which eventually prints a 0, the other of which eventually prints a 1. The appropriate branch of the program is entered before the computation has overwritten the symbol on the preceding square. It is much easier to write the program if we assume that the Turing machine has an extra memory component which can hold one tape symbol at a time. Then if we can show that all references in the program to the extra memory component can be removed by a suitable modification of the program, we shall have indirectly specified the program for **TM** proper. This indirect program-writing strategy turns out to be particularly useful when dealing with standard machines.

5.2.1 DEFINITION

Let **M**, **MN** be machines standard over the same alphabet α and related as follows:

(1) The internal memory of **MN** is $M \times N$ where M is the internal memory of **M** and N is a finite non-empty set with k elements.
(2) A finite set of function and predicate names are interpreted by **MN** as partially defined functions and predicates that operate coordinatewise on the memory extension N. All other non-I/O function and predicate names are interpreted as functions and predicates which act coordinatewise on M and their interpretation is exactly the same as that assigned by **M**.
(3) The extra operations and tests that apply to the memory extension are *completely defined.* That is, given any function or predicate name FP, we can algorithmically determine whether or not FP is the name of an operation or test of the memory extension N, and if it is, for any $n \in N$, whether or not $\mathbf{MN}_{FP}(n) = \boldsymbol{\Omega}$. (Of course if $\mathbf{MN}_{FP}(n) \neq \boldsymbol{\Omega}$ we shall be able to compute its value since every operation and test must be specified by a computable function.) In fact the particular machines that we consider have all their operations and tests completely defined. Complete definition appears here as an explicit requirement to ensure that the program rewrite of algorithm 5.2.2 is indeed an algorithm.
(4) The initial state of $M \times N$ is $\langle m_0, n_0 \rangle$, where m_0 is the initial state of M and n_0 is some fixed element of N designated the *initial state* of the extension.

Then we say that **MN** is a *finite modification* of **M**. ∎

Note that **MN** need not have all the operations and tests of **M**. This is because one or more of the extra operations and tests may have the same name as an internal operation or test of **M**, and the original is then lost.

We now give a method for rewriting any program π to produce a program π' which computes on **M** the function computed by π on **MN**. We do this by removing from π any reference to the memory extension N. The states of N are remembered by storing information in the label names of the modified program.

Thus let L_0 be the label mentioned in the start instruction of π. A completed computation of π on **MN** with input $\sigma \in \alpha^*$ has the form

$$L_0, \langle \Lambda, m_0, n_0, \sigma \rangle, L_1, \langle \sigma_1, m_1, n_1, \sigma'_1 \rangle, \ldots, L_k, \langle \sigma_k, m_k, n_k, \sigma'_k \rangle. \qquad \text{(A)}$$

If we transfer the N-component of the memory elements to the labels we obtain a sequence:

$$\langle L_0, n_0 \rangle, \langle \Lambda, m_0, \sigma \rangle, \langle L_1, n_1 \rangle, \langle \sigma_1, m_1, \sigma'_1 \rangle, \ldots, \langle L_k, n_k \rangle, \langle \sigma_k, m_k, \sigma'_k \rangle, \qquad \text{(B)}$$

which has the form of a computation on **M** of some program π'' in which strings denoting the ordered pairs $\langle L_i, n_i \rangle$ appear as labels. If π'' generates on **M** a completed computation of the form (B) if and only if π generates on **MN** a completed computation of the form (A), then we have $\mathbf{M}_{\pi''}(\sigma) = \mathbf{MN}_{\pi}(\sigma) = \sigma_k$ for all input strings σ.

The algorithm given below constructs the program π'' given π. Actually π'' is not quite a program as defined in chapter 1. In order to ensure that it generates exactly a computation of the form (B), it must include *no-op instructions.* These are instructions of the form,

$$L\text{:GOTO } L';$$

where L,L' are label identifiers. The interpretation of such instructions is obvious; if we have reached the label–memory element pair L_i, m_i in a computation sequence, where L_i is the label of a no-op instruction

$$L_i\text{:GOTO } L_i';$$

then the next label-memory element pair is L_i', m_i. Thus no-op instructions are like the FORTRAN 'CONTINUE' and the ALGOL 68 **skip** statement. Clearly no-op instructions can be dispensed with. Any program containing no-op instructions can be transformed into an equivalent program without no-ops (exercise 5.2.3). Therefore removing the no-op instructions from π'' will give us a program π' such that $\mathbf{MN}_{\pi} = \mathbf{M}_{\pi'}$. We leave the reader to prove that the (no-op) program π'' produced by the algorithm below does indeed produce a completed computation of the form (B) if and only if π produces a completed computation of the form (A). An induction on the length of the computation sequence is required.

5.2.2 ALGORITHM

Beginning with the first instruction of π, we construct π'' using the algorithm below. Initially π'' contains no instructions.

(1) Take next instruction of π.
(2) Instruction is START: GOTO L_0;
Remove the instruction from π and add to π'' the instruction

$$\text{START: GOTO } \langle L_0, n_0\rangle;$$

(3) Instruction is of the form L: HALT;
Remove the instruction from π and add the instruction
$\langle L, n\rangle$: HALT; for each $n \in N$ to π''.
(4) Instruction is of the form L: DO F GOTO L'; where $\mathbf{MN}_F$ is not a function that applies to N.
Remove the instruction from π and add the instruction
$\langle L, n\rangle$: DO F GOTO $\langle L', n\rangle$; for each $n \in N$ to π''.
(5) Instruction is of the form L: DO F GOTO L'; where $\mathbf{MN}_F$ is a function that applies to N.

Remove the instruction from π and add to π'' the instruction
$\langle L, n\rangle$: GOTO $\langle L', n'\rangle$; if $\mathbf{MN}_F(n) = n'$ (this is a no-op instruction),
$\langle L, n\rangle$: DO F GOTO $\langle L, n\rangle$; if $\mathbf{MN}_F(n) = \mathbf{\Omega}$ (this is an Ω-substitution),
for each $n \in N$.

(6) Instruction is of the form L: IF P THEN GOTO L' ELSE GOTO L''; where $\mathbf{MN}_P$ is not a predicate that applies to N.
Remove the instruction from π and add to π'' the instruction

$\langle L, n\rangle$: IF P THEN GOTO $\langle L', n\rangle$ ELSE GOTO $\langle L'', n\rangle$;

for each $n \in N$.

(7) Instruction is of the form L: IF P THEN GOTO L' ELSE GOTO L''; where $\mathbf{MN}_P$ is a predicate that applies to N. Remove the instruction from π and add to π'' the instruction

$\langle L, n\rangle$: GOTO $\langle L', n\rangle$; if $\mathbf{MN}_P(n) =$ true,

$\langle L, n\rangle$: GOTO $\langle L'', n\rangle$; if $\mathbf{MN}_P(n) =$ false,

$\langle L, n\rangle$: DO Ω GOTO $\langle L, n\rangle$; if $\mathbf{MN}_P(n) = \mathbf{\Omega}$,
for each $n \in N$.

(8) Repeat from step 1 until there are no instructions left in π. ▮

The algorithm is illustrated by Figs. 5.2 (π) and 5.3 (π''). $N = \{0, 1\}$ and $N \leftarrow 1$, $N = 0?$ have their obvious interpretations.

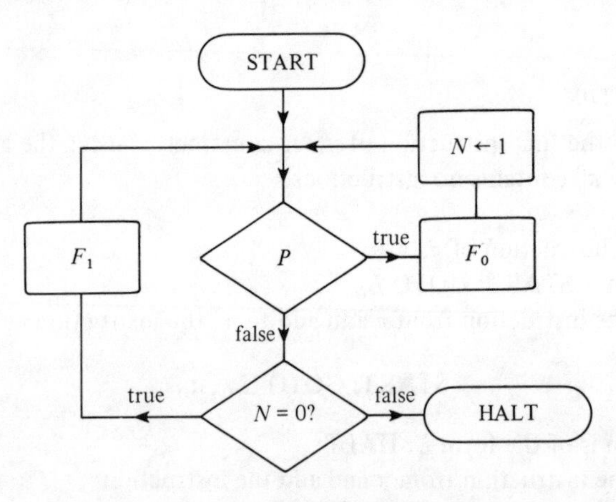

Fig. 5.2

Note π'' does not inherit the structure of π as was the case with the stepwise simulations of chapter 2. In fact, π'', with its jumps to and fro between the copies of π, is highly unstructured! This is not to say that the indirect program-writing strategy–write a program for a finite modification and expand it using the above algorithm–is a bad one. The assumption of a finite memory extension often

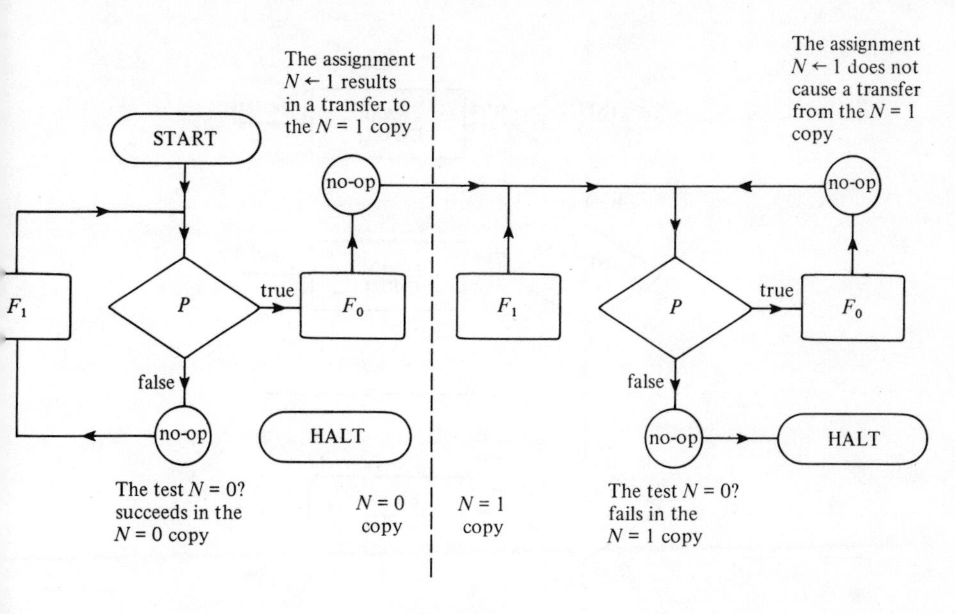

Fig. 5.3

enables us to write a highly structured program π whose correctness proof is quite straightforward. Then the correctness of the unstructured π'' is guaranteed by the correctness of π and our proof that π'' must compute the same function.

5.2.3 EXERCISE

Show that any program containing no-op instructions can be transformed into an equivalent program without no-op instructions. (Remove all no-op instructions and change label identifiers in the rest of the program accordingly; to deal with loops of no-op instructions, introduce Ω-loops.)

5.2.4 THEOREM (FINITE MODIFICATION THEOREM)

If **MN** is a finite modification of **M**, then **M** I/O simulates **MN**.

Proof. Any program π is first rewritten using algorithm 5.2.2 and then the no-ops are removed. The result is a program π' such that

$$\mathbf{MN}_\pi = \mathbf{M}_{\pi'}.$$

Therefore **M** I/O simulates **MN**. ∎

The above theorem has many applications. One in particular will prove to be very useful later on; it tells us that programs for standard machines have equivalent standard forms which are easier to handle.

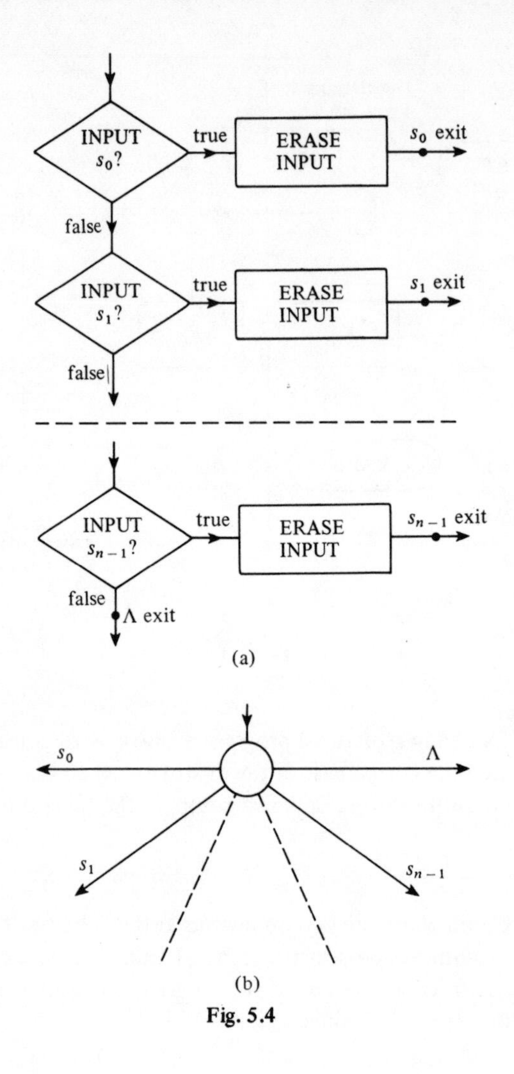

Fig. 5.4

5.2.5 DEFINITION

A program π is in *standard form* with respect to the alphabet $\alpha = \{s_0, s_1, \ldots, s_{n-1}\}$ if all of its pseudo input instructions are grouped in *nodes* which exhaustively test and erase the incoming input symbol as detailed in Fig. 5.4(a). Figure 5.4(b) is shorthand notation for a node. ∎

Henceforth we shall adopt the convention, where α is an arbitrary alphabet, that $s_0, s_1, \ldots, s_{n-1}$ are the symbols of α.

5.2.6 THEOREM

Let **M** be a machine with standard I/O over α. Then any program π is **M**-equivalent to a program π' which is in standard form with respect to α.

Proof. We may suppose, with no loss of generality, that π contains no occurrence of the names END OF INPUT $\leftarrow$ true, END OF INPUT?, $B \leftarrow s_i$ and $B = s_i$? for $0 \leqslant i \leqslant n-1$. If it does we simply invent new names not occurring in π and suitably modify the construction.

We envisage a finite modification **MN** of **M** with memory extension $N = \alpha \times \{\text{true}, \text{false}\}$; the first component is a buffer capable of holding one input symbol and the second is a switch which we shall use to record the state of the input stream—true if this is empty, false if not. **MN** interprets the above names as follows:

Function or predicate name	Result when applied to $\langle s_i, \text{tval}\rangle \in N$
END OF INPUT $\leftarrow$ true	$\langle s_i, \text{true}\rangle$
END OF INPUT?	tval
$B \leftarrow s_j\ (0 \leqslant j \leqslant n)$	$\langle s_j, \text{tval}\rangle$
$B = s_j?\ (0 \leqslant j \leqslant n)$	true if $i = j$, false otherwise

The initial state of N is $\langle s_0, \text{false}\rangle$.

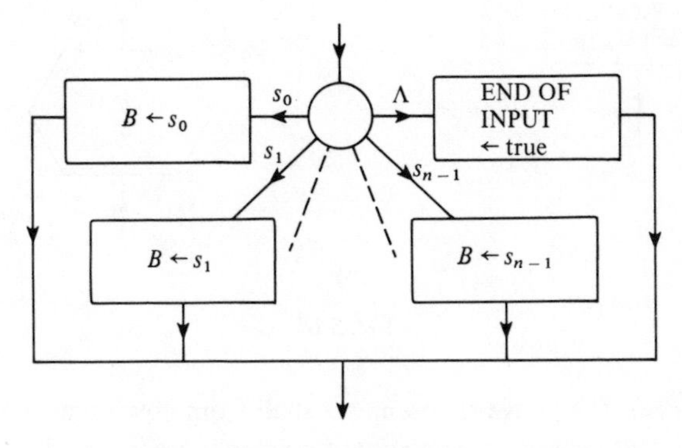

Fig. 5.5 LOAD B

The first step in the rewrite of π is the interpolation of the sequence of code LOAD B given by Fig. 5.5 between the start instruction of π and its successor. LOAD B either transfers the next input symbol to the buffer, or sets the end of input switch to true if there are no more input symbols.

π is now modified so that all input tests are made on the buffer, so that all attempts to erase the input symbol will load the next input symbol into the buffer. This is done by applying the expansions given by Fig. 5.6 to the remainder of π. This will transform π into a program π'' in standard form with respect to α as the only pseudo-input instructions are grouped in nodes in the sequences LOAD B. Clearly $\mathbf{MN}_{\pi''} = \mathbf{M}_{\pi}$. If we now apply the program rewrite described in the proof of theorem 5.2.4, we arrive at a program π', in standard form with respect to α, for which $\mathbf{M}_{\pi} = \mathbf{M}_{\pi'}$ as required. We ask the reader to check that the expansion given by algorithm 5.2.2 does in fact transform standard programs into standard programs, and that removal of no-op instructions does not affect standard form. ∎

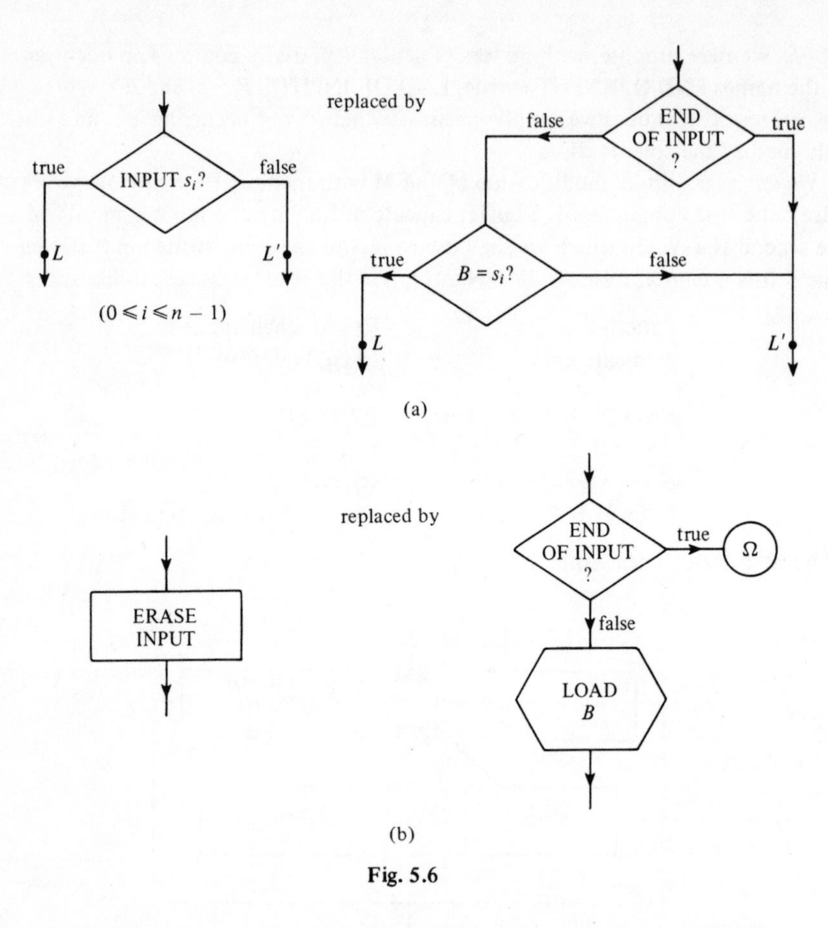

Fig. 5.6

In consequence of the above theorem, we shall from now on assume, unless otherwise stated, that programs for standard machines are in standard form.

Another application of algorithm 5.2.2 is outlined in the following exercise.

5.2.7 EXERCISE*

Show that two standard machines which have the same internal memory and the same repertoire of internal operations and tests are I/O equivalent.

(The machines differ only if they have distinct I/O alphabets. You need only consider the case where one machine (**M**) is standard over Σ and the other (**M'**) is standard over an arbitrary alphabet α as the general case will follow by transitivity of I/O equivalence. It is quite easy to show that **M'** I/O simulates **M**. To prove that **M** I/O simulates **M'**, let g be a symbol-to-byte representation function from α^* to Σ^*. Modify **M** by including a buffer capable of holding k successive input symbols, where k is the byte size, and a switch to signal end of input, with appropriate operations and tests. Give a method for rewriting any program so that it reads m-bytes into the buffer instead of symbols from α and appeal to the finite modification theorem 5.2.4.) ∎

5.2.8 DEFINITION

A standard machine is *finite* if its internal memory is a finite set and its internal operations and tests are completely defined. ∎

5.2.9 THEOREM

All finite standard machines are I/O equivalent.

Proof. By the finite modification theorem 5.2.4 and the last exercise, every finite standard machine is I/O simulated by a standard machine over alphabet Σ with no internal operations and tests. Trivially any standard machine *I/O* simulates such a machine. ∎

This last result leads us naturally to the definition of the simplest possible machine standard over alphabet α.

5.2.10 DEFINITION

The *automaton* **AUT**(α) is the machine standard over the alphabet α with no internal memory at all. That is, the memory set of **AUT**(α) is $\alpha^* \times \alpha^*$ and the only functions and predicates supplied are the pseudo I/O instructions common to all standard machines. ∎

Strictly speaking, the memory set of **AUT**(α) should be $\alpha^* \times M \times \alpha^*$ with M a one-element set. However, it seems more natural to drop the second component when it serves no purpose, as here. We denote **AUT**(Σ) simply by **AUT**. We shall investigate this machine in some depth in the next chapter. It is the ultimate formal model of any physical (and hence finite) machine.

5.3 The pushdown store machine

The reader may now suspect that all standard machines fall into one or other of two categories, depending on whether they have finite or infinite internal memories, all finite machines being equivalent, by theorem 5.2.9, to the automaton, and those with infinite internal memories being able to compute any computable function. In fact the real situation is more complex. Indeed there is a whole spectrum of machines ranging in computing power from the all-powerful machines like **TM** and **R** right down to the automaton, with intermediate levels going beyond the capabilities of finite machines yet unable to simulate **TM** or **R**. In this section we present such a machine, the *pushdown store* machine **PDS**. We shall study examples of functions computable on this machine but not on any finite machine; on the other hand we describe a simple computable function which cannot be computed on **PDS**.

Intuitively, the internal memory of **PDS** is a *pushdown store* or *stack* of 0's and 1's—that is, a finite string of 0's and 1's which may be interrogated, added to or deleted from at one end only by a read/write head (Fig. 5.7). More formally we have the following:

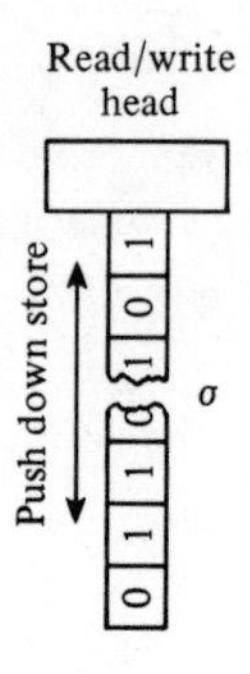

Fig. 5.7

5.3.1 DEFINITION

The *pushdown store machine* **PDS** is the machine with standard I/O over Σ with internal memory set Σ^*, interpreting the function names LOAD 0, LOAD 1 and POP and predicate names 0? and 1? as functions and predicates over the internal memory as follows. Here, if $\sigma \in \alpha^*$, $[\sigma)$ denotes the string obtained from it by erasing its rightmost symbol, being undefined if $\sigma = \Lambda$.

(1) LOAD 0 *and* LOAD 1
Total functions mapping $\sigma \in \Sigma^*$ onto $\sigma 0$ and $\sigma 1$ respectively.

(2) POP
A partial function mapping σ onto $[\sigma)$.

(3) 0? and 1?
Total predicates with value true if $\sigma = (\sigma)0$ ($\sigma = [\sigma)1$ respectively), false otherwise. Note that this allows us to test for empty stack, as then both tests fail.

The initial state of the internal memory is Λ, i.e., empty stack. ∎

We leave it to the reader to provide the formal definition of the pushdown store machine **PDS**(α, β) standard over an alphabet α with stack symbols from an alphabet β (exercise 5.3.4(1)).

What computations can we realize with this machine? Consider the following examples.

5.3.2 EXAMPLE (BALANCED STRINGS)

Call a string $\sigma \in \Sigma^*$ *balanced* if it is either empty, or consists of a 0 followed by a balanced string followed by a 1, or consists of one balanced string followed by another. Thus Λ, 01, 010011, 00010111 and 0100100111 are balanced strings, whereas 0, 1, 10 and 0001011 are not. (It may help to think of a 0 as a left bracket

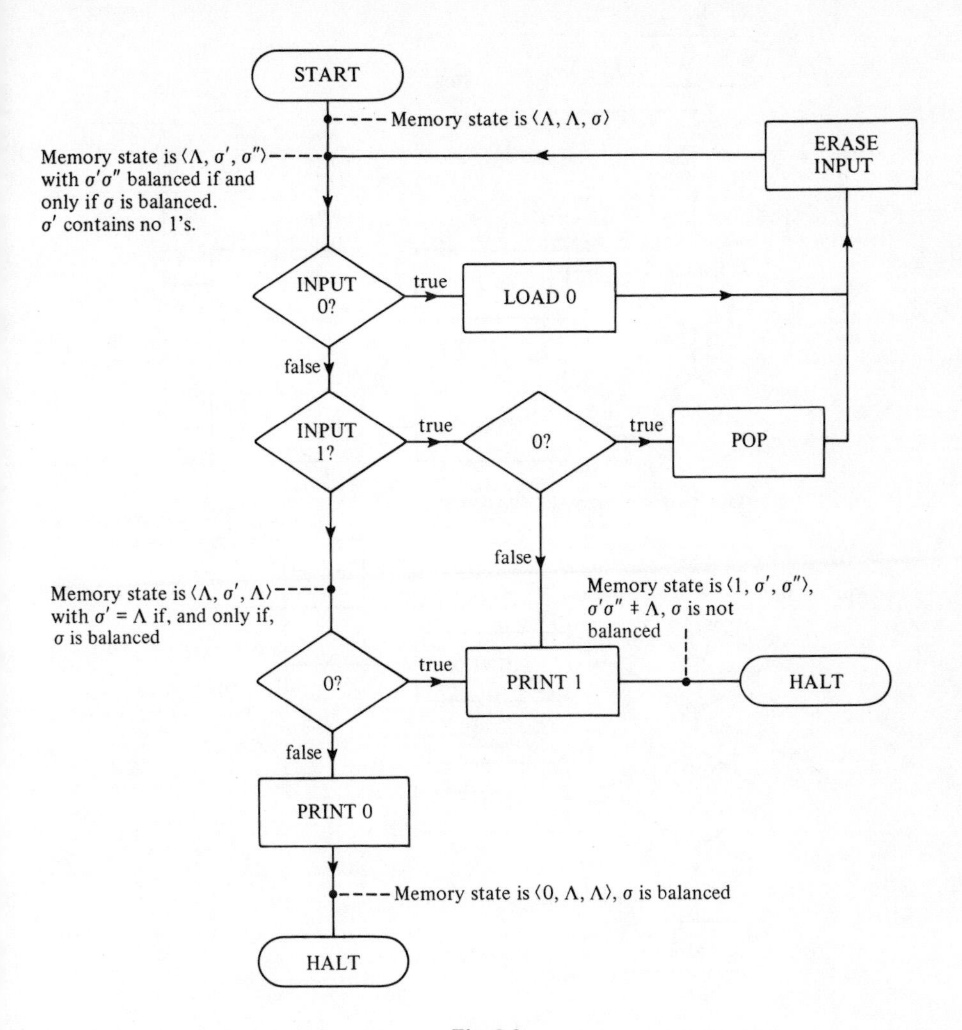

Fig. 5.8

and a 1 as a right bracket. Then a string of brackets is balanced if and only if the brackets nest properly as in ALGOL or FORTRAN arithmetic expressions.) The program Π_b given by Fig. 5.8 is such that $\mathbf{PDS}_{\Pi_b}(\sigma) = 0$ if σ is balanced, 1 if σ is not balanced. (The loop statement is always true as $\sigma'\sigma''$ is balanced if and only if $\sigma'\ 01\ \sigma''$ is. You can prove this by an induction on the number of 01 pairs in $\sigma'\sigma''$.) ∎

5.3.3 EXAMPLE (PALINDROMES)

Recall example 2.4.2. There we gave a program, Π_{pal}, to test whether the string input to **TM** is a palindrome. The program Π_p given by Fig. 5.9 generates the set of even length palindromes when run on **PDS**; that is, each output string is an even palindrome and each even palindrome is the value of $\mathbf{PDS}_{\Pi_p}(\sigma)$ for some in-

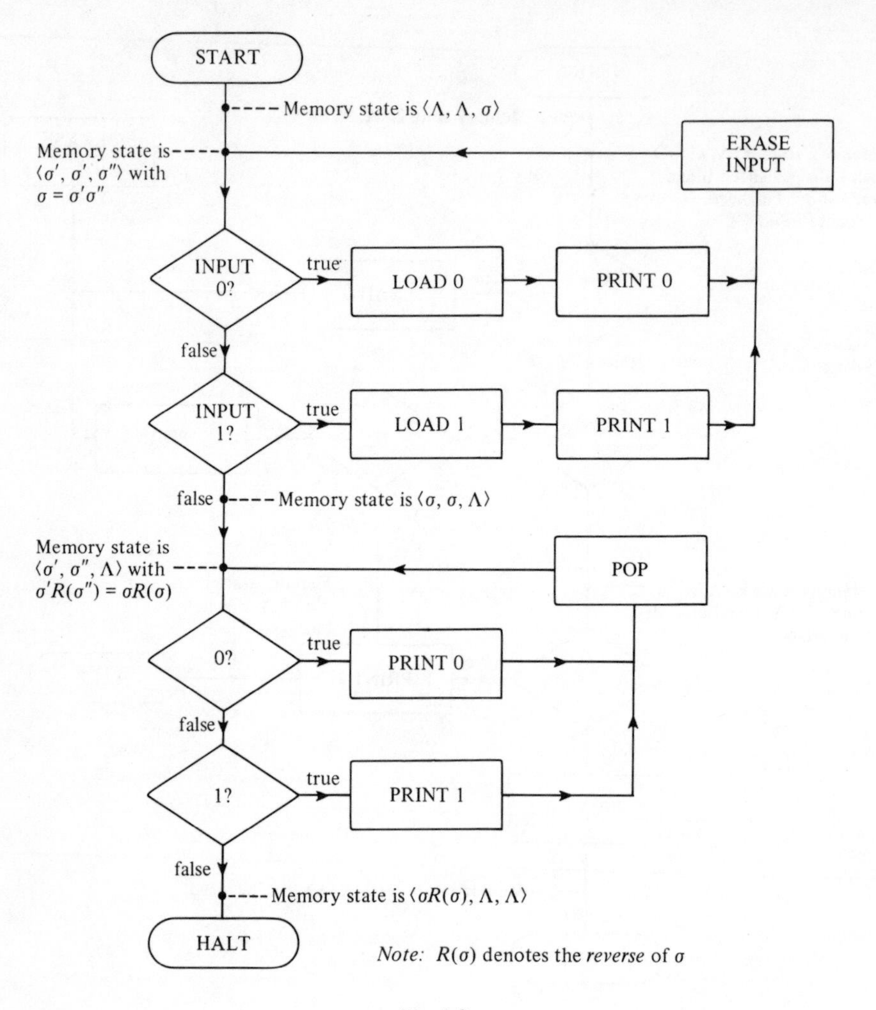

Fig. 5.9

put string σ. (We could have given a program to generate the set of all palindromes, both of even and odd length, but this would have been more complex without being more illuminating. The reader may supply such a program as an exercise.) ∎

What conclusions can one draw from these examples? First, note that neither process described is realizable with a finite internal memory; in both cases there is always an input string which extends the stack beyond any predetermined length, so the unlimited capacity of the stack is essential. Thus the pushdown store machine is more powerful than the automaton.

How does **PDS** compare in computing power with **TM** and **R**? Consider example 5.3.3, which shows that **PDS** generates the set of all even palindromes. Is it also possible to recognize this set of strings on **PDS** in the sense that the computations given by Π_b on **PDS** recognizes the set of balanced strings? In other words, can we construct a program π for **PDS** which will do something noticeably distinct when supplied with an even palindrome–for example, halting with output 0 if and only if the input is such a string? Well, without going into formal details, this is not possible. In order to recognize an even palindrome, the computation must remember the first symbol and compare it with the last when this is read in. However, since the input stream cannot be rewound, it must by that time have checked whether the intervening segment is a palindrome. Since this process requires an arbitrary number of inner palindromes to have been checked out, **PDS** must use its stack to remember the arbitrary number of 'first' symbols–the program itself can remember only a fixed finite number of such first symbols–which are popped off only when the corresponding 'last' symbol is read. The popping of the stack must begin when the innermost two-symbol palindrome has been read. The problem is when to decide to pop–for example, the appropriate point to begin popping the stack to recognize the palindrome 0110 is after the first two symbols have been read. But if the program does this once it will always do it for inputs starting with 01 and it will consequently fail to recognize the palindrome 011110.

But example 2.4.2, with suitable modifications to reject odd palindromes, shows that **TM** can be programmed to recognize even palindromes. Thus we see informally that **TM** is more powerful than **PDS**.

5.3.4 EXERCISES

(1) Give a formal definition of the standard pushdown store machine **PDS** (α, β) over the alphabet α with stack symbols from the alphabet β. Show that all these machines are I/O equivalent, for varying α and β. (See exercise 5.2.7. You will need to use a buffer to hold the top byte of the stack, as well as an input buffer.)

(2)* Construct a program π which generates the set of strings $\{0^n 1^n \mid n \geqslant 0\}$ when run on **PDS**. Give an informal argument to show that the same cannot be done for the set of strings $\{0^n 1^n 0^n \mid n \geqslant 0\}$. Exercise 2.4.3(1) shows that we can realize this latter process on **TM**. Thus we see once more that **TM** is more powerful than **PDS**.

(3)* Show that if we enhance the pushdown store machine by giving it a second stack identical to but independent of the first, then the enhanced machine is I/O equivalent to the standard Turing machine **STM**.

(Use one stack to simulate the portion of the tape to the left of the read/write head of **STM**, the other to simulate the remainder of the tape. Be careful about avoiding stack underflows.) ∎

5.4 Languages associated with machines

If α is a finite alphabet, we call any set of strings in the symbols of α–i.e. any subset of α^*–a *language* over α. Certain classes of language are important because they give us a 'performance measure' or indication of the relative computing powers of machines with standard I/O. We saw something of this in the preceding section, where we indicated that the language of even palindromes over Σ was recognizable by a Turing machine computation but not by any pushdown store machine computation. We shall continue this investigation of languages as a performance measure in chapter 7. Here and in the next two sections we establish certain basic results concerning languages and machines.

With each standard machine we associate three, not necessarily distinct, classes of language.

5.4.1 DEFINITION

Let **M** be a machine with standard I/O over the alphabet α. Then we say that a language $L \subseteq \alpha^*$ is:

(1) *decidable* with respect to **M** if there is a program π such that $\mathbf{M}_\pi(\sigma) = s_0$ if $\sigma \in L$, s_1 if $\sigma \notin L$,
(2) *acceptable* with respect to **M** if there is a program π such that $\mathbf{M}_\pi(\sigma) = s_0$ if and only if $\sigma \in L$,
(3) *generable* with respect to **M** if it is the range of some function computable on **M**; that is, if there is a program π such that

$$L = \{\mathbf{M}_\pi(\sigma) \mid \sigma \in \alpha^*, \mathbf{M}_\pi(\sigma) \neq \Omega\}. \quad \blacksquare$$

In (1) we use the term 'decidable' to indicate that the computation gives us a definite yes-or-no answer to the question 'Is σ in L?'; in (2) we want to convey the feeling that the strings of L are accepted by the computation, but that we don't care what happens when strings not in L are input provided that the computation doesn't tell us that they *are* in L. In (3) the term 'generable' is used as the elements of L are produced by feeding in different inputs from α^*. If $\{\sigma_0, \sigma_1, \ldots, \sigma_k, \ldots\}$ is an enumeration of the strings in α^*—for example the empty string, followed by all strings of length one, followed by all strings of length two, and so on—we may imagine that at each second a fresh computation by π on a new copy of **M** is started with the next string in the enumeration as input, starting with input σ_0. Then a string is in L if and only if it eventually turns up as an output from one of these computations.

What we are doing essentially is to switch our attention from the study of the functions computable by various standard machines to the study of the domains and ranges of such functions. (Recall that in chapter 4 we investigated the subsets of α^* that were the domains and ranges of the **TM**(α) computable functions—i.e., the algorithmically generable languages.) This is borne out by the fact that a set is acceptable with respect to **M** if and only if it is the domain of a function computable on **M**. To see this, first suppose that $L \subseteq \alpha^*$ is acceptable with respect to a machine **M** standard over α. Let π be the accepting program. Appealing to the finite modification theorem, we add a memory component ACCEPTED which may either be true or false, with false as initial state, supplying as additional functions and predicates the obvious interpretations of ACCEPTED $\leftarrow$ true and ACCEPTED?. Then the simple expansions given by Fig. 5.10 convert π into a program which

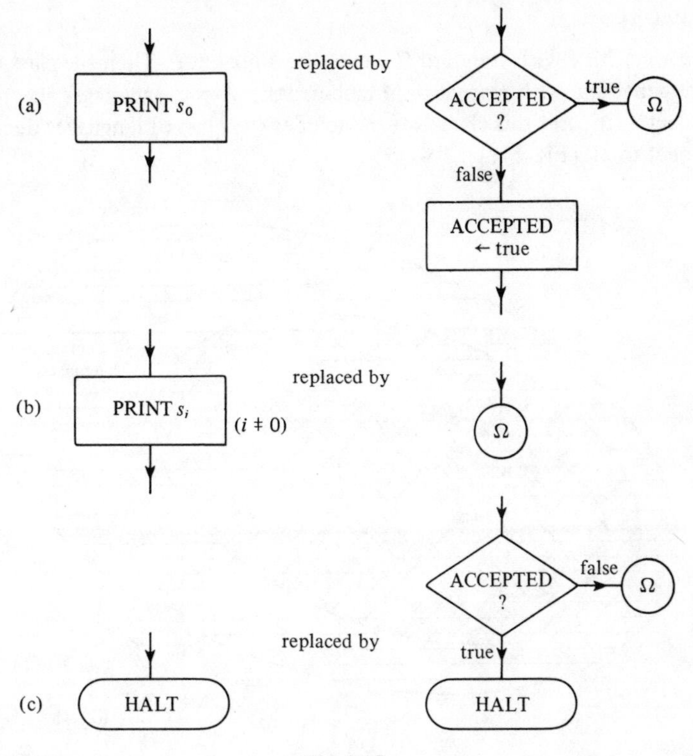

Fig. 5.10

computes a function with domain L on the extension of **M**. (The expanded program halts if and only if the original program halts with output s_0.)

Thus L is the domain of an **M**-computable function as well.

Conversely, if L is the domain of an **M**-computable function, then L is acceptable with respect to **M**. We ask the reader to verify this as an exercise. So we have:

5.4.2 THEOREM

A language $L \subseteq \alpha^*$ is acceptable with respect to a machine **M** standard over α if and only if L is the domain of some function computable on **M**. ∎

Relation between the language classes With respect to a given machine, each decidable language is clearly also acceptable. In turn, each acceptable language is also generable. For, let L be acceptable with respect to some standard machine **M** over α. Then L is the domain of a function $\mathbf{M}_\pi$ for some program π. If we modify π by first removing all print instructions, and then expanding all occurrences of ERASE INPUT into a sequence which prints the current input symbol (if any) before erasing it, we obtain a program π' such that $\mathbf{M}_{\pi'}$ is a partial identity function with domain and range L. To summarize, we have the following result.

5.4.3 THEOREM

Let **M** be a machine with standard I/O over the alphabet α. Then the class of languages generable with respect to **M** includes the class of languages acceptable with respect to **M**, and this class in turn includes the class of languages decidable with respect to **M**. (Fig. 5.11). ∎

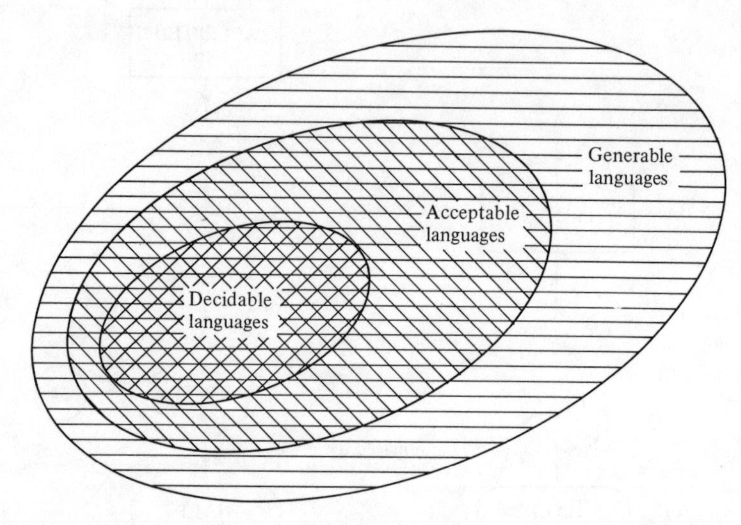

Fig. 5.11

When **M** is some specific machine we can often be more precise about the relation between the language classes. For example, for the Turing machine **STM** the decidable languages are a proper subset of the acceptable languages which are the same as the generable languages. This follows from the results of chapter 4, since by Church's thesis the **STM**-decidable languages are the algorithmically decidable languages and the **STM**-acceptable and -generable languages are the algorithmically generable languages (see theorem 4.1.2 and exercise 4.1.5). For **PDS** we already have the informal result that the even palindromes are generable but not acceptable. Hence the **PDS**-acceptable languages are a proper subset of the **PDS**-generable languages. In the next chapter we shall prove that for the automaton, and hence for all finite machines, the sets of decidable, acceptable and generable languages are identical.

5.4.4 EXERCISE

Show that the complement $\alpha^* \sim L$ of a language L decidable with respect to a machine **M** standard over α is also decidable with respect to **M**. Show that this is not always true if 'decidable' is replaced by 'acceptable' or 'generable' (consider **STM**). ∎

We conclude this section with a technical result needed in the following sections.

5.4.5 THEOREM

If L is an **M**-generable language then it can be generated by a standard program on **M** whose completed computations never apply a test to an empty input stream—i.e., if such a test is applied, then the computation will go undefined.

Proof. We give an outline proof only, leaving the reader to supply the details.

Augment **M** to include a one-symbol input buffer and an end of input flag. Rewrite the generating program so that it uses the buffer and end of input flag for input tests and loads the buffer for an erase. Have the buffer load segment, which must be in standard form, erase *two* symbols for each one loaded into the buffer with the pair $s_0 s_i$ being used to record s_i. If the head of the input stream is a symbol other than s_0 when the buffer is to be loaded, treat this as an end-of-input marker which causes the end-of-input flag to be set. Make the computation go undefined if ever the input is exhausted before an end marker is reached. The range of the computed function is still L. Why? ∎

5.5 Non-deterministic computations

Machines with several I/O streams Our standard machines have just one input and just one output stream. Most digital computers, however, are provided with several distinct I/O devices. We may capture this situation by generalizing definition 5.1.1.

5.5.1 DEFINITION

Let **M** be a machine with standard I/O over the alphabet α. Then the *family* of machines $\{{}_l^k\mathbf{M} : k, l \geqslant 1\}$ *related* to **M** is defined as follows: For each k, l the memory set of ${}_l^k\mathbf{M}$ is $(\alpha^*)^l \times M \times (\alpha^*)^k$, where M is the internal memory of **M**. All internal functions and predicates of **M** are retained, whereas the pseudo I/O instructions are generalized to give the obvious interpretations to the function and predicate names

ERASE INPUT i INPUT i s? PRINT j s

where $s \in \alpha$, i $(1 \leqslant i \leqslant k)$ refers to the ith input stream, and j $(1 \leqslant j \leqslant l)$ refers to the jth output stream. The standard input set for ${}_l^k\mathbf{M}$ is $(\alpha^*)^k$ and the standard output set $(\alpha^*)^l$. The standard encoder e and decoder d are given by

$$e : \langle \sigma_1, \sigma_2, \ldots, \sigma_k \rangle \mapsto \langle \Lambda, \Lambda, \ldots, \Lambda, m_0, \sigma_1, \sigma_2, \ldots, \sigma_k \rangle$$

and

$$d : \langle \sigma_1, \sigma_2, \ldots, \sigma_l, m, \sigma_{l+1}, \sigma_{l+2}, \ldots, \sigma_{l+k} \rangle \mapsto \langle \sigma_1, \sigma_2, \ldots, \sigma_l \rangle,$$

m_0 being the conventional initial state of M. ∎

We denote ${}_1^2\mathbf{M}$ by ${}^2\mathbf{M}$. We shall be interested only in **M** itself or in ${}^2\mathbf{M}$. We are interested in ${}^2\mathbf{M}$ because it provides us with a powerful tool for dealing with **M** and its associated classes of languages. As before, we make no explicit mention of the standard encoding and decoding functions; thus we understand that a program π for ${}^2\mathbf{M}$ computes a function ${}^2\mathbf{M}_\pi : \alpha^* \times \alpha^* \to \alpha^*$.

We could continue by supplying definitions of decidability, acceptability and generability for tuples of languages with respect to a family of machines, perhaps deriving results generalizing those of the preceding section. We shall not pursue this possibility. We refer the interested reader to Scott[1]. However, the introduction of ${}^2\mathbf{M}$ does allow us to define a class of languages possibly distinct from the decidable, acceptable or generable languages.

Weak acceptability

5.5.2 DEFINITION

Let **M** be a machine with standard I/O over the alphabet α. A language $L \subseteq \alpha^*$ is *weakly acceptable* with respect to **M** if there is a program π such that ${}^2\mathbf{M}_\pi(\sigma, \sigma') = s_0$ for some $\sigma' \in \alpha^*$ if and only if $\sigma \in L$. ∎

What we are doing here is to allow for several attempts at accepting the input σ by trying different inputs σ' on the second input stream. Intuitively this second input merely supplies 'noise' to perturb the flow of control until possibly, for some happy choice of σ', the string σ on the first input stream is accepted. To visualize this process, imagine that the set of all possible second inputs σ' is arranged in some order and that at each second we start another computation on a different copy of ${}^2\mathbf{M}$ with first input σ and second input the next σ' in the prescribed order; then σ is weakly accepted if and only if one of these computations halts with output s_0. (Compare this with the intuitive explanation given earlier of generability.)

Non-deterministic programs There is another way of introducing 'noise' into a computation which figures in all the literature on automata theory—namely the use of *non-deterministic programs.* With a (deterministic) program the path of the computation is completely determined given the initial state of the machine. For a non-deterministic program this is no longer true; at certain points in the computation there is a choice of the next instruction to be obeyed. Thus the particular computation sequence generated in one 'run' of the program is just one of the paths along the branches of a computation 'tree' in which there is a branch point each time there is a choice of the next instruction to be obeyed.

For us the format of non-deterministic programs is easily specified. They are simply programs which include extra instructions of the form,

$$L : \text{GOTO } L_1 \text{ OR GOTO } L_2 \text{ OR GOTO } L_3 \ldots \text{OR GOTO } L_k;$$

interpreted by the control as a no-op transfer to any of the instructions labelled $L_1, L_2, \ldots, L_k$. The interaction between a non-deterministic program and a machine can now be defined by a simple elaboration of the definition in chapter 1.

However, when π is a non-deterministic program $\mathbf{M}_\pi$ is a *relation* rather than a function. In particular, when $\mathbf{M}$ is a standard machine,

$$\mathbf{M}_\pi(\sigma) = \{\sigma' \mid \sigma' \text{ is the output string of at least one completed computation of } \mathbf{M}_\pi(\sigma)\}.$$

(Intuitively, $\mathbf{M}_\pi(\sigma)$ comprises the set of output strings that appear at the tips of the branches of the computation 'tree' that are the termination points of completed computations.)

We can now define yet another class of languages.

5.5.3 DEFINITION

Let $\mathbf{M}$ be a machine with standard I/O over α. Language L is *non-deterministically acceptable* with respect to $\mathbf{M}$ if there is a non-deterministic program π such that $s_0 \in \mathbf{M}_\pi(\sigma)$ if, and only if, $\sigma \in L$. ∎

In fact non-deterministic programs give us nothing new; we can use the second 'noise' input stream to achieve the same effect. We shall prove that non-deterministic and weak acceptability are equivalent language properties.

First, suppose that L is non-deterministically acceptable with respect to $\mathbf{M}$. We may assume, with no loss of generality, that the non-deterministic program accepting L with respect to $\mathbf{M}$ only has two-way non-deterministic jumps of the form

$$L_1 \text{: GOTO } L_2 \text{ OR GOTO } L_3;$$

as we can replace an m-way jump by $m-1$ such two-way jumps. If we now replace each two-way jump by a sequence as shown in Fig. 5.12, we obtain a deterministic program which weakly accepts L with respect to $\mathbf{M}$. (The fact that the erasure of the incoming symbol on the second input stream may occasionally lead to an undefined result is immaterial; what is important is that if $\sigma \in L$, then there is always a string σ' of sufficient length to supply to the second input stream so that this does not happen.)

Now suppose that L is weakly acceptable with respect to $\mathbf{M}$. Using the program modification of theorem 5.4.5, we rewrite the program that weakly accepts L so that its completed computations never apply a test to the *second* input stream when it is empty. This produces a program with all the tests and erases on the second input stream grouped in nodes with each Λ-exit leading to an Ω-loop. We

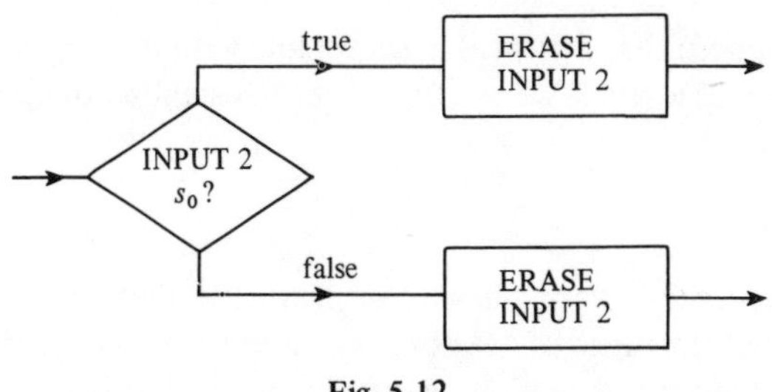

Fig. 5.12

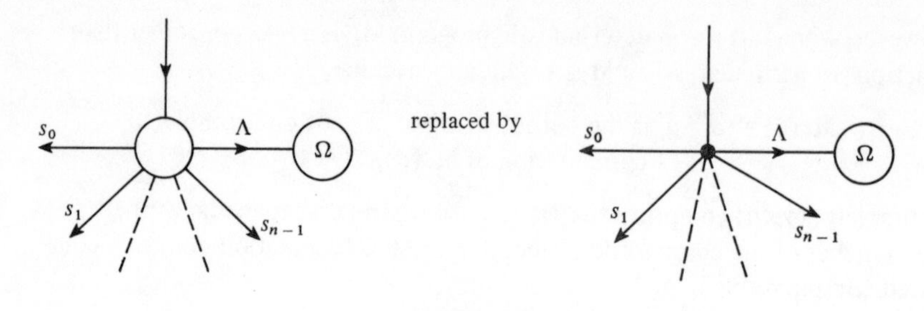

Fig. 5.13

simply replace these nodes by non-deterministic jumps as indicated in Fig. 5.13, thus removing all reference to the second input stream.

We have proved

5.5.4 THEOREM

With respect to a given standard machine, non-deterministic and weak acceptability are equivalent language properties. ∎

How does weak, or non-deterministic, acceptability fit in with the other language properties? Well, let $L \subseteq \alpha^*$ be generable with respect to a standard machine **M** over α. We shall show that L is also weakly acceptable.

Thus let π be a program for **M** such that L is the range of the function $\mathbf{M}_\pi$. By replacing all occurrences of the instructions ERASE INPUT and INPUT s? for $s \in \alpha$ in π by ERASE INPUT 2 and INPUT 2 s? respectively we obtain a program π_0 which looks only at the second input stream of ${}^2\mathbf{M}$, such that the range of ${}^2\mathbf{M}_{\pi_0}$ is also L. If we now apply the expansions given by Fig. 5.14 to π_0, we obtain a program π_1 such that ${}^2\mathbf{M}_{\pi_1}(\sigma, \sigma')$ is defined for some $\sigma' \in \alpha^*$ if and only if $\sigma \in L$. It is now easy to construct a program π_2 from π_1 such that ${}^2\mathbf{M}_{\pi_2}(\sigma, \sigma') = s_0$ for some σ' if and only if $\sigma \in L$; i.e. L is weakly acceptable.

5.5.5 EXERCISE

Prove that the program π_1 has the stated property and give the construction of π_2 from π_1. ∎

Conversely, suppose that L is weakly acceptable with respect to **M**. We shall show that L is generable. First we ask the reader to establish an intermediate result:

5.5.6 EXERCISE*

Show that, if L is weakly acceptable with respect to **M**, then there is a standard program π such that the range of ${}^2\mathbf{M}_\pi$ is L, and a completed computation of π on **M** never applies an input test to either input stream when it is empty. (See theorems

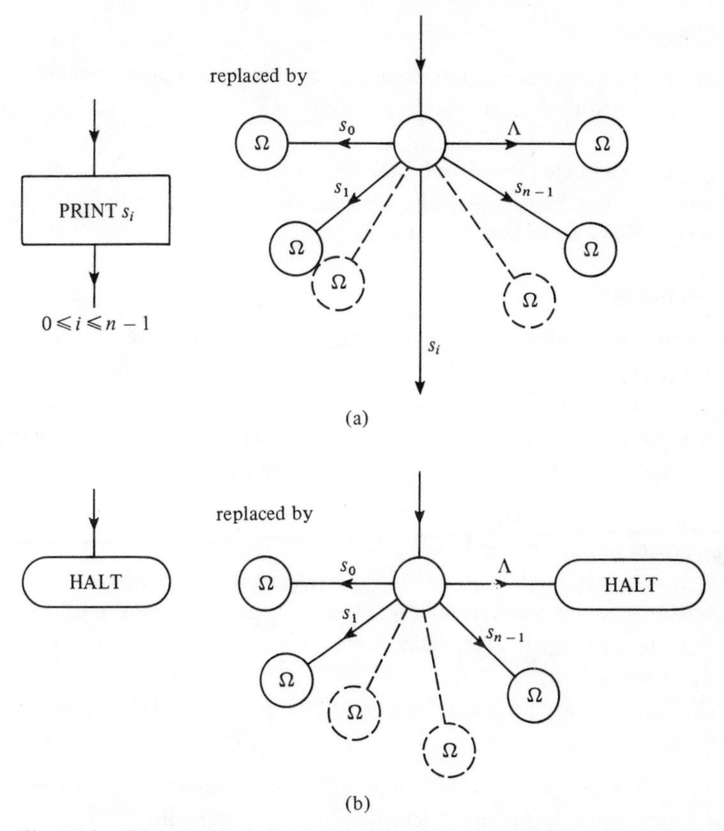

Fig. 5.14 The nodes in the replacing segments are on the first input stream

5.4.3 and 5.4.5.) Intuitively the program does not need to test for emptiness of either input stream, and if ever it does the computation goes undefined. ∎

We then simply rewrite π so that all its tests and erases are made on the first input stream. Now for every completed computation of the original program on ${}^2\mathbf{M}$, there is a merging together of the segments of the two input streams read in during the computation that is exactly right for the single input computation. Conversely, for every completed computation using the single input stream, there is a decomposition of the segment read in into the segments that were read in by the input nodes corresponding to the old first and second stream input nodes respectively. These two segments would be exactly right as inputs for the original ${}^2\mathbf{M}$ computation to produce the same output string.

5.5.7 THEOREM

With respect to a given standard machine, generability and weak acceptability are equivalent language properties. ∎

Thus, using weak acceptability as an intermediate concept, we have proved

5.5.8 THEOREM

With respect to a given standard machine, generability and non-deterministic acceptability are equivalent language properties. ∎

As we shall see in chapters 6 and 7 the characterization of the generable languages as the non-deterministically acceptable languages greatly facilitates proofs about the generable languages of particular machines.

5.5.9 EXERCISE*

(1) Show that if we allow $k \geqslant 2$ input streams instead of just two in the definition of weak acceptability, then the defined property remains unchanged. (Merge $k-1$ of the input streams into one.)
(2) Give definitions analogous to those for non-deterministic and weak acceptability, for non-deterministic and weak decidability and generability. Show:

(a) that non-deterministic and weak decidability are equivalent language properties with respect to a given standard machine,
(b) that non-deterministic generability, weak generability and generability are equivalent language properties with respect to a given standard machine,
(c) that the language of even palindromes (example 5.3.3) is non-deterministically decidable with respect to **PDS**,
(d) that each weakly decidable language with respect to **STM** is algorithmically decidable.

Thus from (c) and (d), weak or non-deterministic decidability is in general equivalent neither to decidability, acceptability nor generability. ∎

5.6 Regular operations on languages

There are various simple operations that we can perform on languages over a fixed alphabet α. As subsets of α^*, for instance, we have the familiar set-theoretic operations of union, intersection and complementation in α^*. As sets of strings there are other operations of interest.

5.6.1 DEFINITION

Let L_1 and L_2 be languages over α. The *concatenation* or *product* $L_1 \cdot L_2$ of L_1 and L_2 is the language of all strings of the form $\sigma_1\sigma_2$ where $\sigma_1 \in L_1$ and $\sigma_2 \in L_2$. The *closure* L_1^* of L_1 is the language of all strings which consist of an arbitrary number (including zero) of strings from L_1; that is,

$$L_1^* = \{\sigma_1\sigma_2 \ldots \sigma_m \mid \sigma_i \in L_1 \text{ for } 1 \leqslant i \leqslant m \ (m \geqslant 0)\}. \quad ∎$$

Note that $\Lambda \in L^*$ for any language L as Λ is of the given form for $m = 0$. An equivalent definition of L^* is

$$\{\Lambda\} \cup L \cup L \cdot L \cup L \cdot L \cdot L \cup \cdots.$$

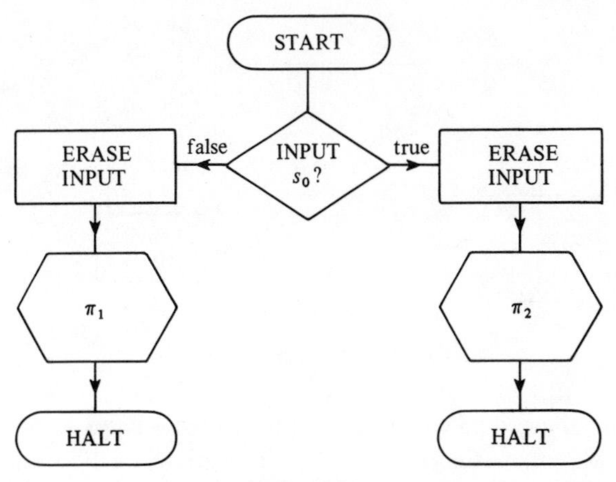

Fig. 5.15

* is a *closure operation* (hence the name)—that is, application of * any number of times is equivalent to a single application (the reader may readily verify this). If we identify α with the language over α consisting of all strings of length one, then we see that α^* is precisely the set of all strings, including Λ, in the symbols of α. This is why we have been using the notation α^* so far.

Do any of these operations preserve any of the language properties we have been investigating? Well, we know (exercise 5.4.4) that, with respect to a given standard machine, the complement of a decidable language is decidable. There is another very easily proved property concerning the union: If L_1 and L_2 are generable with respect to a given standard machine **M**, then so is $L_1 \cup L_2$. To see this, let π_1 be a program such that L_1 is the range of $\mathbf{M}_{\pi_1}$ and π_2 a program such that L_2 is the range of $\mathbf{M}_{\pi_2}$. Then if π is the program given by Fig. 5.15, the range of $\mathbf{M}_\pi$ is clearly $L_1 \cup L_2$

If we impose on **M** the restriction that it must be able to 'reset' its internal memory, i.e., there is a sequence of code RESET which will always leave the internal memory in its initial state m_0 without performing any I/O (all our machines have this capability), then we are also able to show that $L_1 \cdot L_2$ and L_1^* are generable. But this is not quite so simple as the argument for generability of $L_1 \cup L_2$. The difficulty is this: We might expect that the programs of Figs. 5.16 and 5.17 would generate $L_1 \cdot L_2$ and L_1^* respectively. But this will not do—the computation of π_1 may gobble up all the input, leaving none for the subsequent execution of π_2 or for repeat executions of π_1. The solution is to modify π_1 as in the proof of theorem 5.4.5, so that it generates L in such a way that its completed computations never test for empty input stream. This program modification ensures that when

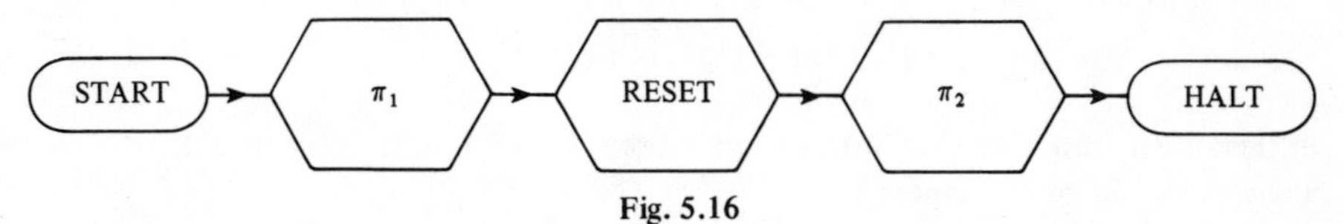

Fig. 5.16

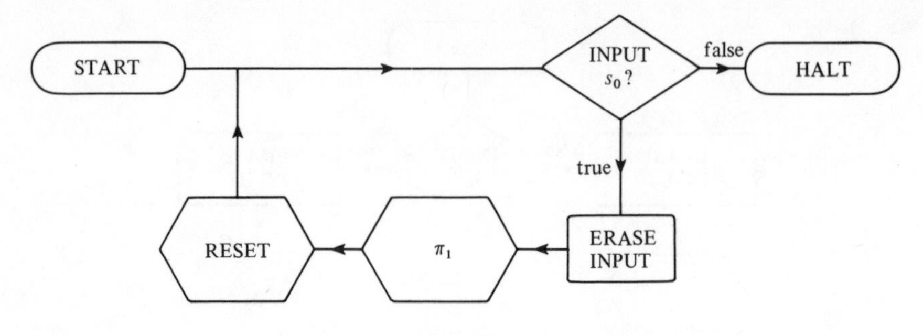

Fig. 5.17

σ'' is the output for a completed computation that reads input string σ, then it is also the output for input strings of the form $\sigma\sigma'$, with all of the arbitrary string σ' left unread on the input stream at the end of the computation.

We leave it to the reader to check that, with this modification made to π_1, the above constructions do indeed give programs generating $L_1 \cdot L_2$ and L_1^* respectively. This gives

5.6.2 THEOREM

Let **M** be a machine with standard I/O over the alphabet α which has the reset property. Let L_1 and L_2 be languages over α generable with respect to **M**. Then the languages $L_1 \cup L_2, L_1 \cdot L_2$ and L_1^* are also generable with respect to **M**. ∎

Remarks We call the operations of union, product and closure the *regular* operations over languages. Clearly any language consisting of a single string is generable with respect to any standard machine whose alphabet includes all the symbols in the string. Theorem 5.6.2 then shows us that any language obtainable from such single-string languages by a finite number of applications of regular operations is also generable. We shall investigate this class of languages, called the *regular* languages, in some detail in the next chapter. There we shall see that finite machines (i.e. the automaton) can generate nothing but regular languages. In effect this means that the study of finite-state devices reduces very largely to the study of regular languages. ∎

5.6.3 EXERCISES

(1) Write a program to generate the regular language

$$(\{0\} \cdot \{1\}^*) \cup (\{1\} \cdot \{0\}^*)^*$$

on the automaton. (We shall introduce a more succinct notation for regular languages in the next chapter.)

(2) Let L be a language over the alphabet α. Define $HEADS(L)$, $TAILS(L)$ and $BITS(L)$ by

$$HEADS(L) = \{\sigma \in \alpha^* : \sigma\sigma' \in L \text{ for some } \sigma' \in \alpha^*\},$$

$$TAILS(L) = \{\sigma' \in \alpha^* : \sigma\sigma' \in L \text{ for some } \sigma \in \alpha^*\},$$

$$BITS(L) = \{\sigma \in \alpha^* : \sigma \text{ is obtained from some } \sigma' \in L \text{ by deletion of an arbitrary number of symbols}\}.$$

Show that $HEADS(L)$, $TAILS(L)$ and $BITS(L)$ are all generable with respect to a machine standard over α if L is. ∎

5.7 Notes and references

Nearly all the concepts of this chapter derive from Scott[1].

References

1. Scott, D., 'Some definitional suggestions for automata theory,' *J. Comp. Sys. Sci.*, 1, 187–212 (1967)

6 The automaton

6.1 Regular languages

In the last section of the preceding chapter we saw that any machine standard over the alphabet α is capable of generating all of the regular languages over α. In this chapter we show that the converse is true for the automaton—all the languages generable with respect to **AUT**(α) are in fact regular. We shall also see that each regular language is decidable with respect to the automaton.

We start by reminding the reader of just what a regular language is:

6.1.1 DEFINITION

Let α be an arbitrary alphabet. Then

(1) The empty subset and all one-element subsets of α^* are regular.
(2) If languages L_1 and $L_2 \in \alpha^*$ are regular, then so are the languages $L_1 \cup L_2$, $L_1 \cdot L_2$ and L_1^*.
(3) A language $L \subseteq \alpha^*$ is regular only if it can be shown to be so by a finite number of applications of (1) and (2). ▮

Set-theoretic notation for representing regular languages can be rather clumsy, so we introduce some notational simplifications. For a string $\sigma \in \alpha^*$ no distinction will be made between σ and $\{\sigma\}$, the set whose only element is σ. We often omit the concatenation operator, simply denoting it by juxtaposition of its operands. To avoid excessive use of brackets we assume that * has precedence over • and • over ∪. Brackets will be used to override these precedences. Expressions built up in this way from the symbols of α are called *regular expressions* and we shall say that they *represent* the corresponding regular languages. For example,

1	represents	$\{1\}$,
$1 \cup 01$	represents	$\{1, 01\}$,
$0^*\,1^* \cup 10^*$	represents	$(\{0\}^* \cdot \{1\}^*) \cup (\{1\} \cdot \{0\}^*)$,

and so on. Note that a regular expression represents more than just a set of strings; it also contains structural information, information about how the language being represented is constructed from elementary building blocks. That there may be more than one way of constructing a given regular language is reflected in the fact that many different regular expressions may represent the same language—for example the expressions $(0 \cup 1)^*$ and $(0^*1^*)^*$ both represent Σ^*, the set of all strings of 0's and 1's including the empty string.

6.2 Transition graphs

In this section we introduce *transition graphs*, and a compact notation for them, as a normal form for accepting programs for **AUT**(α). This notation is an elaboration of the standard form of the previous chapter.

Deterministic transition graphs If the Λ-exit of a node of a standard program leads to the sequence

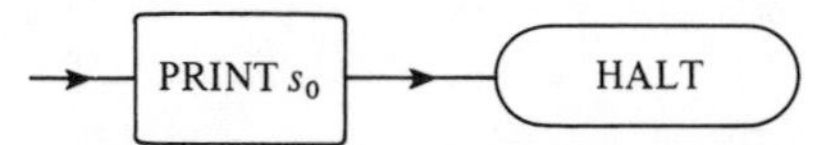

we shall call it a *success node* and we denote this by a double circle with no Λ-exit as in Fig. 6.1. If the Λ-exit of a node leads to the sequence

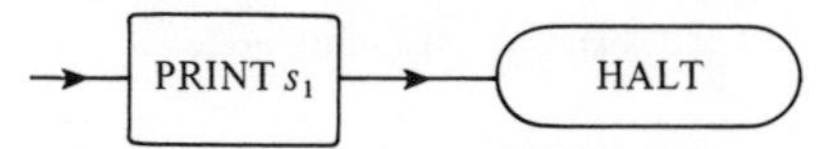

we call it a *failure node*, and we denote this simply by a node with no Λ-exit as in Fig. 6.2. If the start instruction flows directly into a node, we call that node the *start node* of the program, and we denote this by an arrow leading into the node from nowhere. A label name appearing inside a node denotes the label of the first instruction in that node. We shall normally use $q_1, q_2, \ldots, q_k$ to denote these labels. As an illustration, Fig. 6.3(a) is an **AUT**-program consisting of two success nodes and a failure node, and Fig. 6.3(b) is the same program expressed in the new notation.

6.2.1 DEFINITION

A (*deterministic*) *transition graph* over a given alphabet α is a program π for **AUT**(α) which is constructed entirely from success and failure nodes. ∎

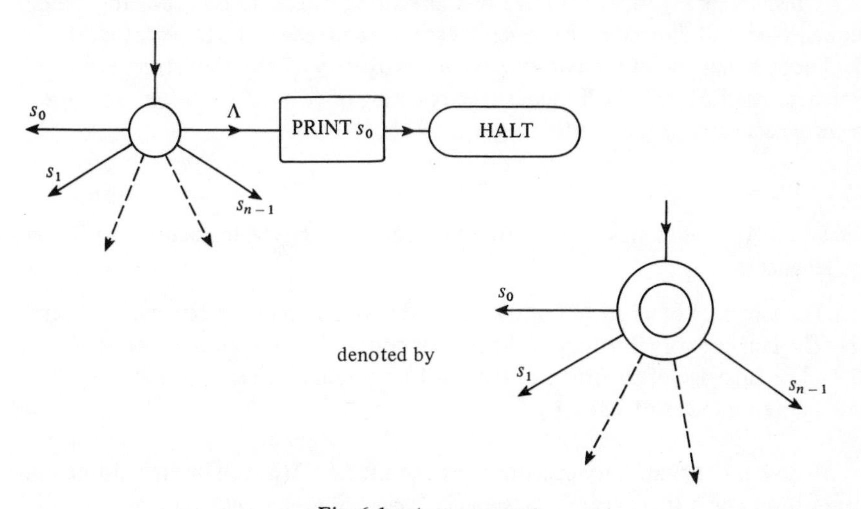

Fig. 6.1 A success node

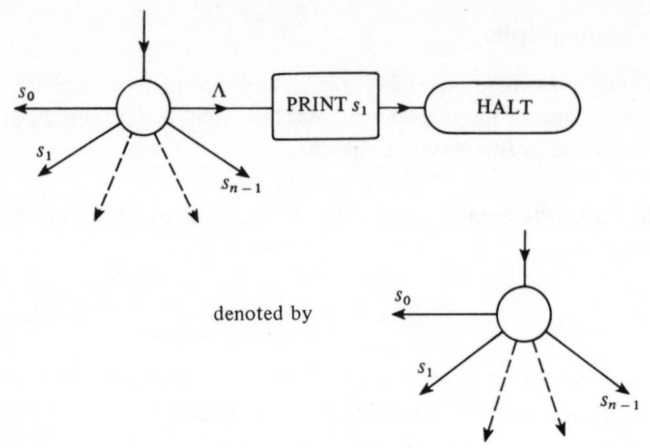

Fig. 6.2 A failure node

The program of Fig. 6.3 is a transition graph.

If a language L is accepted by a transition graph π with respect to **AUT**(α), we shall simply say that L is accepted by π. We may determine whether or not a string σ belongs to L as follows:

Let $\sigma \in \alpha^*$. Beginning with the start node of π and the leftmost symbol of σ, we repeat the following until the right end of σ is reached:

Scan the next symbol of σ. Proceed along the arc labelled with that symbol from the current node to the next node. Delete the incoming symbol.

When the end of σ is reached, $\sigma \in L$ if and only if the final node is a success node.

Note, in consequence, that a transition graph is a deciding program and that the language it accepts is therefore an **AUT**(α)-decidable language.

By inspecting Fig. 6.3(b), we see that any string consisting of a (possibly empty) sequence of 0's followed by a (possibly empty) sequence of 1's is accepted, the final node being one of the two success nodes q_1 or q_2; any other string is rejected, as the final node will then be the rejecting node q_3. Thus we see that the language accepted is the regular language 0^*1^*.

6.2.2 EXERCISE

Construct **AUT**-programs in the form of transition graphs which accept the following languages:

(1) The language of all strings of 0's and 1's in which no two successive 0's occur.
(2) The language of all strings of 0's and 1's containing an even number of 0's.
(3)* The language of all strings of 0's and 1's containing an even number of 0's and an even number of 1's. ∎

We now prove that every accepting program for **AUT**(α) can be transformed into a transition graph that accepts the same language. Since a transition graph is a

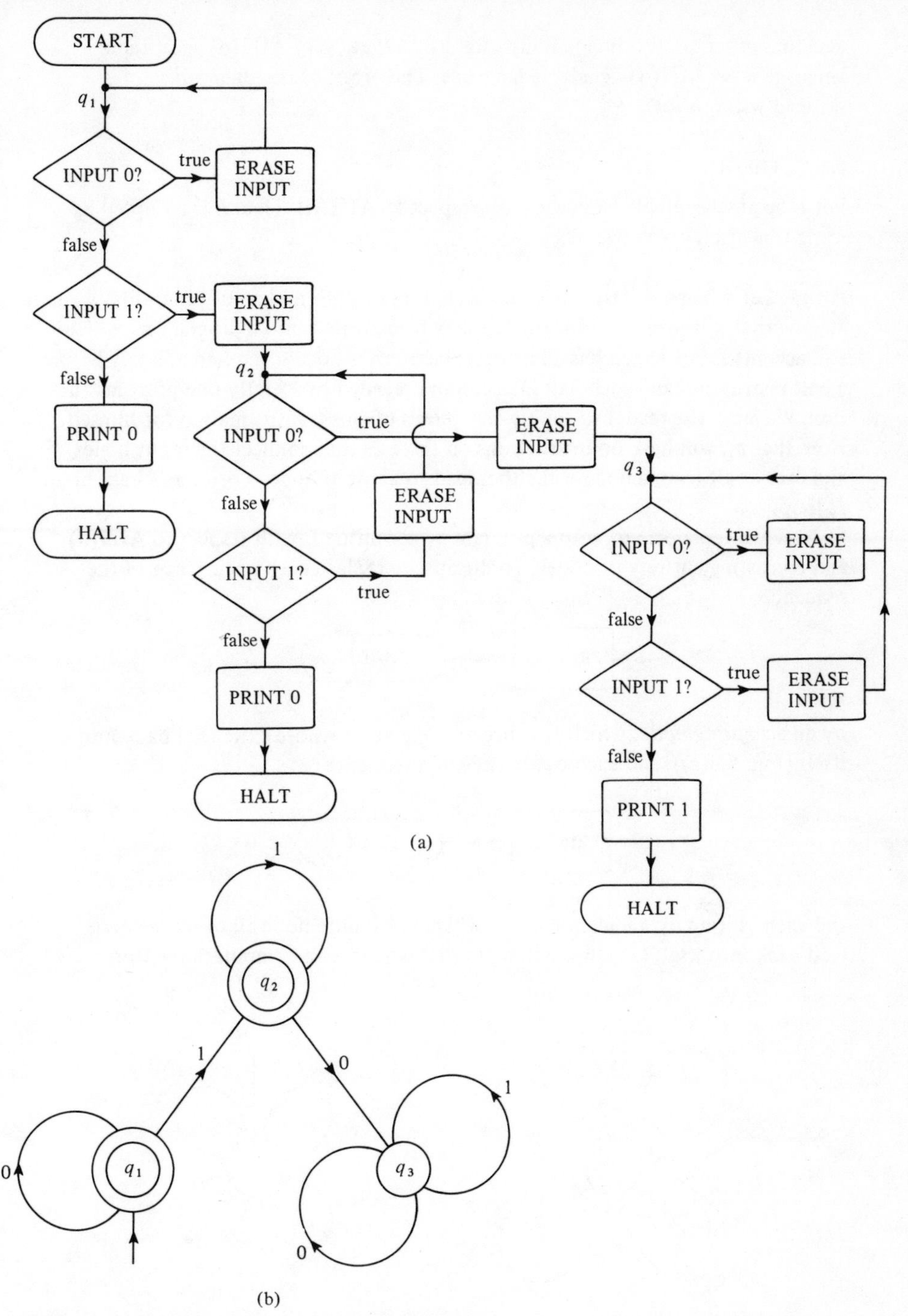

Fig. 6.3 (a) An **AUT**-program with two success nodes and one failure node (b) The flowchart of (a) using the compact notation. q_1 is the start node

deciding program, this incidentally establishes that every **AUT**(α)-acceptable language is an **AUT**(α)-decidable language. The proof of the theorem can be skipped without loss.

6.2.3 THEOREM

Let L be an acceptable language with respect to **AUT**(α). Then L is accepted by some transition graph over α.

Proof. Let π be an **AUT**(α)-program accepting L. With no loss of generality, we may assume that π is in standard form. We now transform π into a program π_0 which still accepts L but which has all its print instructions occurring immediately before a halt instruction and each halt instruction preceded by exactly one print instruction. We leave the reader to supply the details of this transformation for himself. Note that π_0 will have no instructions on the arcs that connect the input nodes, and every exit from a node will either lead to another node, a print and halt, or an Ω-loop.

Now we transform π_0 into a program π_1 accepting L with respect to **AUT**(α) and consisting entirely of nodes. To do this we replace each occurrence of the sequence

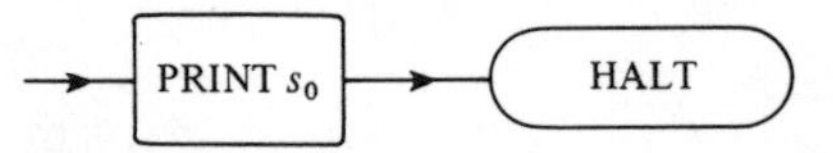

by an *accepting node*, which is a success node all of whose exits feed back into itself (Fig. 6.4(a)), and each occurrence of a sequence

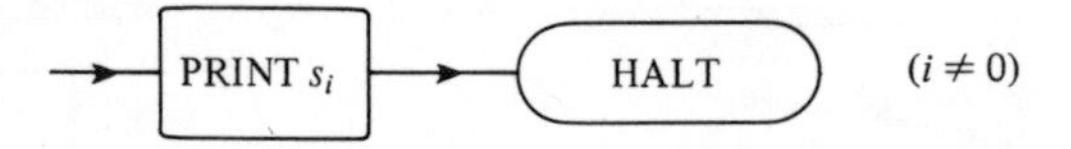

and each Ω-loop by a *rejecting node*, which is a failure node all of whose exits feed back into itself (Fig. 6.4(b)). Note that whenever a computation enters an

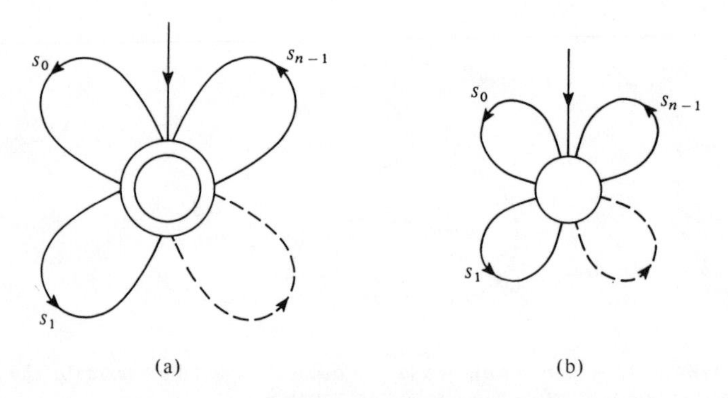

Fig. 6.4 (a) An accepting mode (b) A rejecting mode

accepting (rejecting) node the corresponding input string is accepted (rejected) with the input stream being read in until it is empty. Moreover, every completed computation of the program empties the input stream.

Finally we convert all the input nodes of π_1 into success or failure nodes (by getting rid of their Λ-exits): If the Λ-exit of a node leads directly to a success (failure) node, then we delete the Λ-exit and turn that node into a success (failure) node. We repeat this process until no further nodes can be added to the collections of success or failure nodes. Now each of the remaining nodes is such that it is not connected to a halt instruction by a path of Λ-exits Therefore any computation which enters such a node with empty input stream cannot be completed, which in turn means that the original input string cannot be accepted. Hence we may turn each of these nodes into failure nodes. This gives us the desired transition graph π'. ∎

6.2.4 COROLLARY

The classes of languages decidable and acceptable with respect to the automaton are identical. They are the languages accepted by transition graphs. ∎

Non-deterministic transition graphs What can we say about generability? The characterization of generability as non-deterministic acceptability suggests that we consider *non-deterministic transition graphs*:

6.2.5 DEFINITION

A *non-deterministic node* is an input node for which there can be more than one exit labelled with a given input symbol s, indicating a non-deterministic jump on this exit path (Fig. 6.5(a)). A non-deterministic node is a *success* or *failure* node if it has only one Λ-exit and this Λ-exit leads directly to the sequence PRINT s_0 followed by halt (respectively, PRINT s_1 followed by halt).

A *non-deterministic transition graph* over a given alphabet α is a non-deterministic program for **AUT**(α) which is constructed entirely from non-deterministic success or failure nodes. ∎

Figure 6.5(b) depicts a non-deterministic transition graph over Σ.

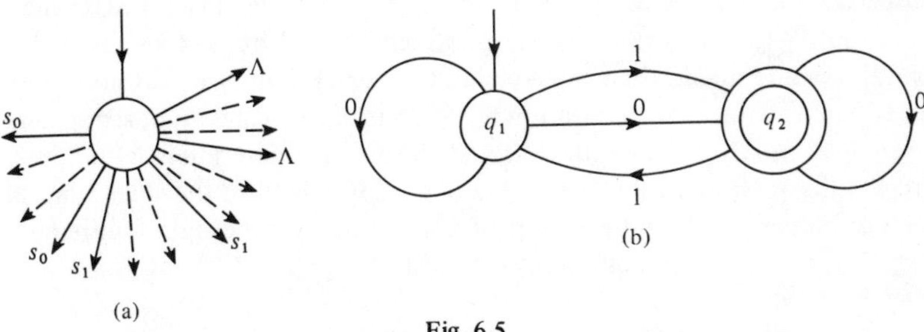

Fig. 6.5

If a language L is accepted by a non-deterministic transition graph π with respect to **AUT**(α), we shall simply say that L is accepted by π.

The following theorem is the analogue of theorem 6.2.3 for non-deterministic transition graphs. Again the proof can be skipped without loss.

6.2.6 THEOREM

Let L be a language generable with respect to **AUT**(α). Then L is accepted by some non-deterministic transition graph over α.

Proof. By the results of the previous chapter, there is a standard program π for ^{2}**AUT**(α) which weakly accepts L. Since the algorithm that transforms a program into standard form inserts a switch on the input immediately after the start instruction, we may assume that there is such a switch (for the first input stream) at the beginning of the program. We now rewrite π so that all its prints occur before a halt and each halt is preceded by exactly one print as in the proof of theorem 6.2.3. Applying the program rewrite of theorem 5.5.4, we convert this program into a non-deterministic accepting program. This rewrite will not alter the juxtaposition of prints with halts. Moreover, it is such that all the non-deterministic jumps appear on the exit paths of input nodes.

We now construct the required non-deterministic transition graph from this program. As in the proof of theorem 6.2.3, each sequence

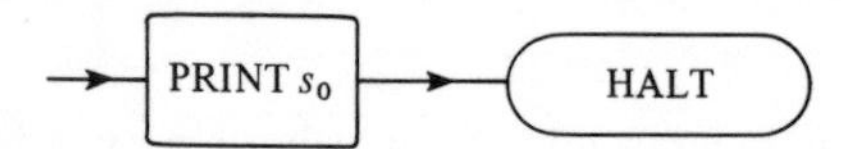

is converted into an accepting node, and each sequence

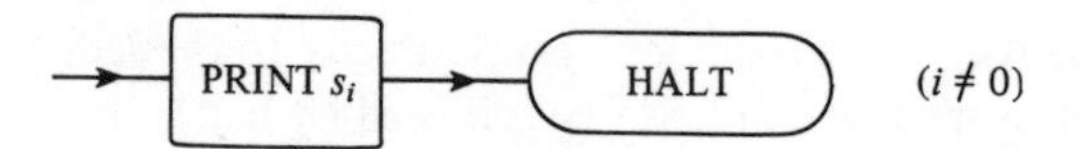

and each Ω-loop is converted into a rejecting node. The final step, getting rid of unwanted Λ-exits, is slightly different from the construction given before, as the nodes may have several Λ-exits. If *at least one* Λ-exit of a node leads directly to a success node, this indicates that any computation which arrives at that node with the input stream exhausted results in acceptance of the original input string by choosing a Λ-exit leading to a success node, and we may delete all Λ-exits and turn the node into a (non-deterministic) success node. If *all* Λ-exits of a node lead directly to failure nodes, then any computation which arrives at that node with input stream exhausted must result in rejection of the original input string, and we may delete all Λ-exits and turn the node into a (non-deterministic) failure node. We repeat this process until no further nodes can be added to the collections of success or failure nodes, and then turn all the remaining nodes into failure nodes. This gives the desired non-deterministic transition graph. ∎

For the automaton, non-determinism adds nothing new:

6.2.7 THEOREM

For every non-deterministic transition graph π over α there is a deterministic transition graph π' over α accepting exactly the same language.

Proof. Given a string $\sigma \in \alpha^*$, let $Q(\sigma)$ be the set of nodes of π accessible from the start node by a path whose labels comprise the symbols of σ (these labels are, of course, the alphabet symbols on the arcs of π rather than the node labels of π). Note that σ is accepted by π if and only if $Q(\sigma)$ contains at least one success node. This provides the key to the construction of π', which keeps track of the subset of nodes $Q(\sigma)$ that the computation may be at in the non-deterministic transition graph after reading in σ.

The nodes of π' are each labelled by some non-empty subset of the set of node labels of π. (Thus there are at most $2^k - 1$ nodes in π' where k is the number of nodes of π.) A node of π' is a success node if and only if its label set contains the label of some success node of π. The start node of π' is the node labelled $\{q_1\}$, where q_1 is the start node of π. Finally the arcs between the nodes of π' are constructed as follows. There is an arc labelled s directed from node P to node R of π' if and only if the nodes of π named in the label set of R are precisely those nodes accessible in π from one or other of the nodes named in the label set of P, by an arc labelled s.

To see that π and π' accept the same language, note the following points:

(1) $Q(\Lambda)$ is the start node $\{q_1\}$ of π'.
(2) There is an arc labelled s from the node $Q(\sigma)$ to the node $Q(\sigma s)$ in π'.
(3) For input σ, the computation given by π' halts at the node $Q(\sigma)$. (This follows from (1) and (2) by an induction on $|\sigma|$.)
(4) π accepts a string σ if and only if $Q(\sigma)$ contains a success node of π if and only if $Q(\sigma)$ is a success node of π' if and only if π' accepts σ. ∎

6.2.8 EXAMPLE

Consider the non-deterministic transition graph π given by Fig. 6.6(a). Applying the construction used in the proof of theorem 6.2.7, we arrive at the deterministic transition graph π' given by Fig. 6.6(b), which accepts the same language as π.

The nodes of π' are labelled $\{q_1\}$, $\{q_2\}$ and $\{q_1, q_2\}$, these being the non-empty subsets of the node labels of π. The node $\{q_1\}$ is the start node of π'; $\{q_2\}$ and $\{q_1, q_2\}$ are both accepting nodes as they contain the accepting node q_2 of π. There is an arc labelled 0 from $\{q_1, q_2\}$ back to itself because q_1 and q_2 are both accessible from either q_1 or q_2 by an arc labelled 0 in π. The reader should check that each of the other arcs of π' are correctly labelled. ∎

6.2.9 EXERCISE

Verify (1), (2), (3) and (4) in the proof of theorem 6.2.7. ∎

In all we have proved

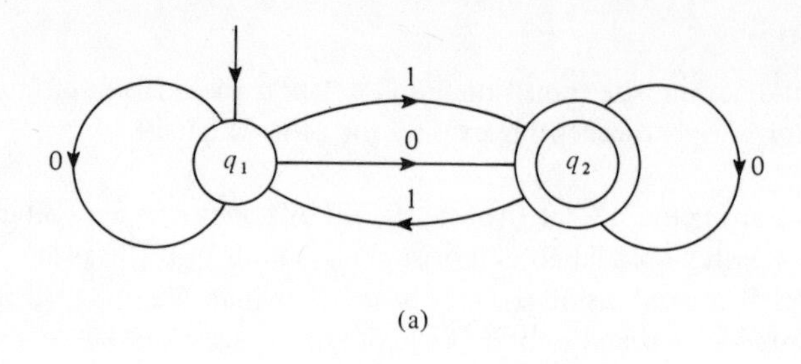

(a)

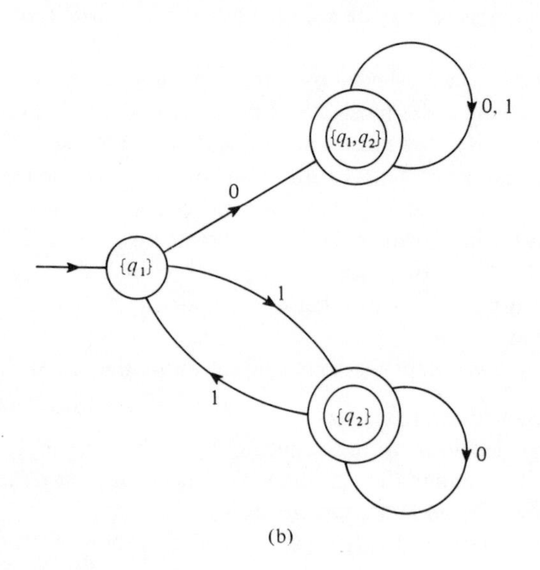

(b)

Fig. 6.6

6.2.10 THEOREM

With respect to **AUT**(α), decidability, acceptability and generability are equivalent language properties. ∎

6.2.11 EXERCISES

(1) Construct non-deterministic transition graphs accepting
 (a) the language $1(0^* \cup 1^*)$,
 (b) the language of all strings of 0's and 1's containing at least two consecutive 0's or at least two consecutive 1's.

(2) Construct a deterministic transition graph accepting the same language over Σ as the non-deterministic transition graph given by Fig. 6.7. ∎

A set-theoretic characterization* We may define deterministic and non-deterministic transition graphs over an alphabet α, and the languages accepted by them, without recourse to the program/machine theory expounded in this book.

Consider the transition graph of Fig. 6.8. We may describe it unambiguously by specifying its set of nodes $Q = \{q_1, q_2, q_3\}$, its input alphabet $\alpha = \{0, 1\}$, its

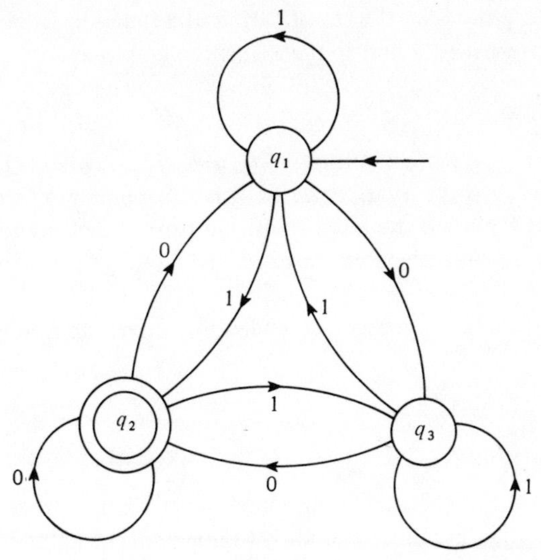

Fig. 6.7

start node q_1, its set of success nodes $S = \{q_2, q_3\}$, and the arcs between nodes and their labels. These arcs and labels can be specified by means of a table which gives for each node q and input symbol s the node q' to which q is connected by an arc leaving q labelled s:

$$\langle q_1, 0\rangle \to q_1$$
$$\langle q_1, 1\rangle \to q_2$$
$$\langle q_2, 0\rangle \to q_3$$
$$\langle q_2, 1\rangle \to q_2$$
$$\langle q_3, 0\rangle \to q_1$$
$$\langle q_3, 1\rangle \to q_2$$

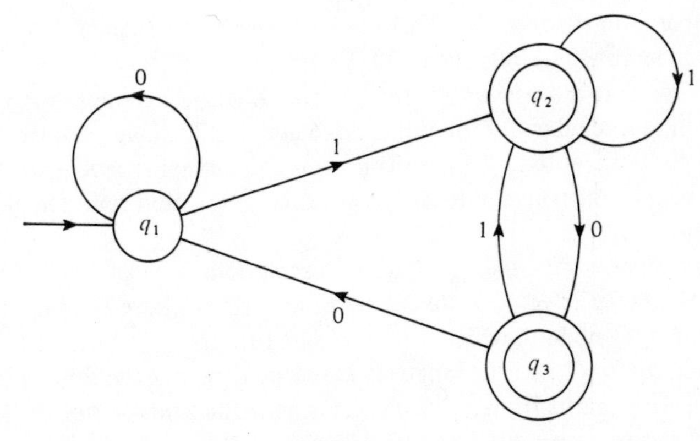

Fig. 6.8

This table is no more than the specification of a function from $Q \times \alpha$ to Q. So we may give an alternative definition of transition graphs as

6.2.12 DEFINITION

A *transition graph* π over α is a quintuple $\langle Q, \alpha, \delta, q_1, S\rangle$, where Q is a finite non-empty set of *nodes*, α is the *input alphabet*, δ is a mapping of $Q \times \alpha$ into Q (intuitively, if $\delta(q, s) = q'$ then there is a transition from node q to node q' via an arc labelled s), $q_1 \in Q$ is the designated *start node* and $S \subseteq Q$ the set of *success nodes.* ∎

The transition function δ may be extended inductively to a function $\hat{\delta} : Q \times \alpha^* \to Q$:

$$\hat{\delta}(q, \Lambda) = q,$$
$$\hat{\delta}(q, \sigma s) = \delta(\hat{\delta}(q, \sigma), s) \quad \text{for all } \sigma \in \alpha^*, s \in \alpha.$$

Intuitively $\hat{\delta}(q, \sigma) = q'$ if the transitions along the arcs which trace out the symbols of σ send the transition graph from node q to node q'. The extended transition function allows us to define the language accepted by a transition graph also in a purely set-theoretic form:

6.2.13 DEFINITION

The language L *accepted* by a transition graph $\pi = \langle Q, \alpha, \delta, q_1, S\rangle$ is given by

$$L = \{\sigma \mid \hat{\delta}(q_1, \sigma) \text{ is in } S\}. \quad ∎$$

6.2.14 EXERCISE*

Give purely set-theoretic definitions of non-deterministic transition graphs and the languages accepted by them, analogous to definitions 6.2.12 and 6.2.13 for deterministic transition graphs. ∎

6.3 Kleene's theorem

The regular operation theorem 5.6.2 tells us that each regular language over an alphabet α is generable with respect to **AUT**(α).

We shall prove that the converse is true—every language generable with respect to **AUT**(α) is in fact regular. By theorems 6.2.6 and 6.2.7, all we need demonstrate is that the language accepted by an arbitrary transition graph π is regular. We give an algorithm which constructs inductively a regular expression representing the language accepted by π.

Thus let π have nodes $q_1, q_2, \ldots, q_m$, with start node q_1. For $1 \leqslant i \leqslant m$, $1 \leqslant j \leqslant m$, $0 \leqslant k \leqslant m$, let R_{ij}^k denote the set of all strings whose symbols label a path from node q_i to node q_j which does not pass through (i.e., both enter and leave) any node q_l for $l > k$. The language L accepted by π is the set of all strings whose symbols label paths from q_1 to a success node, and this is the (finite) union of the sets R_{1j}^m, where q_j is a success node. Thus we need only show that each set

R_{ij}^k is regular to prove that L is regular. We do this by an induction on k. Note first that

$$R_{ij}^0 = \alpha_{ij} \cup \Lambda_{ij}, \tag{A}$$

where $\alpha_{ij} \subseteq \alpha$ is the set of all symbols labelling arcs from q_i to q_j and $\Lambda_{ij} = \Lambda$ if $i = j$, empty if $i \neq j$. Now if $\sigma \in R_{ij}^k$ for $k \geqslant 1$, then either σ traces out a path which does not pass through q_k, in which case $\sigma \in R_{ij}^{k-1}$, or σ traces out a path which

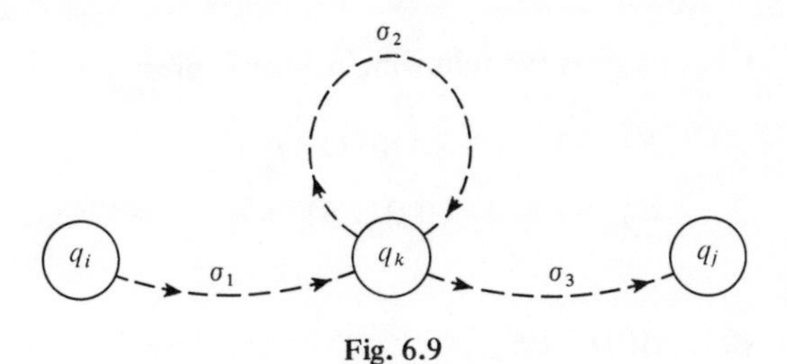

Fig. 6.9

passes through q_k an arbitrary number of times greater than zero, in which case we can write $\sigma = \sigma_1\sigma_2\sigma_3$, where $\sigma_1 \in R_{ik}^{k-1}$, $\sigma_2 \in (R_{kk}^{k-1})^*$ and $\sigma_3 \in R_{kj}^{k-1}$ (see Fig. 6.9). Thus we can write

$$R_{ij}^k = R_{ij}^{k-1} \cup R_{ik}^{k-1}(R_{kk}^{k-1})^* R_{kj}^{k-1} \tag{B}$$

for $k \geqslant 1$, and it follows from (A) and (B) by induction on k that each R_{ij}^k is regular.

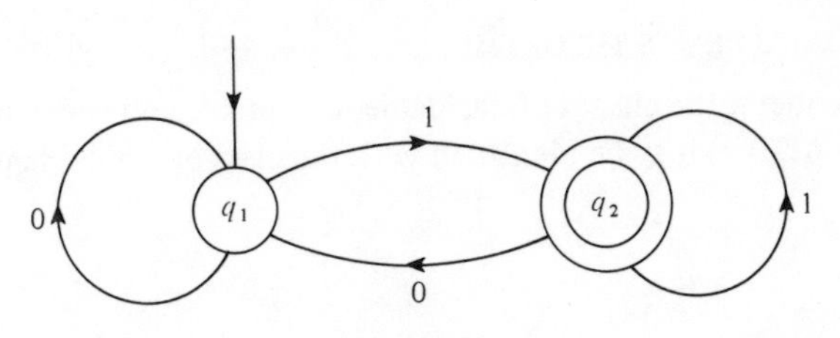

Fig. 6.10

As an illustration of this algorithm, consider the transition graph over Σ given by Fig. 6.10. As there is only one success node q_2, the language L accepted is R_{12}^2. Applying (B) three times, we see that

$$R_{12}^2 = R_{12}^1 \cup R_{12}^1(R_{22}^1)^* R_{22}^1,$$

where

$$R_{12}^1 = R_{12}^0 \cup R_{11}^0(R_{11}^0)^* R_{12}^0$$

and

$$R_{22}^1 = R_{22}^0 \cup R_{21}^0(R_{11}^0)^* R_{12}^0.$$

Applying (A) four times, we see that

$$R_{11}^0 = 0 \cup \Lambda,$$
$$R_{12}^0 = 1,$$
$$R_{21}^0 = 0,$$
$$R_{22}^0 = 1 \cup \Lambda.$$

Substituting back, this gives the following regular expressions:

$$R_{12}^1 = 1 \cup (0 \cup \Lambda)(0 \cup \Lambda)^* 1,$$
$$R_{22}^1 = 1 \cup \Lambda \cup 0(0 \cup \Lambda)^* 1$$

and finally

$$L = R_{12}^2 = 1 \cup (0 \cup \Lambda)(0 \cup \Lambda)^* 1 \cup \{1 \cup (0 \cup \Lambda)(0 \cup \Lambda)^* 1\} \{1 \cup \Lambda \cup 0(0 \cup \Lambda)^* 1\}^* \{1 \cup \Lambda \cup 0(0 \cup \Lambda)^* 1\}.$$

This algorithm is not to be used for practical purposes–in fact, for the example given, a much simpler regular expression for the language accepted is

$$(0 \cup 11^*0)^* 11^*.$$

To summarize the results obtained so far, we have

6.3.1 THEOREM (KLEENE'S THEOREM)

For a given alphabet α the classes of decidable, acceptable and generable languages with respect to **AUT**(α) may be identified with the class of regular languages over α. ∎

6.3.2 EXERCISE*

(1) If E is a regular expression representing a regular language L, describe the construction of a transition graph π_E accepting L. (Use the results of sections 5.6 and 6.2.

(2) Given transition graphs π_1 and π_2 accepting languages L_1 and L_2 respectively over alphabet α, show directly how to construct transition graphs π_3 accepting $\alpha^* \sim L_1$, π_4 accepting $L_1 \cap L_2$ and π_5 accepting $L_1 \cup L_2$.

(Note that this proves that the class of regular languages over α is closed under complementation in α^* and under intersection. The construction of π_3 is quite straightforward; π_4 has nodes labelled by ordered pairs $\langle q, q' \rangle$ where q is a node label of π_1 and q' of π_2, with the appropriate start node, success nodes and transitions. π_5 may be constructed from π_3 and π_4 by noting that

$$L_1 \cup L_2 = \alpha^* \sim ((\alpha^* \sim L_1) \cap (\alpha^* \sim L_2)).)$$ ∎

6.4 Some solvability results

In chapter 1 we established some elementary results on program equivalence; for example, every program is equivalent to one containing just one halt instruction. In chapter 3 we established the negative result that the equivalence of programs with respect to **TM** or **R** is not solvable.

We now have enough material to establish the most important positive result on program equivalence–namely, that there is a decision procedure for the equivalence of two programs with respect to all machines. We do this by showing that the problem of program equivalence reduces to the problem of whether or not the language accepted by a given transition graph is empty. This latter problem is solvable.

6.4.1 THEOREM

There is an algorithm to determine whether or not the language L accepted by a given transition graph π over alphabet α is empty.

Proof. We show that if L contains any strings at all, then it contains a string of length less than m, where m is the number of nodes in π. The decision procedure is then to feed every string over α of length less than m into π; L is empty if and only if all of these strings are rejected.

If L is non-empty, then it must contain a string of minimum length. Let σ be such a string. If $|\sigma| < m$, there is nothing to prove, so we suppose that $|\sigma| \geqslant m$. As π has only m nodes, at least one node q_i, say, must be passed through twice in accepting σ. It follows that we can write σ in the form $\sigma_1\sigma_2\sigma_3$, where σ_1 takes π from the start node q_1 to node q_i, σ_2 takes π from node q_i back to node q_i and σ_3 takes π from q_i to some success node q_j. As q_i is passed through twice, $\sigma_2 \neq \Lambda$. But this contradicts the assumption, as the string $\sigma_1\sigma_3$, of length less than $|\sigma|$, is also accepted by omitting the loop from q_i back to q_i again. ∎

The essential step in this proof is illustrated by Fig. 6.11.

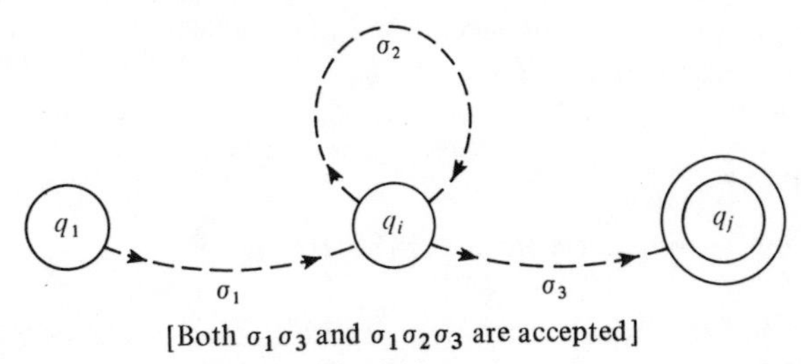

[Both $\sigma_1\sigma_3$ and $\sigma_1\sigma_2\sigma_3$ are accepted]

Fig. 6.11

6.4.2 THEOREM

There is an algorithm to determine whether or not two transition graphs π_1 and π_2 over an alphabet α accept the same language.

Proof. Let π_1 accept language L_1 and π_2 accept language L_2. We construct a transition graph π accepting the language

$$L = \{L_1 \cap (\alpha^* \sim L_2)\} \cup \{L_2 \cap (\alpha^* \sim L_1)\}$$

(see exercises 6.3.2(2)) and note that L is empty if and only if $L_1 = L_2$. The result then follows immediately from theorem 6.4.1. ∎

6.4.3 EXERCISE

Show that there is an algorithm for the equivalence of two regular expressions–in other words, that the problem 'Do the regular expressions E_1 and E_2 represent the same language?' is solvable. ∎

Solvability of program equivalence* Let π_1 and π_2 be any two programs. We want to determine whether they are equivalent or not. Let $P_1, P_2, \ldots, P_k$ denote the test names and $F_1, F_2, \ldots, F_l$ denote the operation names occurring in either program. Our strategy is to construct transition graphs π'_1 and π'_2 which accept the same language if and only if π_1 and π_2 are equivalent programs, and then appeal to theorem 6.4.2.

Let **M** be any machine and m_0 be any element of its memory set M. (If **M** is a standard machine M includes the input and output streams.) Suppose that $\mathbf{M}_{\pi_1}(m_0) \neq \Omega$. Let $f_1, f_2, \ldots, f_n$ be the names of the operations of **M** applied in computing $\mathbf{M}_{\pi_1}(m_0)$ in the order that they were applied. For $1 \leqslant i \leqslant n$, let $m_i = f_i(m_{i-1})$; then $\mathbf{M}_{\pi_1}(m_0) = m_n$. For each state m_i there is a k-tuple of T's, F's and U's indicating the outcomes of the tests named by $P_1, P_2, \ldots, P_k$ – T for true, F for false and U for Ω. Denote this k-tuple by $\langle m_i \rangle$. (The fact that we may not be able to decide which k-tuple corresponds to m_i is immaterial; all we need know is that such a k-tuple exists.) Let us call the alternating sequence of k-tuples and operation names

$$\langle m_0 \rangle f_1 \langle m_1 \rangle f_2 \cdots \langle m_{n-1} \rangle f_n \langle m_n \rangle,$$

the *computation record* or *trace* generated by running π_1 on **M** with initial state m_0. The set of all such traces, for varying **M** and m_0 which give a completed computation, we call the *trace set* $T(\pi_1)$ of π_1.

6.4.4 EXERCISE**

Prove that π_1 and π_2 are equivalent if $T(\pi_1) = T(\pi_2)$. ∎

Let α be the alphabet whose symbols comprise all the k-tuples of T's, F's and U's together with all the operation names $F_1, F_2, \ldots, F_l$. (We assume, with no loss of generality, that no operation name is a k-tuple.) Then the trace sets $T(\pi_1)$ and $T(\pi_2)$ are languages over α. In fact, they are regular languages; by applying the expansions given by Fig. 6.12 to π_1 and π_2, we obtain programs π''_1 and π''_2 which compute functions over **AUT**(α) with domains $T(\pi_1)$ and $T(\pi_2)$ respectively.

6.4.5 EXERCISES

(1) Check that this assertion is true by an induction argument on the number of operation names in the computation record.
(2) Prove that $T(\pi_1) = T(\pi_2)$ if π_1 and π_2 are equivalent. (If $T(\pi_1) \neq T(\pi_2)$, then π_1'' and π_2'' are not automaton equivalent; deduce that π_1 and π_2 are not equivalent. ∎

We now have the main result of this section:

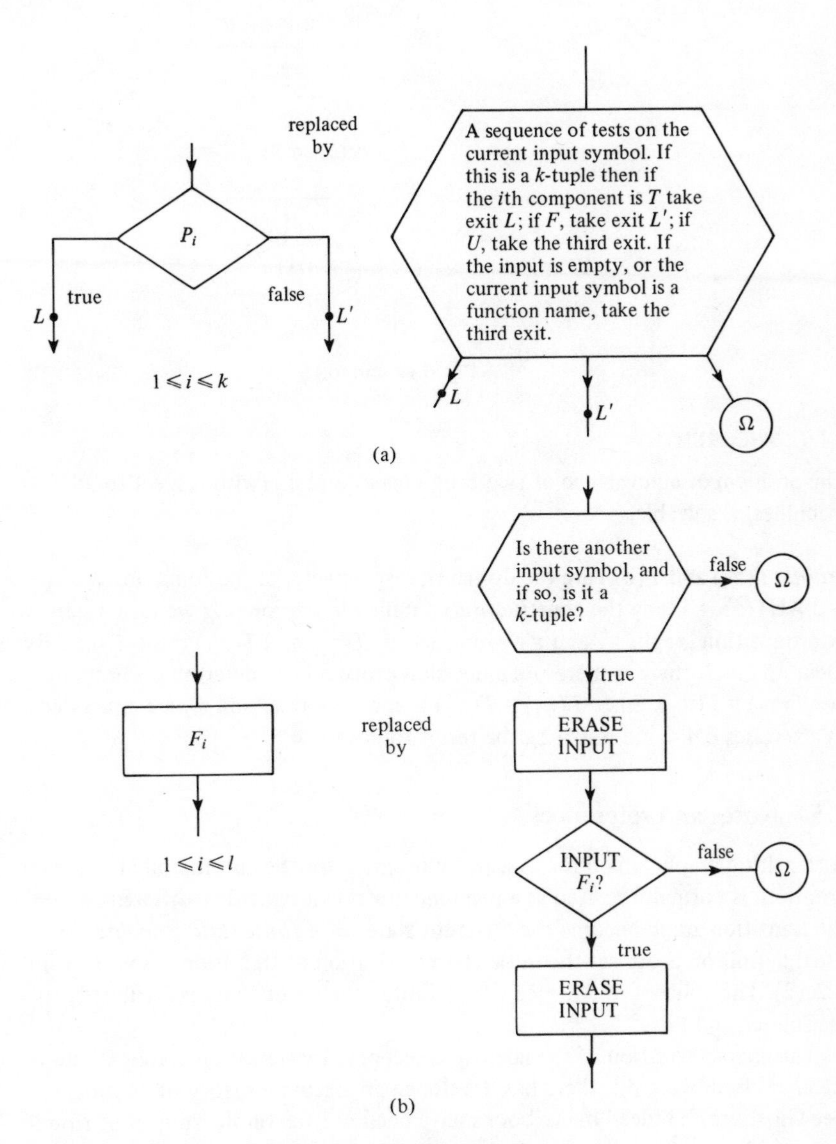

Fig. 6.12 (continued overleaf)

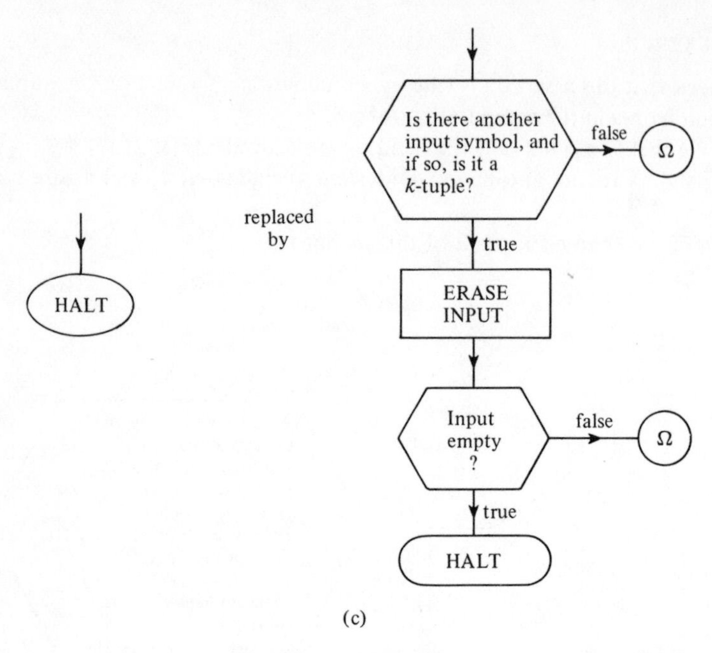

(c)

Fig. 6.12 (contd.)

6.4.6 THEOREM

The problem of equivalence of two programs π_1 and π_2 (with respect to all machines) is solvable.

Proof. $T(\pi_1)$ and $T(\pi_2)$ are the domains, respectively, of the functions $\mathbf{AUT}(\alpha)_{\pi_1''}$ and $\mathbf{AUT}(\alpha)_{\pi_2''}$. Using the constructions detailed in section 6.2, we turn π_1'' and π_2'' into transition graphs π_1' and π_2' which accept $T(\pi_1)$ and $T(\pi_2)$ respectively. By theorem 6.4.2, there is therefore a decision procedure to determine whether or not $T(\pi_1) = T(\pi_2)$. Since $T(\pi_1) = T(\pi_2)$ if and only if π_1 and π_2 are equivalent, by exercises 6.4.4 and 6.4.5(2), the result follows. ∎

6.5 Notes and references

A transition graph, which for us is just a program for the automaton in compact notation, is normally treated as a machine in its own right. The different nodes of the transition graph become the different states of a *finite-state machine.* The usual definition is our set-theoretic characterization of transition graphs (definition 6.2.12). The concept of a device with a finite number of states is attributed to McCulloch and Pitts[8].

The characterization of the languages accepted by transition graphs is due to Kleene[5]. Following this there has developed an algebraic theory of automata (see Ginzburg)[3]. Indeed many books have been written on the subject of finite-state machines[1, 2].

Theorem 6.4.2 essentially proves that the problem of whether two programs compute functions on the automaton which have the same domain is solvable. In fact the more general problem of whether two programs compute the same function on the automaton is solvable. Solvability questions for finite-state machines were first considered by Moore[9]. See also Rabin and Scott[11].

Except that we allow partial functions and predicates as values for the function and predicate names our programs are essentially Ianov schemas. The equivalence for these schemas was first proved by Ianov[4]. Solvability questions for more elaborate program schemas are treated by Paterson[10] and Luckham, Park and Paterson[6]. Manna[7] devotes a chapter to these topics.

References

1. Booth, T. L., *Sequential Machines and Automata Theory*, Wiley, New York (1967)
2. Gill, A., *Introduction to the Theory of Finite State Machines*, McGraw-Hill, New York (1962)
3. Ginzburg, A., *Algebraic Theory of Automata*, Academic Press, New York (1968).
4. Ianov, Y. I., 'The logical schemes of algorithms', in *Problems of Cybernetics*, Vol. 1, pp. 82–140, Pergamon Press, New York (1960)
5. Kleene, S. C., 'Representation of events in nerve nets and finite automata', in Ref. 12
6. Luckham, D. C., D. M. R. Park, and M. S. Paterson, 'On formalised computer programs', *J. Comp. Sys. Sci.*, **4**(3), 220–249 (1970)
7. Manna, Z., *Mathematical Theory of Computation*, McGraw-Hill, New York (1974)
8. McCulloch, W. S. and W. Pitts, 'A logical calculus of the ideas immanent in nervous activity', *Bull. Math. Biophys.*, **5**, 115–133 (1943)
9. Moore, E. F., 'Gedanken experiments on sequential machines', in Ref. 12
10. Paterson, M. S., Program Schemata, in D. Michie (ed.), *Machine Intelligence*, Vol. 3, pp. 19–31, Edinburgh University Press, Edinburgh (1967)
11. Rabin, M. O., and D. Scott, 'Finite automata and their decision problems', *IBM J. Res.*, **3**(2), 115–125 (1959)
12. Shannon, C. E., and J. McCarthy (eds.), *Automata Studies* (*Ann. of Math. Studies.* No. 34), Princeton University Press, Princeton, N.J. (1956)

7 Grammars and machines

7.1 Grammars

In the last two chapters, we have presented the idea of using languages over an alphabet α as a 'performance measure' for machines standard over α. In order to develop this idea effectively, we need some way of describing languages independently from the particular machines with respect to which they may be decidable, acceptable or generable. If a language L is finite, this is easy; one simply lists all strings in L. If L is infinite—and most interesting languages are—we have to find some other means of description.

In this chapter, we shall use *grammars* as a new descriptive tool for languages. The idea of a grammar is a very natural concept with a long history, originally formalized by linguists in their search for an adequate structural description of the sentences in a natural language, and more recently used, with more success, by computer scientists for use in the structural description of programs in a given programming language such as ALGOL. Before giving the formal definition of a grammar, let us look at a few examples.

7.1.1 EXAMPLE

Consider the English sentence 'The little boy ate a big sandwich'. This sentence may be broken down or 'parsed' into two constituents, a noun phrase 'The little boy' followed by a verb phrase 'ate a big sandwich'. The noun phrase may be parsed further as a noun 'boy' modified by an article 'The' and an adjective 'little', and the verb phrase as a verb 'ate' modified by a noun phrase 'a big sandwich' which may then be parsed into its constituents. This parse is illustrated in detail by Fig. 7.1.

The rules used in this parse may be written as follows:

⟨sentence⟩ → ⟨noun phrase⟩⟨verb phrase⟩
⟨noun phrase⟩ → ⟨article⟩⟨noun phrase⟩
⟨noun phrase⟩ → ⟨adjective⟩⟨noun⟩
⟨verb phrase⟩ → ⟨verb⟩⟨noun phrase⟩
⟨article⟩ → The
⟨article⟩ → a
⟨adjective⟩ → little
⟨adjective⟩ → big
⟨noun⟩ → boy
⟨noun⟩ → sandwich
⟨verb⟩ → ate

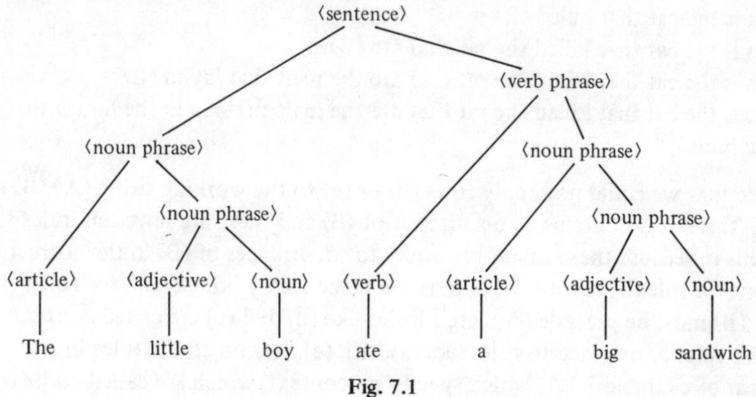

Fig. 7.1

Each rule indicates that the item to the left of the arrow may be replaced by the item or items to the right of the arrow. The names of parts of sentences such as ⟨noun phrase⟩ and ⟨article⟩ are enclosed in angle brackets to avoid confusion with the actual phrases and words that appear in the parsed sentence. The grammar may be used to generate the example sentence and many more besides. To generate a sentence, we start with the term ⟨sentence⟩ and replace it, according to the first rule, by ⟨noun phrase⟩ followed by ⟨verb phrase⟩. Subsequently we may select one of the two rules for replacing ⟨noun phrase⟩ and apply it. This process continues until no further application of the rules is possible. Since both the second and fourth rules may be applied any number of times, an infinite number of sentences, most of them making no sense in English, may be generated. These nonsensical sentences may be eliminated by suitably modifying the rules. However, our purpose is simply to demonstrate that an infinite number of sentences may be described by a finite set of rules for generating sentences. Each of the generated sentences is correct according to the given grammar. ∎

7.1.2 EXAMPLE

Consider the following rewriting rules:

⟨sentence⟩ → ⟨A⟩⟨B⟩	(a)
⟨A⟩ → This is	(b)
⟨A⟩ → ⟨A⟩ the cat that killed	(c)
killed ⟨B⟩ → killed the rat that ate ⟨B⟩	(d)
ate ⟨B⟩ → ate the malt that lay in ⟨B⟩	(e)
⟨B⟩ → the house that Jack built	(f)

By applying the rules in the sequence (a), (c), (b), (d), (e), (f) we obtain the derivation

⟨sentence⟩ ⇒
⟨A⟩⟨B⟩ ⇒
⟨A⟩ the cat that killed ⟨B⟩ ⇒

This is the cat that killed ⟨B⟩ ⇒
This is the cat that killed the rat that ate ⟨B⟩ ⇒
This is the cat that killed the rat that ate the malt that lay in ⟨B⟩ ⇒
This is the cat that killed the rat that ate the malt that lay in the house that Jack built

Note that we could not apply rules (d) or (e) to the working string ⟨A⟩⟨B⟩ even though this string contains an occurrence of ⟨B⟩ and these are rewriting rules for ⟨B⟩. This is because these rules only apply to occurrences of ⟨B⟩ in the correct context; for rule (d) to apply, ⟨B⟩ must be preceded by 'killed' and for rule (e) to apply, ⟨B⟩ must be preceded by 'ate'. Rules like (d) and (e) are called *context-sensitive* rules as opposed to rules like (a), (b), (c), (f) and all the rules in the grammar of example 7.1.1, which specify no context, which are called *context-free* rules. ∎

In general a language L may be grammatically described by specifying four things: the set of words or symbols of the language whose sentences are to be generated (called the alphabet of terminals), the set of syntactic categories which correspond to sentences and components of sentences (called the alphabet of non-terminals), the rewriting rules, and the distinguished syntactic category (called the start symbol) which starts any derivation of a sentence. More formally:

7.1.3 DEFINITIONS

A *grammar* G is a quadruple $\langle \alpha, \beta, R, S \rangle$, where α, β and R are finite sets of *terminal symbols, non-terminal symbols* and *rewriting rules* or *productions* respectively. α and β are disjoint, and we shall denote $\alpha \cup \beta$ by V. The set R consists of expressions or rules of the form $\sigma_1 \to \sigma_2$, where $\sigma_1 \in V^+$ and $\sigma_2 \in V^*$. (This is new notation. For any alphabet A we denote $A^* \sim \{\Lambda\}$ by A^+. The right-hand side of a production may be the null string, but the left-hand side may not.) S is the distinguished *start* symbol in R.

The *language* $L(G)$ *generated* by G is defined using relations $\Rightarrow_G$ and $\Rightarrow_G^*$ between strings in V^*. If $\sigma_1 \to \sigma_2$ is a production and γ and δ are any two strings in V^*, then $\gamma\sigma_1\delta \Rightarrow_G \gamma\sigma_2\delta$, and we say that $\gamma\sigma_1\delta$ *directly produces* $\gamma\sigma_2\delta$. In other words $\Rightarrow_G$ relates two strings exactly when the second is obtained from the first by the application of a single rewriting rule. If $\sigma_0, \sigma_1, \ldots, \sigma_k$ are strings in V^* such that $\sigma_i \Rightarrow_G \sigma_{i+1}$ for $0 \leqslant i \leqslant k-1$, then we say that σ_0 *produces* σ_k and we write $\sigma_0 \Rightarrow_G^+ \sigma$. Finally $\sigma \Rightarrow_G^* \sigma'$ if $\sigma \Rightarrow_G^+ \sigma'$ or $\sigma = \sigma'$. For convenience, we drop G if it is obvious from the context. Then

$$L(G) = \{\sigma \mid \sigma \in \alpha^* \text{ and } S \Rightarrow^* \sigma\}.$$

In other words, a string is in $L(G)$ if and only if it consists solely of terminals and it can be produced from S. We shall call a production of a string σ from S a *derivation* of σ.

A string in V^* is called a *sentential form* if it can be produced from S. Thus we may characterize $L(G)$ as the set of all sentential forms containing only terminals. ∎

Types of grammar By imposing restrictions on the form of the productions we can identify four different types of grammar. This classification into types is due to Chomsky[5].

Type 0 No restriction on the form of the productions. This is the most general type.

Type 1 Let $G = \langle \alpha, \beta, R, S \rangle$. If

(a) the start symbol S does not appear on the right-hand side of any production,
(b) with the possible exception of the rule $S \to \Lambda$ each production $\sigma_1 \to \sigma_2$ has $|\sigma_1| \leqslant |\sigma_2|$,

then we call G a type 1 or *context-sensitive grammar*. These restrictions ensure that $L(G)$ is a decidable set (theorem 7.1.4).

Type 2 A grammar $G = \langle \alpha, \beta, R, S \rangle$ is type 2 or *context free* if each production is context free–i.e., each production is of the form $A \to \sigma$ with $A \in \beta$ and $\sigma \in V^*$.

The reader is probably familiar with the Backus–Naur Form (BNF) grammar for ALGOL 60. This is a type 2 grammar. Since the publication of the ALGOL 60 Report[12], BNF has become synonymous with the terms type 2 and context free. This type of grammar is of great practical importance as it is powerful enough to describe most features of the syntax of a programming language like ALGOL 60, and there exist many efficient algorithms for the 'parsing problem'–that is, given a string σ in $L(G)$, construct a derivation of σ in the form of a parse tree such as Fig. 7.1. These algorithms break down in the presence of context-sensitive productions.

Type 2 is not as it stands a restriction of type 1, as we allow productions of the form $A \to \Lambda$ with $A \neq S$ (for example, the BNF grammar for ALGOL 60 contains the production $\langle \text{empty} \rangle \to \Lambda$, whereas the start symbol is $\langle \text{program} \rangle$), and we allow S to appear on the right-hand side of productions. However, theorem 7.4.9 below proves that, given a type 2 grammar G, we can construct another type 2 grammar G', which also satisfies the type 1 restrictions, such that $L(G) = L(G')$.

Type 3 A grammar G is type 3 or *regular* if each production is of the form $A \to aB$, $A \to a$ or $A \to \Lambda$, where A and B are non-terminals and a is a terminal. This is clearly a restriction of type 2. The importance of this very simple type of grammar will become clear in the next section.

A language L is called type i if there is a type i grammar G such that $L = L(G)$ ($i = 0, 1, 2$ or 3)–and we shall say that G is *for* L. We see that each type 3 language is also type 2, each type 2 language is also type 1 (anticipating theorem 7.4.9) and each type 1 language is also type 0. These inclusions are in fact strict, as we shall see (theorem 7.4.14) that there is a type 0 language which is not type 1, a type 1 language which is not type 2 and a type 2 language which is not type 3.

It should be clear to the reader that a grammar as defined above is nothing more than a non-deterministic mechanical device for generating strings. This makes us seek some connection between, say, the class of languages generated by certain classes of grammar—the types defined above, for example—and the class of languages generable with respect to certain standard machines. In fact it turns out that we may identify the type 0 languages with the class of languages generable with respect to the Turing machine, the type 2 languages with the class of languages generable with respect to the pushdown store machine and the type 3 languages with the class of languages generable with respect to the automaton—i.e., the regular languages (and hence the synonym 'regular' for 'type 3'). We shall establish these facts in the following sections.

As it happens, there is no such result for the type 1 languages—any standard machine capable of generating the type 1 languages is powerful enough to generate all the type 0 languages as well (exercise 7.1.7(5)).

The principal reason for identifying the type 1 languages as a separate type is

7.1.4 THEOREM

Every type 1 language is decidable.

Proof. Let $G = \langle \alpha, \beta, R, S \rangle$ be a type 1 grammar.

We suppose first that $S \to \Lambda$ is not one of the productions. Let $\nu \in \alpha^*$ with $|\nu| = k$. We indirectly specify an algorithm which will tell us whether or not $\nu \in L(G)$. Define the set T_m to be the set of strings σ in V^+, of length at most k, such that $S \Rightarrow^* \sigma$ by a derivation of at most m steps. As the productions in R do not decrease the length of a sentential form, the sets T_m may be defined inductively:

$$T_0 = S,$$

$$T_{m+1} = T_m \cup \{\sigma \mid \text{for some } \sigma' \text{ in } T_m, \sigma' \Rightarrow \sigma \text{ and } |\sigma| \leqslant k\}.$$

Clearly $T_m \subseteq T_{m+1}$ and $T_m \subseteq V^{(k)}$, where $V^{(k)}$ is the finite set of all strings in V^+ of length at most k. It follows that there is a value of m for which $T_m = T_{m+1}$. Since T_{m+1} depends only on T_m, $T_{m+1} = T_{m+2} = T_{m+3} = \cdots$. Now $\nu \in L(G)$ if and only if $\nu \in T_i$ for some i. But we can decide whether this is so or not by calculating $T_0, T_1, T_2, \ldots$ until for some m, $T_{m+1} = T_m$, and then finding out whether $\nu \in T_m$ or not. Thus $L(G)$ is decidable.

If $S \to \Lambda$ is one of the productions in R, we remove it, giving a grammar G' generating the language $L(G') = L(G) \sim \{\Lambda\}$ which is decidable by the above reasoning. Since a string is in $L(G)$ if and only if it is the empty string or it is in $L(G')$, it follows that $L(G)$ is also decidable. ∎

We conclude this section with two more examples of grammars which will be needed later on.

7.1.5 EXAMPLE

Let G be the context free grammar with terminal alphabet Σ, non-terminal alphabet $\{S\}$, start symbol S and productions

$$(1)\ S \to 0S1, \quad (2)\ S \to \Lambda.$$

Then $L(G) = \{0^n 1^n : n \geqslant 0\}$.

To see this, note that each sentential form can contain at most one occurrence of S, so after applying (2) for the first time the sentential form is a terminal string. Thus all derivations must consist of $n \geqslant 0$ applications of (1), followed by a single application of (2), giving

$$S \Rightarrow^* 0^n S 1^n \Rightarrow 0^n 1^n. \quad ∎$$

7.1.6 EXAMPLE

Let G be the context-sensitive grammar with terminal alphabet $\{a, b, c\}$, non-terminal alphabet $\{S, A, B, C\}$, start symbol S and productions

$$\begin{array}{ll}(1)\ S \to ABC, & (2)\ A \to aABC, \\ (3)\ A \to a, & (4)\ CB \to BC, \\ (5)\ aB \to ab, & (6)\ bB \to bb, \\ (7)\ bC \to bc, & (8)\ cC \to cc.\end{array}$$

Then $L(G) = \{a^n b^n c^n : n \geqslant 1\}$.

To see this, note first that $L(G)$ contains $a^n b^n c^n$ for each $n \geqslant 1$, since we can use production (1), followed by production (2) $n - 1$ times, followed by production (3) to get $S \Rightarrow^* a^n (BC)^n$. Production (4) then enables us to arrange the B's and C's so that all B's precede all C's. Thus, $S \Rightarrow^* a^n B^n C^n$. Next we use production (5) once and production (6) $n - 1$ times to get $S \Rightarrow^* a^n b^n C^n$, and finally production (7) once and production (8) $n - 1$ times to get $S \Rightarrow^* a^n b^n c^n$.

Conversely, consider the following statements about a string σ:

There are an equal number of a's (capital or lower case), b's (capital or lower case) and c's (capital or lower case) in σ.

There is no occurrence of an a or A in σ to the right of a b, B, c or C.

There is no occurrence of a b in σ to the right of a c or C.

These statements are trivially true for the start symbol S. Furthermore they are *production invariants*—if they are *all* true for a sentential form σ, and σ' is derived from σ by one of the productions (1) to (8), then they are also true for σ' (we ask the reader to verify this). It follows that these statements are true for all sentential forms σ. Since the only terminal strings possessing these properties are the strings $a^n b^n c^n$ for $n \geqslant 1$, these are the only possible strings in $L(G)$. ∎

7.1.7 EXERCISES

(1) Construct context-free grammars G_1 and G_2 so that $L(G_1)$ is the language of all balanced strings of 0's and 1's and $L(G_2)$ is the language of all even palindromes over the alphabet Σ. (Recall examples 5.3.2 and 5.3.3.)
(2) Construct a context-sensitive grammar for the language of all strings of a's, b's and c's containing an equal number of a's, b's and c's.
(3) Given a grammar G, describe informally a machine **M**, standard over the terminal alphabet of G, and a program π such that $L(G)$ is the range of $\mathbf{M}_\pi$. (Use the input string as a coded sequence to decide which production to apply next.) Show that if G is type 3, then **M** need only have a finite internal memory. Deduce that all type 3 languages are regular.
(4)** Show that there is a decidable language over Σ which is not type 1. (List all type 1 grammars with terminal alphabet Σ and diagonalize.)
(5)* Suppose that there is a collection of standard machines $\mathbf{M}(\alpha)$, for varying I/O alphabet α, each with the same internal memory and the same repertoire of internal operations and tests. Suppose further that each $\mathbf{M}(\alpha)$ may generate all the type 1 languages over α. Show that $\mathbf{M}(\alpha)$ may generate all the type 0 languages over α also.

(Let $L \subseteq \alpha^*$ be generated by a type 0 grammar G. Modify G as follows: Let # be a new terminal symbol. Add enough #'s to the right-hand side of each shrinking production to make it non-shrinking. Add productions $\#A \to A\#$ for each terminal or non-terminal symbol A. Finally, introduce a new start symbol S' and add the production $S' \to S$ where S is the old start symbol. Denote the modified type 1 grammar by G'. Check that each string in $L(G')$ gives rise to a string in L upon deletion of the #'s and that each string in L may be so obtained. By hypothesis, $L(G')$ is generable with respect to $\mathbf{M}(\alpha \cup \{\#\})$. Deduce that L is also, by omitting all PRINT # instructions from the generating program, and hence that L is generable with respect to $\mathbf{M}(\alpha)$.)
(6) Show that each type 0 language has a type 0 grammar in which there is only one shrinking production, of the form $\# \to \Lambda$. ∎

7.2 Type 3 grammars and the automaton

Exercise 7.1.7(3) suggests that the type 3 languages may be identified with the regular languages. To show this, we first show that, given any transition graph π, we may construct a type 3 grammar generating the same language as that accepted by π; and conversely that, given any type 3 grammar G we may construct a non-deterministic transition graph accepting the same language as that generated by G.

7.2.1 THEOREM

The type 3 languages are precisely the regular languages.

Proof. Consider the transition graph over Σ given by Fig. 7.2. We want to construct a type 3 grammar G whose productions mimic the transitions in the graph. There

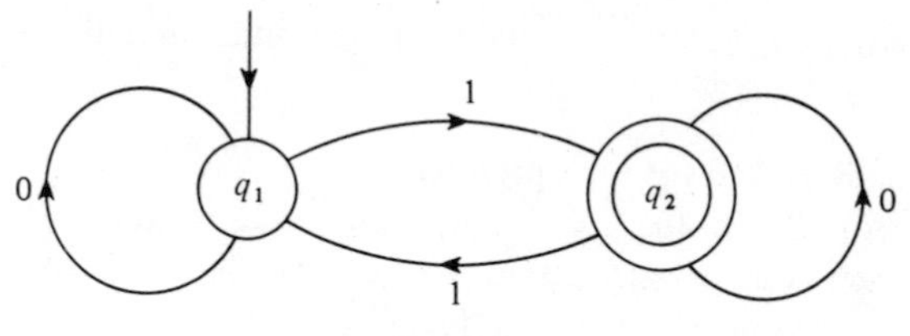

Fig. 7.2

are four transitions altogether—one labelled 0 from node q_1 back to node q_1, one labelled 0 from node q_2 back to node q_2, one labelled 1 from node q_1 to node q_2, and one labelled 1 from node q_2 to node q_1. We shall mimic these transitions in our grammar by having non-terminals S_1 (to represent q_1) and S_2 (to represent q_2), with productions $S_1 \to 0S_1, S_2 \to 0S_2, S_1 \to 1S_2$ and $S_2 \to 1S_1$. As q_2 is a success node, we include the production $S_2 \to \Lambda$ and we make S_1 the start symbol of G as the corresponding node q_1 is the start node of the transition graph. Consider the string 001110. This is accepted by the transition graph. For each transition, apply the corresponding production in the grammar, starting at S_1. This gives

$$S_1 \Rightarrow 0S_1 \Rightarrow 00S_1 \Rightarrow 001S_2 \Rightarrow 0011S_1 \Rightarrow 00111S_2 \Rightarrow 001110S_2,$$

and at this stage we may apply the production $S_2 \to \Lambda$ so that 001110 is also generated by the grammar. In fact, the transitions made in accepting σ exactly correspond to the sequence of productions required to generate σ by the grammar.

In general, let π be a transition graph over some alphabet α, with nodes $q_1, q_2, \ldots, q_m$ and start node q_1. We may define a type 3 grammar G which will generate the language accepted by π. The terminal alphabet of G is α, the non-terminal alphabet is $\{S_1, S_2, \ldots, S_m\}$, the start symbol is S_1 and the productions are defined as follows:

For each transition from a node q_i to a node q_j via an arc labelled s, include the production $S_i \to sS_j$.
For each success node q_i of π, include the production $S_i \to \Lambda$.

By an induction on the length of σ it is trivial to establish that σS_i is a sentential form derived from S_1 after $|\sigma|$ productions if and only if the transition graph would be at node q_i after reading in σ. Since $S_i \to \Lambda$ if and only if q_i is a success node, $S_1 \Rightarrow^* \sigma$ if and only if σ is accepted by the transition graph.

The other way around, let G be a type 3 grammar with terminal alphabet α, non-terminal alphabet $\{S_1, S_2, \ldots, S_m\}$ and start symbol S_1. We may construct a non-deterministic transition graph π over α which will accept $L(G)$. The graph π has nodes $q_1, q_2, \ldots, q_m$ corresponding to $S_1, S_2, \ldots, S_m$, and two extra nodes—a success node q_0 and a rejecting node q_{m+1}. (Recall the definition of a rejecting node. This is a failure node all of whose exits lead straight back into itself.) The transitions of π mimic the productions of G as follows:

For each production $S_i \to sS_j$, we include a transition from node q_i to node q_j via an arc labelled S.

For each production $S_i \to s$, we include a transition from node q_i to the success node q_0 via an arc labelled s.

The start node is q_1 and for each production $S_i \to \Lambda$ we make q_i a success node; all other nodes from the set $\{q_1, q_2, \ldots, q_m\}$ are made failure nodes. Finally, we make sure that each node has at least one exit arc labelled s, for each $s \in \alpha$, by adding arcs where necessary from the nodes $q_0, q_1, \ldots, q_m$ to the rejecting node q_{m+1}. Note that this makes all the exits from q_0 lead to q_{m+1}.

Again by a trivial induction on the length of a derivation, we have σS_i as a sentential form if and only if the transition graph is at node q_i after having read in σ; then σ is accepted if and only if $S_i \to \Lambda$ is in the grammar, i.e., if and only if $S_1 \Rightarrow^* \sigma$; and σs is accepted if and only if $S_i \to s$ is in the grammar, i.e., if and only if $S_1 \Rightarrow^* \sigma s$.

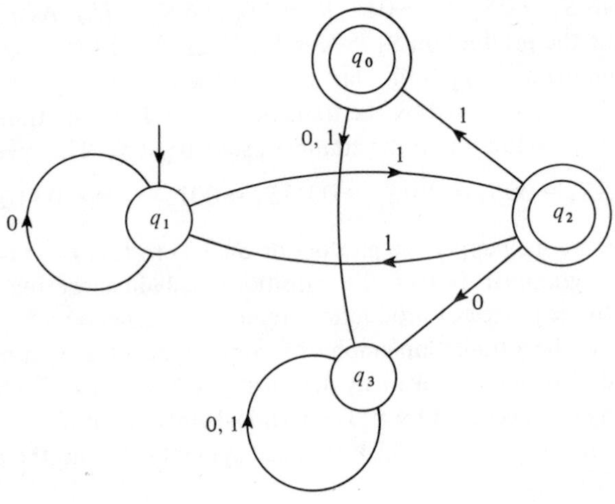

Fig. 7.3

As an example of this construction, consider the grammar G with terminal symbols 0, 1, non-terminal symbols S_1, S_2, start symbol S_1 and productions $S_1 \to 0S_1$ $S_1 \to 1S_2$, $S_2 \to 1$, $S_2 \to 1S_1$ and $S_2 \to \Lambda$. The corresponding non-deterministic transition graph is illustrated by Fig. 7.3. ∎

7.2.2 EXERCISES

(1) Construct a type 3 grammar generating the same language over Σ as that accepted by the transition graph shown in Fig. 7.4.

(2) Let G be the type 3 grammar with terminal alphabet Σ, non-terminal alphabet $\{S_1, S_2, S_3\}$, start symbol S_1 and productions $S_1 \to 0S_1, S_1 \to 0S_2$, $S_2 \to 1S_2, S_2 \to 1S_3, S_3 \to 0, S_3 \to \Lambda$. Construct a non-deterministic transition graph accepting $L(G)$.

(3) (a) A grammar G has productions of the form $A \to \sigma B$ or $A \to \sigma$, where A and B are non-terminals and σ is a possibly empty string of terminals. Show that $L(G)$ is regular.

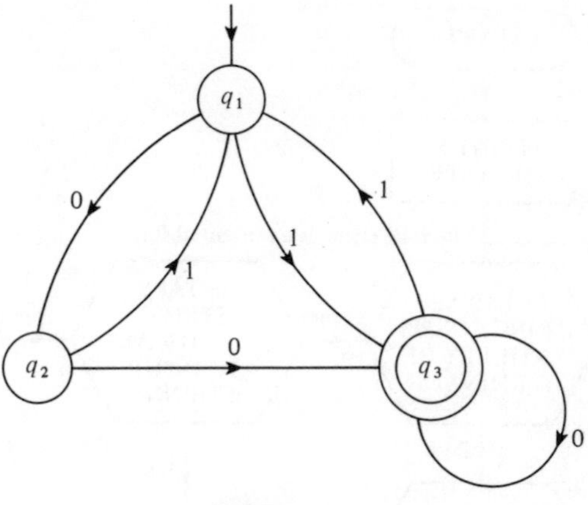

Fig. 7.4

(b)* A grammar G has productions of the form $A \to Ba$ or $A \to a$ or $A \to \Lambda$, where A and B are non-terminals and a is a terminal. Show that $L(G)$ is regular. ∎

7.3 Type 0 grammars and the Turing machine

We now go to the other end of the spectrum to establish the analogue of theorem 7.2.1 for type 0 languages; namely that they are precisely the languages generable with respect to the Turing machine. We shall prove this in two parts.

7.3.1 THEOREM

If $L \subseteq \alpha^*$ is type 0, then it is generable with respect to **STM**(α, V) for some alphabet V. (Recall the definition of **STM**(α, V); α is the I/O alphabet, V the alphabet of tape symbols and the internal memory has a blank tape as initial state.)

Proof. We could simply appeal to Church's thesis to establish this result, grammars clearly being effective devices for generating languages. However, a direct proof is more satisfying and is indeed quite straightforward. Thus let G be a type 0 grammar such that $L = L(G)$. We shall demonstrate that L is non-deterministically acceptable with respect to **STM**(α, V), where V is the union of the terminal alphabet α and non-terminal alphabet β of G. The result then follows from the equivalence of non-deterministic acceptability with generability (theorem 5.5.8). The required program Π, which non-deterministically generates a derivation in G of a string in L and compares this with the input, is given in outline by Fig. 7.5, where we assume that the productions are ordered in some way.

The program follows just one of the possible derivations from the start symbol S. If the computation halts, the input string is a member of L. Conversely if the input string is a member of L, then some choice of exits from the non-deterministic jumps in Π will result in acceptance. ∎

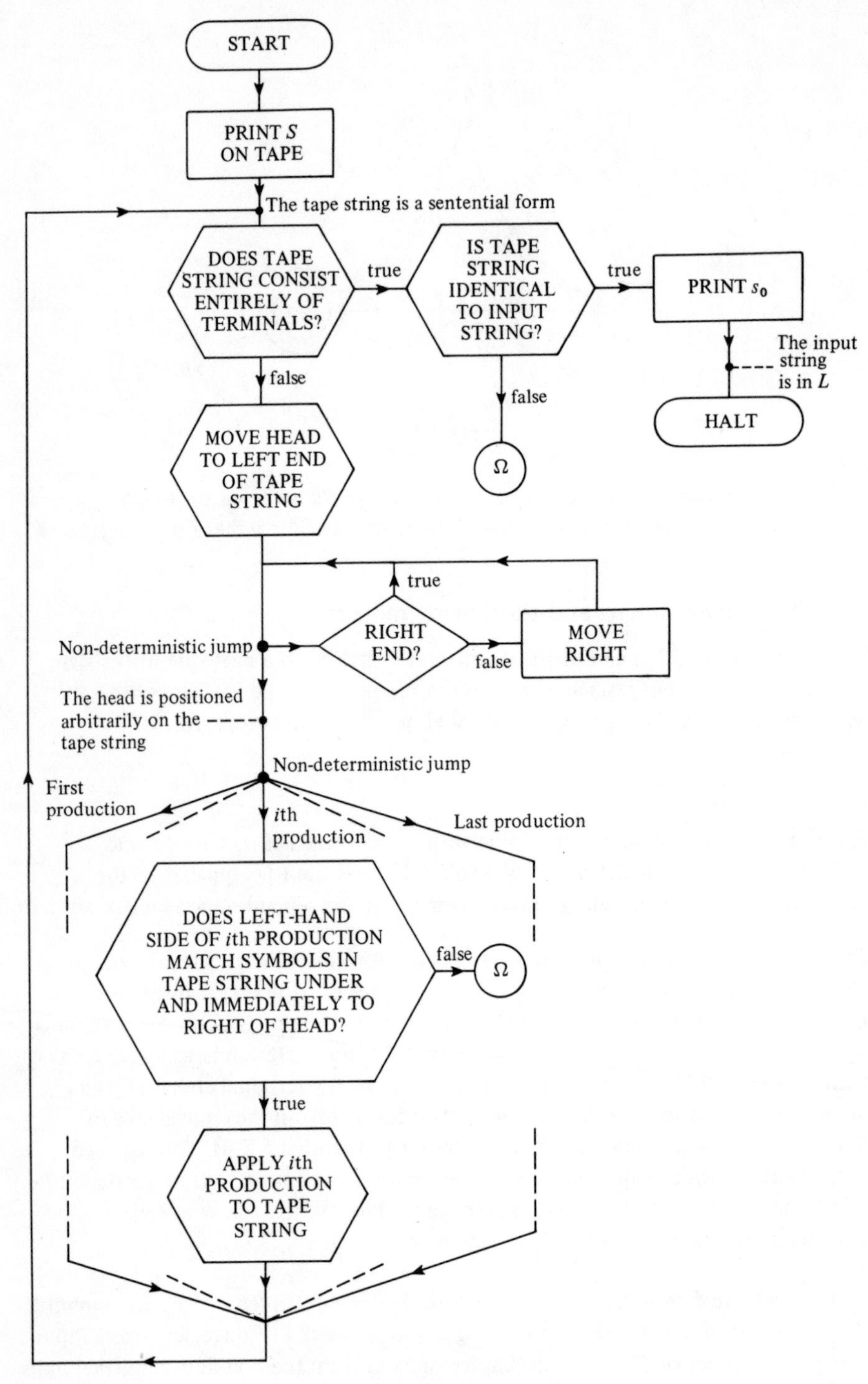
START
PRINT S ON TAPE
The tape string is a sentential form
DOES TAPE STRING CONSIST ENTIRELY OF TERMINALS?
true
IS TAPE STRING IDENTICAL TO INPUT STRING?
true
PRINT s_0
The input string is in L
HALT
false
false
Ω
MOVE HEAD TO LEFT END OF TAPE STRING
true
Non-deterministic jump
RIGHT END?
false
MOVE RIGHT
The head is positioned arbitrarily on the tape string
Non-deterministic jump
First production
ith production
Last production
DOES LEFT-HAND SIDE OF ith PRODUCTION MATCH SYMBOLS IN TAPE STRING UNDER AND IMMEDIATELY TO RIGHT OF HEAD?
false
Ω
true
APPLY ith PRODUCTION TO TAPE STRING

Fig. 7.5

The other way around, we want to demonstrate the existence of a type 0 grammar G such that the range of $\mathbf{STM}(\alpha, \beta)_\pi$ is $L(G)$, for given alphabets α and β and a given program π. In fact it is much easier to work with the non-standard version of the Turing machine than with the standard version. Since these are equivalent (exercise 5.1.3) we lose nothing by doing so.

7.3.2 THEOREM

Given any program π for $\mathbf{TM}(\alpha)$, there is a type 0 grammar G such that $L(G)$ is the set of all final tape strings of completed computations of π on $\mathbf{TM}(\alpha)$.

Proof. The terminal alphabet of G is α. The non-terminal alphabet is $\{S, T, \#, L_0, L_1, \ldots, L_p\}$, where $L_0, L_1, \ldots, L_p$ are the labels of π and L_0 is the start label–i.e., the label mentioned in the start instruction. (We are assuming that all these symbols are distinct and that none of them belong to α.) $s_0 \in \alpha$ is the tape-initializing symbol and S is the start symbol of G. The productions of G 'simulate' the computations of π in the following way. First the productions of group (1) below generate a sentential form $\#\sigma L_0 \sigma' \#$. In this $\sigma\sigma'$ is some arbitrary initial tape string, the #'s are endmarkers and L_0, the non-terminal corresponding to the start label, positioned at the left end of σ', indicates that the head is scanning the left-most symbol of σ'. Each of the productions in groups (2)–(8) below now corresponds to a possible transition from one label–state pair to the next in the computation of π. More formally if one step in the computation is from

$$L', \langle \sigma', k' \rangle \quad \text{to} \quad L'', \langle \sigma'', k'' \rangle,$$

then there is exactly one direct production

$$\#\sigma_1' L' \sigma_2' \# \Rightarrow \#\sigma_1'' L'' \sigma_2'' \#,$$

where $\sigma_1'\sigma_2' = \sigma'$, $|\sigma_1'| = k' - 1$ and similarly for σ_1''. During this phase of the derivation, there is a one-to-one correspondence between steps in the derivation and steps in the computation. If and when the computation halts, the productions of group 9 are applied, which transform the sentential form into the required output string of the computation. The reader is asked to verify that, for any derivation of a terminal string, there is another derivation of the same string in which the two applications of the production $\# \to \Lambda$ to erase the endmarkers are the last two productions applied. Thus, premature erasure of the endmarkers does not affect the language generated. The productions follow. Before proceeding, the reader is advised to remind himself of the definitions of the operations and tests of $\mathbf{TM}(\alpha)$.

(1) Productions to generate the input. These are

$$S \to \#L_0\# \quad S \to \#Ts\# \quad T \to sT \quad T \to Ts \text{ (all } s \in \alpha) \quad T \to L_0.$$

(2) Productions which simulate MOVE LEFT. For each instruction

L_i: DO MOVE LEFT GOTO L_j;

in π, we include the productions

$$sL_i \to L_js \quad \#L_is \to \#L_js_0s \quad L_i\# \to L_j\# \quad (\text{all } s \in \alpha)$$

(3) Productions which simulate MOVE RIGHT. For each instruction

$$L_i\text{: DO MOVE RIGHT GOTO } L_j;$$

in π, we include the productions

$$L_ist \to sL_jt \quad L_is\# \to sL_js_0\# \quad L_i\# \to L_j\# \quad (\text{all } s, t \in \alpha).$$

(4) Productions which simulate PRINT s (all $s \in \alpha$). For each instruction

$$L_i\text{: DO PRINT } s \text{ GOTO } L_j;$$

in π, we include the productions

$$L_it \to L_js \quad L_i\# \to L_js\# \quad (\text{all } t \in \alpha).$$

(5) Productions which simulate ERASE. For each instruction

$$L_i\text{: DO ERASE GOTO } L_j;$$

in π, we include the productions

$$sL_itu \to sL_jtu \quad L_i\# \to L_j\# \quad \#L_is \to \#L_j \quad sL_it\# \to L_js\# \quad (\text{all } s, t, u \in \alpha).$$

(6) Productions which simulate s? (all $s \in \alpha$). For each instruction

$$L_i\text{: IF } s \text{ ? THEN GOTO } L_j \text{ ELSE GOTO } L_k;$$

in π, we include the productions

$$L_is \to L_js \quad L_it \to L_kt \quad L_i\# \to L_k\# \quad (\text{all } t \in \alpha, t \neq s)$$

(7) Productions which simulate LEFT END?. For each instruction

$$L_i\text{: IF LEFT END ? THEN GOTO } L_j \text{ ELSE GOTO } L_k;$$

in π, we include the productions

$$\#L_i \to \#L_j \quad sL_i \to sL_k \quad (\text{all } s \in \alpha).$$

(8) Productions which simulate RIGHT END ?. For each instruction

$$L_i\text{: IF RIGHT END ? THEN GOTO } L_j \text{ ELSE GOTO } L_k;$$

in π, we include the productions

$$L_i\# \to L_j\# \quad L_is\# \to L_js\# \quad L_ist \to L_kst \quad (\text{all } s, t \in \alpha).$$

(9) Productions which simulate a halt. For each instruction

$$L_i\text{: HALT;}$$

in π, we include the productions

$$L_i \to \Lambda \quad \# \to \Lambda. \quad \blacksquare$$

7.4 Context-free grammars and derivation trees

Consider the context-free grammar

$$G = \langle\{(,)\}, \{S\}, \{S \to SS, S \to (S), S \to ()\}, S\rangle.$$

The string $()(())$ is in $L(G)$ and may be derived using one of the following:

$$S \Rightarrow SS \Rightarrow ()S \Rightarrow ()(S) \Rightarrow ()(())$$

$$S \Rightarrow SS \Rightarrow S(S) \Rightarrow S(()) \Rightarrow ()(())$$

$$S \Rightarrow SS \Rightarrow S(S) \Rightarrow ()(S) \Rightarrow ()(()).$$

Clearly these derivations do not differ in any essential respect. Since each non-terminal in a context-free grammar may be replaced in a sentential form independently of the substitutions for the other non-terminals, the order in which they are replaced does not affect the terminal string eventually derived. Thus a more appropriate, 'canonical' representation of a context-free derivation is a *derivation tree.* Figure 7.6 is the derivation tree corresponding to each of the above derivations of $()(())$.

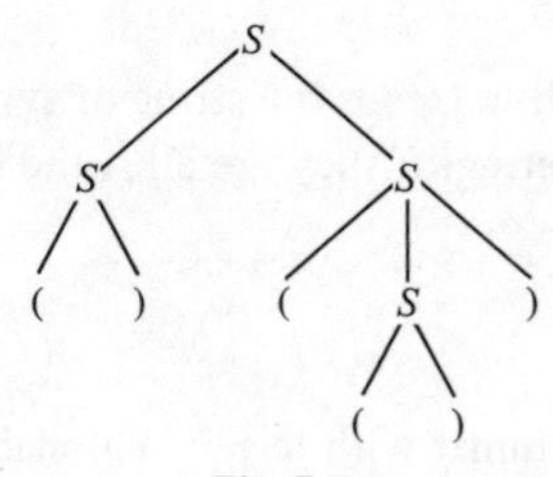

Fig. 7.6

7.4.1 DEFINITIONS

A *tree* is a finite set of nodes connected by directed edges such that

(1) there is exactly one node, the *root*, for which there is no entering edge,
(2) every other node is connected to the root by a unique path comprising a sequence of directed edges,
(3) exactly one edge enters each non-root node.

The *depth* of a node in a tree is the number of edges on the path from the root to that node.

A node n is a *son* of a node m if there is an edge leaving m and entering n.

A node is a *leaf* node of it has no sons.

A node n is a *descendant* of a node m if it is either m itself or a descendant of a son of m.

A tree T_2 is a *sub-tree* of a tree T_1 if T_2 consists of a node of T_1 together with all its descendants in T_1. If $T_2 \neq T_1$ then T_2 is a *proper* subtree of T_1.

A tree is *ordered* if the sons of every node are linearly ordered. Then if n_1 and n_2 are sons of a node m, with n_1 earlier in the ordering than n_2, we say that n_1 and all its descendants are to the *left of* n_2 and all its descendants. Thus if n_1 and n_2 are any two nodes such that neither is a descendant of the other, then there is some node m, common to their respective paths to the root, such that n_1 and n_2 are descendants of nodes n'_1 and n'_2, respectively, which are distinct sons of m. Therefore either n_1 is to the left of n_2 or vice-versa. In particular all the leaf nodes are linearly ordered by this *left of* relation. ∎

7.4.2 DEFINITION

A *derivation tree* labelled in accordance with a context-free grammar G is an ordered tree such that

(1) every node is labelled by a terminal or non-terminal symbol of G, or by Λ.
(2) every non-leaf node is labelled by a non-terminal symbol A of G and if its sons are labelled, in the left-to-right ordering, with symbols $A_1, A_2, \ldots, A_k$, then

$$A \to A_1 A_2 \cdots A_k$$

is a production of G.

The *leaf string* of a derivation tree is the string of symbols that label the leaf nodes in the left-to-right ordering. If they are all Λ the leaf string is Λ. Otherwise Λ labels are ignored.

7.4.3 EXAMPLE

Let G be the context-free grammar with terminal alphabet $\{a, b\}$, non-terminal alphabet $\{S, A, B\}$, start symbol S and productions

$$S \to AB, \quad A \to a,$$
$$B \to ab, \quad B \to b,$$
$$A \to aa.$$

Then

```
            B                   S                    S
(1)         |          (2)     / \          (3)     / \
            b                 A   B                A   B
                                                   |  / \
                                                   a a   b
```

and

(4) 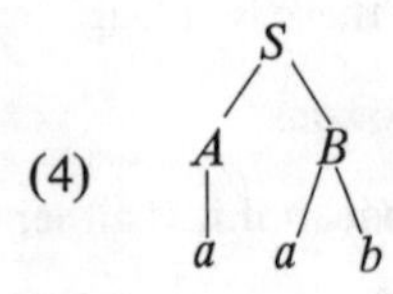

are all derivation trees labelled in accordance with G. Note that the leaf strings of (3) and (4) are identical although they are distinct derivation trees. ∎

It is obvious that the leaf string of every non-trivial (i.e., more than one node) derivation tree is derivable from the non-terminal symbol that labels the root using productions of the grammar. (This can be proved formally by an induction on the number of non-leaf nodes in the tree.) Likewise for every sequence of productions that derives a string σ from a non-terminal symbol A there is a corresponding derivation tree with root labelled A and leaf string σ. (Again this can be established formally by an induction on the length of the derivation.)

7.4.4 DEFINITION

A context-free grammar is *ambiguous* if there is some string in the language generated by the grammar, for which there are two derivations with distinct derivation trees. ∎

Thus the very simple grammar of example 7.4.3 is ambiguous.

When a context-free grammar is used to specify the syntax of a programming language it is clearly important that the grammar be unambiguous. For, since the productions used in the generation of a program indicate the way the program should be 'parsed' and its meaning derived, the existence of two distinct parses for the same program might lead to an interpretation of the program by the compiler different from the interpretation intended by the programmer. We mention this only in passing, for we shall not investigate ambiguity further. We shall just record the fact that the ambiguity problem of an arbitrary context-free grammar is unsolvable. We refer the reader to Hopcroft and Ullman[10] for a proof of this and other results concerning ambiguity.

7.4.5 DEFINITION

A *left-most* (*right-most*) *derivation* of a string σ from a non-terminal A of a context-free grammar is a derivation

$$A \Rightarrow \sigma_1 \Rightarrow \sigma_2 \Rightarrow \cdots \Rightarrow \sigma_k = \sigma$$

such that σ_{i+1} is directly produced from σ_i by replacing the left-most (right-most) non-terminal of σ_i, for $1 \leqslant i \leqslant k-1$. ∎

7.4.6 EXERCISE

Prove that if $A \Rightarrow^* \sigma$ using the productions of some context-free grammar, then there is a left-most (right-most) derivation of σ from A. (Use the characterization of derivations as derivation trees.) ∎

Derivation trees are the key to proofs of several results concerning context-free grammars.

7.4.7 THEOREM

It is solvable whether or not the language generated by a given context-free grammar G is empty.

Proof. Let S be the start symbol and m the number of non-terminals of G. The algorithm is to construct in turn each of the finite number of derivation trees with root labelled S, which have no leaf node of depth greater than m. If one of these trees has each leaf node labelled by a terminal symbol or Λ, then $L(G)$ is non-empty, otherwise $L(G)$ is empty.

To see that we need only consider this subset of all derivation trees, suppose that $L(G)$ is non-empty. Let T be a derivation tree for some string in $L(G)$. If no leaf node of T has depth greater than m, there is nothing more to prove. If some leaf node k has depth greater than m, then the path from the root to k passes through more than m nodes (we include the root node) labelled by non-terminals.

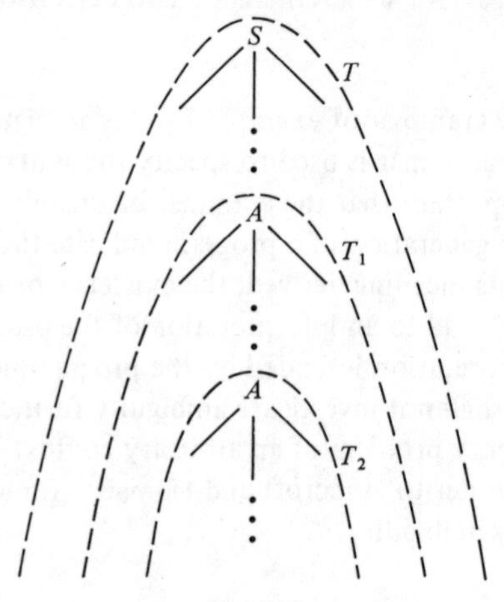

Fig. 7.7

Hence at least two nodes are labelled by the same non-terminal A, say, and T has the form depicted by Fig. 7.7, containing sub-trees T_1 and T_2 such that both have root nodes labelled A, T_2 is itself a proper sub-tree of T_1 and k is a leaf node of T_2. Thus the derivation tree which has T_1 replaced by T_2 corresponds to a derivation of another terminal string. Moreover, we have reduced the depth of leaf node k by at least one. This operation may be repeated until k has depth less than or equal to m. The ultimate result of this 'tree truncation' applied to every path from the root of length greater than m is a derivation tree for a terminal string in which no leaf node has depth greater than m. ▮

7.4.8 EXERCISES

(1) Let G be a context-free grammar. Prove that it is solvable whether or not $\Lambda \in L(G)$. (Show that only a finite number of derivation trees need investigating, by a tree-truncation argument similar to that used in the proof of theorem 7.4.7. Note that this result does *not* follow trivially from the decidability of each context-sensitive language (theorem 7.1.4), as we do not yet know that all context-free languages are also context-sensitive. Indeed this is the import of the next theorem, which uses this exercise as a lemma.)

(2)** Show that the emptiness problem for contest-sensitive (and therefore also for type 0) grammars is *totally unsolvable.* (Reduce the problem of whether an arbitrary program computes the totally undefined function on **TM**(α), which we know to be totally unsolvable from chapter 4, to this emptiness problem by a suitable modification to the grammar constructed in the proof of theorem 7.3.2. ∎

7.4.9 THEOREM

Let $G = \langle \alpha, \beta, R, S \rangle$ be a context-free grammar. Then there is another context-free grammar $G' = \langle \alpha, \beta', R', S' \rangle$, which also satisfies the contect-sensitive restrictions, such that $L(G) = L(G')$.

Proof. G only needs altering if it contains productions $A \to \Lambda$ where $A \neq S$, or if S appears on the right-hand side of a production.

The first step is to find all non-terminals A such that $A \Rightarrow^* \Lambda$. We do this by applying the algorithm of exercise 7.4.8(1) to the grammars $\langle \alpha, \beta, R, A \rangle$ for each $A \in \beta$.

Let $A_1, A_2, \ldots, A_m$ be the non-terminals from which Λ may be derived. Set $\beta' = \beta \cup \{S'\}$, where S' is an entirely new symbol, and construct a new set R' of productions as follows.

(1) Delete all the productions $A \to \Lambda$ from R but retain all other productions.
(2) If $S \Rightarrow^* \Lambda$, add the productions $S' \to \Lambda$ and $S' \to S$, otherwise just add the production $S' \to S$.
(3) For each other production $A \to \sigma$ in R, add each of the productions $A \to \sigma'$ where $\sigma' \neq \Lambda$ and is obtained from σ by deleting some or all of the non-terminals $A_1, A_2, \ldots, A_m$ that appear in it. (For example, suppose that $A \to BCD$ is a production in R where Λ may be derived from each of the non-terminals B, C and D. Then we add the productions $A \to CD, A \to BD, A \to BC, A \to B, A \to C, A \to D$ but not $A \to \Lambda$.) These extra productions cover the possibilities that some of the A_i might be erased in subsequent steps of a derivation in the original grammar G. ∎

7.4.10 EXERCISES*

(1) Complete the proof of theorem 7.4.9 by verifying that $L(G) = L(G')$. (It should be obvious that $L(G') \subseteq L(G)$. To prove that $L(G) \subseteq L(G')$, show that whenever $S \Rightarrow_G^* \sigma$, $\sigma \neq \Lambda$, then $S \Rightarrow_{G'}^* \sigma$, by induction on the length of the derivation in G. If $\Lambda \in L(G)$ then $\Lambda \in L(G')$ because of the production $S' \to \Lambda$.)
(2) Prove that every context-free language can be generated by a context-free grammar satisfying the context-sensitive restrictions, in which there are no productions of the form $A \to B$ with B a non-terminal. ∎

7.4.11 THEOREM (THE *uvwxy* THEOREM)

If L is a context-free language, then there is an integer N such that every string in L of length greater than N can be written as the concatenation of five substrings

$$uvwxy,$$

where either $v \neq \Lambda$ or $x \neq \Lambda$, in such a way that all the strings of the form

$$uv^iwx^iy \quad (i \geqslant 0)$$

are also in L.

Proof. By exercise 7.4.10(2), we may assume that $L = L(G)$ for some context-free grammar G whose start symbol S does not occur on the right-hand side of any production, which contains no productions of the form $A \to B$ with B a non-terminal and which contains no shrinking productions except, possibly, $S \to \Lambda$.

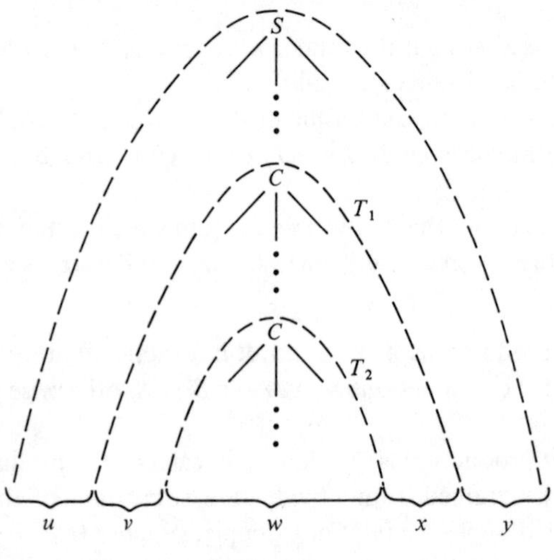

Fig. 7.8

Suppose that k is the maximum length of the string on the right-hand side of a production in G. Then the maximum length of the leaf string of a derivation tree labelled according to G, for which the leaf depth does not exceed d, is k^d. (True when $d = 0$. If true for some $d \geqslant 0$ then true for depth $d + 1$ since the worst case has each of the k^d leaf nodes of the tree of maximum leaf depth d linked to k new leaf nodes in the tree with maximum leaf depth $d + 1$. The length of the new leaf string in this case is $k \times k^d = k^{d+1}$. Therefore the general case follows by induction on d.) Thus the derivation tree of any string σ in $L(G)$ of length greater than $N = k^m$, where m is the number of non-terminals of G, must contain a leaf node whose path to the root has at least two nodes labelled with the same non-terminal C (q.v. proof of theorem 7.4.7). This tree has the form depicted by Fig. 7.8, where the segments of the leaf string are u, v, w, x and y with $\sigma = uvwxy$. From the form of the derivation tree we see that $C \Rightarrow^+ vCx$, and by the restrictions imposed on G it follows that either $v \neq \Lambda$ or $x \neq \Lambda$. In the tree, we can replace sub-tree T_1 by its sub-tree T_2, producing a derivation tree with leaf string uwy. Alternatively, we may replace T_2 by a copy of T_1, producing a derivation tree with leaf string $uvvwxxy$. Repeating this operation $i - 1$ times produces a derivation tree with leaf string uv^iwx^iy for all $i > 1$. Therefore all the strings uv^iwx^iy with $i \geqslant 0$ are in $L(G)$. ∎

The $uvwxy$ theorem tells us something about the structure of context-free languages. It enables us to prove that languages lacking this structure are not context free.

7.4.12 EXAMPLE

The language $L = \{a^n b^n c^n : n \geqslant 1\}$ is not context free.

For suppose it is. Then there is some N such that any string in L of length greater than N can be written $uvwxy$ as in the theorem. In particular,

$$a^N b^N c^N = uvwxy$$

for some u, v, w, x, y with v and x not both empty, with uv^iwx^iy for $i \geqslant 0$ also in L. But we shall show that, whatever the decomposition of $a^N b^N c^N$ as $uvwxy$, the string $uvvwxxy$ cannot be in L. This contradiction proves that L is not context free.

First note that v and x cannot be substrings that have a mixture of a's, b's and c's. For example v cannot contain both a's and b's; if it did then $uvvwxxy$ would have some b's before an a which places it outside the language L. The same argument applies to all other combinations. In that case at least one of a, b or c cannot be in the substrings v and x. Thus when we double up v and x to produce the string $uvvwxxy$ we are not increasing the number of occurrences of this symbol in the string. Since one of v and x is not empty, we must at the same time be increasing the number of occurrences of at least one of the other two symbols, giving us a string not of the form $a^n b^n c^n$. ∎

7.4.13 EXERCISES

(1) The analogue of the $uvwxy$ theorem for regular languages is the vwx theorem—there is an integer N such that any string σ of length greater than N which is in the language can be decomposed $\sigma = vwx$, such that $w \neq \Lambda$ and every string of the form vw^ix, $i \geqslant 0$, is also in the language. Prove this result. (Use transition graphs.)
(2) Use (1) to prove that the language $\{0^n 1^n : n \geqslant 0\}$ is not regular.
(3) Show that the languages

$$\{a^m b^m c^n : m \geqslant 1, n \geqslant 1\} \quad \text{and} \quad \{a^m b^n c^n : m \geqslant 1, n \geqslant 1\}$$

are context-free. Deduce that the context-free languages are not closed under intersection or complementation.
(4)* Show that the languages

$$\{\sigma \# R(\sigma) \# \sigma : \sigma \in \Sigma^*\} \quad \text{and} \quad \{0^n : n \text{ is a perfect square}\}$$

are not context free. ($R(\sigma)$ is the *reverse* of σ). ∎

Example 7.4.12, together with example 7.1.6 which established that $\{a^n b^n c^n : n \geqslant 1\}$ is context sensitive, proves that the context-free languages form a proper subset of the context-sensitive languages. Exercise 7.4.13(2) together with example 7.1.5, which established that $\{0^n 1^n : n \geqslant 0\}$ is context free proves that the regular languages are a proper subset of the context-free languages. Finally theorems 7.3.1 and 7.3.2 prove that the type 0 languages are the algorithmically generable languages and theorem 7.1.4 proves that each context-sensitive language is algorithmically decidable. Thus

7.4.14 THEOREM

The type 3 languages form a proper subset of the type 2 languages, which form a proper subset of the type 1 languages, which form a proper subset of the type 0 languages. ∎

7.5 Context-free grammars and the pushdown store machine

Our final aim is to establish that the context-free languages are precisely the languages generable with respect to the pushdown store machine. Half of the proof is very similar to the corresponding result for type 0 languages and the Turing machine (theorem 7.3.1).

7.5.1 THEOREM

If $L \subseteq \alpha^*$ is context free, then it is generable with respect to **PDS**(α, V) for some alphabet V. (Recall the definition of **PDS**(α, V); α is the I/O alphabet, V the alphabet of stack symbols and the internal memory has an empty stack as initial state.)

Proof. Again we use the equivalence of non-deterministic acceptability with generability (theorem 5.5.8). Let $G = \{\alpha, \beta, R, S\}$ be a context-free grammar such that $L = L(G)$. We know that each $\sigma \in L(G)$ can be produced by a left-most derivation (exercise 7.4.6). We therefore construct a non-deterministic program for **PDS**(α, $\alpha \cup \beta$) of the form depicted in Fig. 7.9, which uses the stack to generate left-most derivations of sentential forms. We assume that the productions for each non-terminal A_i, $1 \leqslant i \leqslant m$, are ordered in some way. The attached assertions guarantee that every string accepted by the computation of this program is in $L(G)$. We need only note that for every string in $L(G)$ there is a left-most derivation, and a corresponding sequence of choices of exit for the non-deterministic jump, to see that if $\sigma \in L(G)$, then there is some computation of the program which halts accepting σ. ∎

Top-down and bottom-up parsers It is quite easy to transform the accepting program of the above proof into a *parsing* program. That is, a program that will print out on the output stream some string representation of a derivation tree for the input $\sigma \in L(G)$. One possible string representation of a derivation tree is a bracketed expression in which the depth of nesting within brackets corresponds

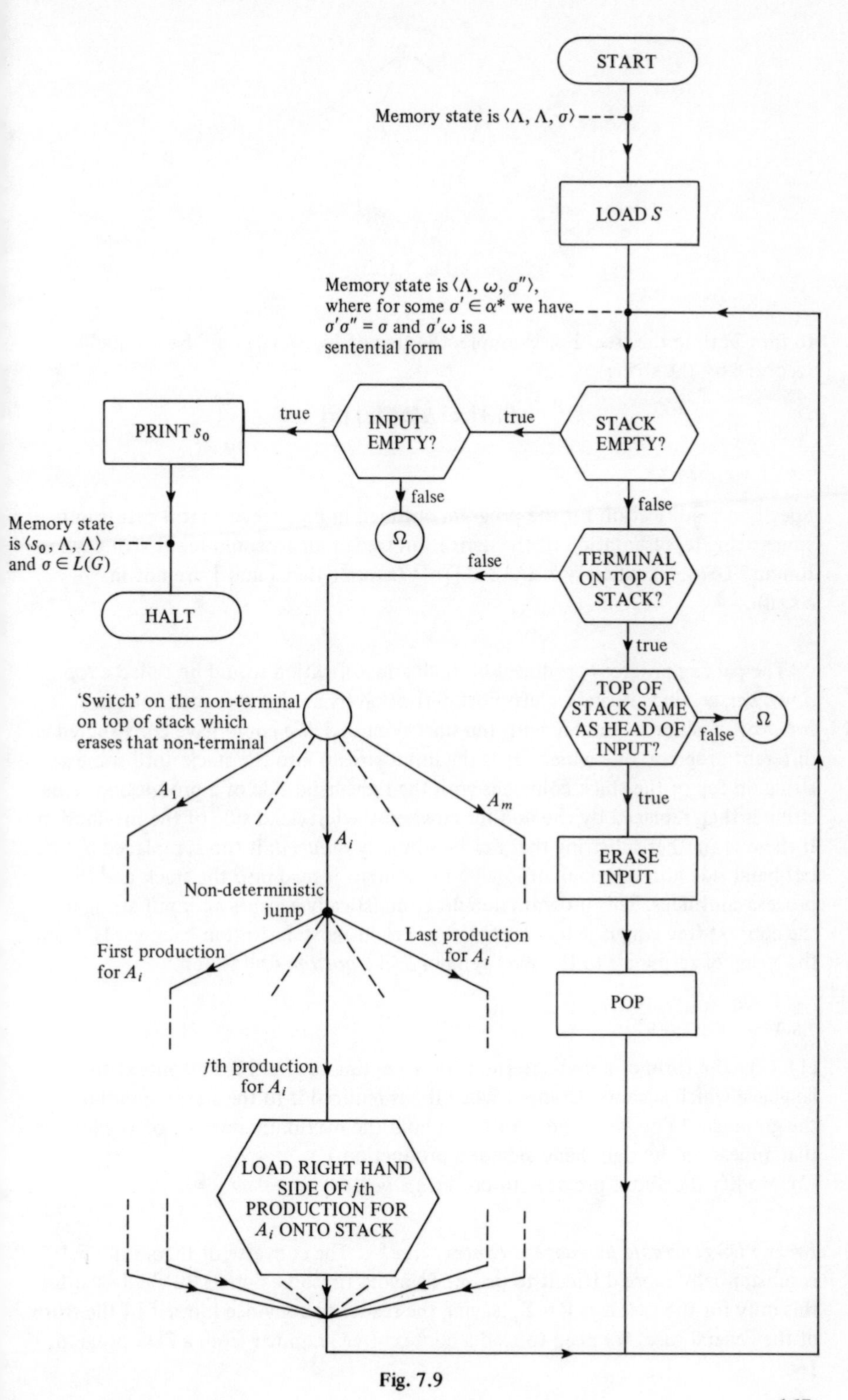
START
Memory state is $\langle \Lambda, \Lambda, \sigma \rangle$
LOAD S
Memory state is $\langle \Lambda, \omega, \sigma'' \rangle$, where for some $\sigma' \in \alpha^*$ we have $\sigma'\sigma'' = \sigma$ and $\sigma'\omega$ is a sentential form
STACK EMPTY?
true
INPUT EMPTY?
true
PRINT s_0
Memory state is $\langle s_0, \Lambda, \Lambda \rangle$ and $\sigma \in L(G)$
HALT
false
Ω
false
TERMINAL ON TOP OF STACK?
false
true
TOP OF STACK SAME AS HEAD OF INPUT?
false
Ω
true
ERASE INPUT
POP
'Switch' on the non-terminal on top of stack which erases that non-terminal
A_1
A_i
A_m
Non-deterministic jump
First production for A_i
Last production for A_i
jth production for A_i
LOAD RIGHT HAND SIDE OF jth PRODUCTION FOR A_i ONTO STACK

Fig. 7.9

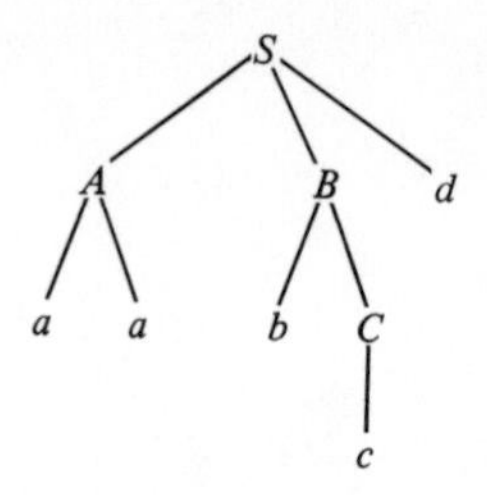

Fig. 7.10

to the depth in the tree. For example, the tree of Fig. 7.10 could be uniquely recorded by the string

$$S[A[aa]B[bC[c]]d].$$

7.5.2 EXERCISE*

Specify a modification for the program outlined in Fig. 7.9 so that it prints out some string representation of the derivation tree of an accepted input string when run on **PDS**(γ, γ), where $\gamma = \alpha \cup \beta \cup \{[,]\}$ (assume that [and] are not in $\alpha \cup \beta$). ∎

The parsing program produced by such a modification would be called a *top-down parser*, since it finds a left-most derivation by applying productions in a *top-down* fashion beginning with the start symbol S. We could have constructed a different program; one which reads the input stream into the stack until some substring on top of the stack coincides with the right-hand side of a production. This string is then replaced by the non-terminal on the left-hand side of the production. If there is another substring that can be similarly *reduced*, it too is replaced by the left-hand side non-terminal, otherwise more input is read into the stack and the process continues. This program non-deterministically accepts an input string in the context-free language by constructing a right-most derivation backwards, from the string of terminals to the start symbol S in a *bottom-up* fashion.

7.5.3 EXERCISES*

(1) Give the form of a non-deterministic accepting program for a context-free language which accepts the input when it has reduced it to the start symbol of the grammar. (You will need a buffer to hold the maximum number of symbols that appear on the right-hand side of a production.)
(2) Modify the above program to produce a *bottom-up parser.* ∎

Every* PDS*-generable language is context free* The converse of theorem 7.5.1 is substantially more difficult to prove. To avoid tiresome details we shall establish this only for the case $\alpha = V = \Sigma$, leaving the reader to convince himself of the truth of the general case. We need to read a context-free grammar from a **PDS** program such that it generates exactly the set of output strings that are produced by computations of the program on **PDS**. To do this in a reasonably straightforward way we need to assume that the program is in a special form.

7.5.4 DEFINITION

A **PDS** *stack switch* is a group of instructions of the form indicated in Fig. 7.11 and represented in the string version of the program by the 'macro' instruction

$$L_i\text{: switch}(L_j, L_k),$$

where L_i is the label of a switch macro and $L_{0(i)}$ denotes the label of the 0 exit and $L_{1(i)}$ the label of the 1 exit. Thus for the switch shown in Fig. 7.11, $0(i) = j$ and $1(i) = k$. ∎

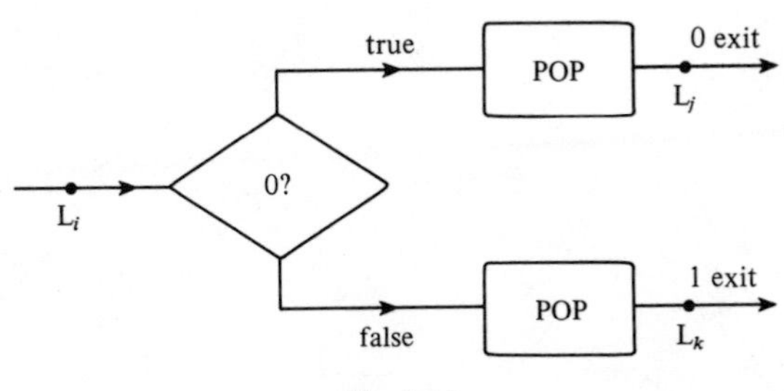

Fig. 7.11

7.5.5 LEMMA

For every **PDS** program π there is a program π', which non-deterministically generates on **PDS** exactly the same set of output strings as π, but which

(1) contains no instructions referring to the input stream,
(2) has all tests and POPs of the stack grouped as stack switches and
(3) has a single halt instruction and leaves the stack empty when it halts.

Proof. With no loss of generality we may assume that π is in standard form with respect to Σ, has a single halt instruction and never applies a test to an empty input stream (theorems 5.2.6 and 5.4.5). We first modify π so that it satisfies (3) above and never needs to test for empty stack. This is done by working in code on the stack, with symbol pairs 00 and 11 representing 0 and 1 respectively, and the pair 01 as a bottom-of-stack marker which is loaded at the start of the computation. Just before the halt instruction, the coded stack entries are erased until the bottom-of-stack marker is detected, then this is erased leaving the stack empty. The details of this modification, producing a program π_1, are left to the reader as an exercise. If we now apply the expansions given by Fig. 7.12 to π_1, we obtain a program π_2, generating on **PDS** exactly the same set of output strings as π, which satisfies (2) and (3) above. (Note that the expansion of the test for 0 on top of the stack never gives an undefined result as the original test in π_1 is never applied to an empty

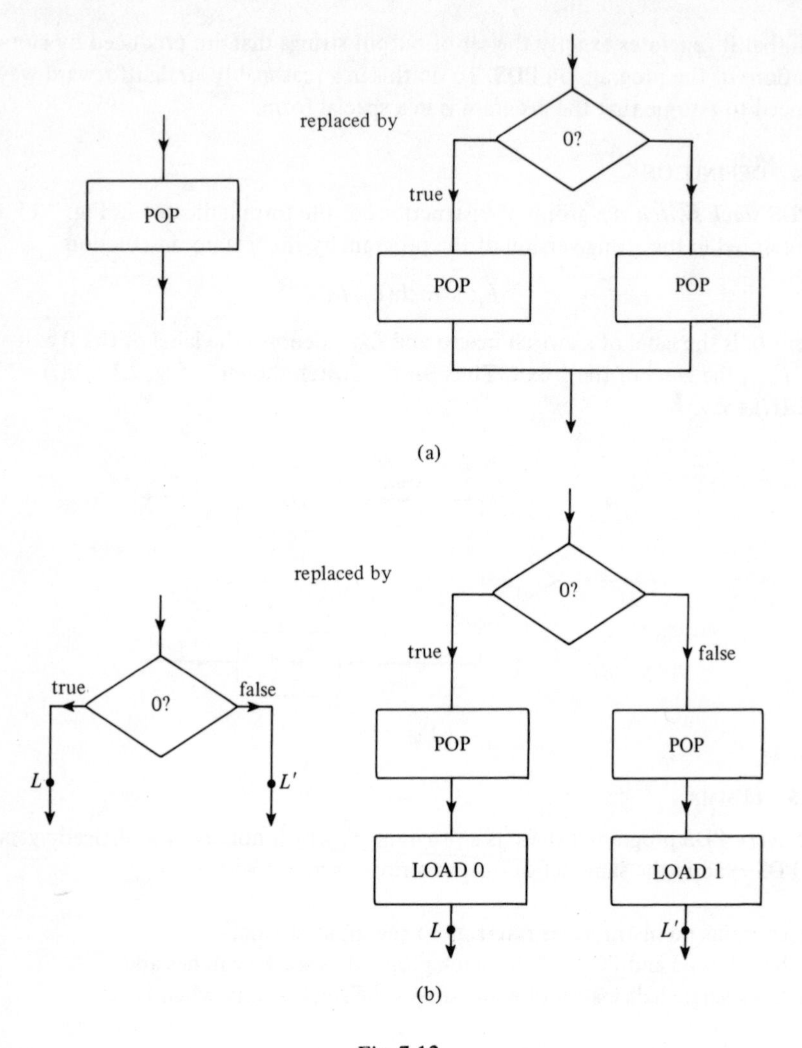

Fig. 7.12

stack.) The required non-deterministic program π' is now obtained from π_2 by replacing the input nodes by non-deterministic jumps as in the proof of theorem 5.5.4. ∎

7.5.6 THEOREM**
Every **PDS** generable language is context free.

Proof. By lemma 7.5.5, we may assume that L comprises the set of output strings of terminating computations of some non-deterministic program π on **PDS**, which apart from one start and one halt instruction, uses only instructions of the form:

$$L_i\text{: GOTO } L_j \text{ OR GOTO } L_k;$$

$$L_i\text{: LOAD 0 GOTO } L_j;$$

$$L_i\text{: LOAD 1 GOTO } L_j;$$

$$L_i\text{: PRINT 0 GOTO } L_j;$$

$$L_i\text{: PRINT 1 GOTO } L_j;$$

and 'macros'

$$L_i\text{: switch}(L_j, L_k)$$

and which leaves the stack empty on termination.

Let $L_0, L_1, \ldots, L_p$ be the labels used in this program with L_0 the start label and L_p the label of the halt instruction. We construct a context-free grammar in which the non-terminals are the set of superscripted labels $L_0^r, L_1^r, \ldots, L_p^r$ for all r such L_r is the halt label (i.e., $r = p$) or the label of a stack switch macro. Thus if there are n stack switches, there are $(p + 1)(n + 1)$ non-terminals. Let R denote the set of superscripts r. The start symbol of the grammar is L_0^p and the productions are derived from the instructions of the program as follows:

For each instruction

$$L_i\text{: GOTO } L_j \text{ OR GOTO } L_k;$$

in π, we include the productions

$$L_i^r \to L_j^r \quad L_i^r \to L_k^r \quad (\text{all } r \in R).$$

For each instruction

$$L_i\text{: PRINT 0 GOTO } L_j;$$

in π, we include the productions

$$L_i^r \to 0L_j^r \quad (\text{all } r \in R),$$

and similarly for PRINT 1. For each instruction

$$L_i\text{: LOAD 0 GOTO } L_j;$$

in π, we include the productions

$$L_i^r \to L_j^s L_{0(s)}^r \quad (\text{all } r, s \in R, s \neq p).$$

For each instruction

$$L_i\text{: LOAD 1 GOTO } L_j;$$

in π, we include the productions

$$L_i^r \to L_j^s L_{1(s)}^r \quad (\text{all } r, s \in R, s \neq p).$$

For the stack switches and halt instruction we simply include the productions

$$L_r^r \to \Lambda \quad (\text{all } r \in R).$$

The terminal alphabet is of course Σ.

A left-most derivation in the grammar that eventually produces a string of terminals ω corresponds to some computation of π which eventually halts with output string ω in the following sense. At the nth step in the computation, which has not yet halted, control is at label L_i with σ as the current output string and $m \geqslant 0$ symbols on the stack, if and only if the nth sentential form in the derivation is the string

$$\sigma L_i^{s_1} L_{t_1}^{s_2} L_{t_2}^{s_3} \cdots L_{t_{m-1}}^{s_m} L_{t_m}^{p}$$

(if $m = 0$ it is simply σL_i^p). This sentential form records the nth step of the computation, and certain aspects of its future course, as follows. The leading string σ of terminals gives the output string. The subscript of the first non-terminal indicates that control is at label L_i. If $m > 0$ the sequence of superscript–subscript pairs

$$\langle s_1, t_1 \rangle, \langle s_2, t_2 \rangle, \cdots \langle s_m, t_m \rangle$$

implicitly records the stack string. For each s_i, $1 \leqslant i \leqslant m$, L_{s_i} is the label of a stack switch macro. It is precisely the label of the stack switch that will eventually pop the symbol that is currently the ith symbol on the stack. Moreover L_{t_i} is one of the exit labels of this stack switch macro, being the 0 exit label if the ith stack element is 0, the 1 exit label if it is 1. Finally, if the computation is about to halt, then the stack is empty, i.e., $m = 0$, control is at L_p so L_p^p is replaced by Λ giving the output string ω as the terminal string.

We leave the reader to verify this correspondence between *left-most* derivations of terminal strings and the computations of π. An induction on n, the length of the computation and corresponding derivation, is required. Finally, note that if the 'wrong' choice of production is made corresponding to a load instruction, then no terminal string will be obtained as each load production must anticipate the stack switch which will eventually erase the symbol being loaded. ∎

7.6 Notes and references

The concept of a grammar used in this chapter, and the classification by type, is due to Chomsky[5]. The original work on type 2 grammars appears in Chomsky[4,5], and Bar-Hillel, Perles, and Shamir[3]. The results relating type 3 grammars and the automaton were established by Chomsky and Miller[7], the results relating type 0 grammars and the Turing machine were established by Chomsky[5], and the relationship between type 2 grammars and the pushdown store machine was established independently by Chomsky[6] and Evey[8].

This chapter has been a necessarily brief introduction to grammars and automata. The reader is referred to texts such as Arbib[2], Hopcroft and Ullman[10], and Kain[11] for further information. For the specific application of type 2 grammars to compiler construction, consult Gries[9] and Aho and Ullman[1], volume 1.

References

1. Aho, A. V., and J. D. Ullman, *Theory of Parsing, Translation and Compiling*, Vols 1 and 2, Prentice-Hall (1973)
2. Arbib, M. A., *Theories of Abstract Automata*, Prentice-Hall (1969)
3. Bar-Hillel, Y., M. Perles, and E. Shamir, 'On formal properties of simple phrase structure grammars', in *Language and Information* (Y. Bar-Hillel, ed.), Addison-Wesley (1961)
4. Chomsky, N., 'Three models for the description of language', *IRE Trans*, **IT-2**, 113-24 (1956)
5. Chomsky, N., 'On certain formal properties of grammars', *Inf. and Control*, **2**, 2, 137–67 (1959)
6. Chomsky, N., 'Context-free grammars and pushdown storage', *MIT Res. Lab. Electron. Quart. Prog. Rep. 65*, 187–94 (1962)
7. Chomsky, N., and G. A. Miller 'Finite state languages', *Inf. and Control*, **1**, 2, 91–112 (1958)
8. Evey, J., *The Theory and Application of Pushdown Store Machines*, Doctoral Thesis, Harvard University, Cambridge, Mass., (1963)
9. Gries, D., *Compiler Construction for Digital Computers*, Wiley (1971)
10. Hopcroft, J. E., and J. D. Ullman, *Formal Languages and Their Relation to Automata*, Addison-Wesley (1969)
11. Kain, R., *Automata theory: Machines and Languages*, McGraw-Hill (1972)
12. Naur, P. (ed.), 'Revised report on the algorithmic language ALGOL 60', *Comm. ACM*, **6**, 1, 1–17 (1963)

Index

Printed in Great Britain by William Clowes & Sons Ltd.,
London, Colchester and Beccles